Contemporary Art 1942-72
Collection of the Albright-Knox Art Gallery

Contemporary Art 1942–72

Collection of the Albright-Knox Art Gallery

Praeger Publishers
New York · Washington · London
In association with the
Albright-Knox Art Gallery, Buffalo, New York

PRAEGER PUBLISHERS
111 Fourth Avenue, New York, N.Y. 10003, U.S.A.
5 Cromwell Place, London SW7 2JL, England

Published in the United States of America in 1973
by Praeger Publishers, Inc.
in association with the Albright-Knox Art Gallery

Printed in the United States of America

Contents

Preface

Since the organization of The Buffalo Fine Arts Academy in 1862, the acquisition of the work of contemporary artists has been a consistent policy. The first painting acquired was The "Marina Piccola" in Capri with the Faraglioni Rock in the Background, 1859, by Albert Bierstadt, a gift of the artist in 1863. At present, over one-half of the entire Gallery collection is of paintings and sculptures dated 1942–72. This catalogue begins with the revolutionary American movement Abstract Expressionism and includes the many innovations of later years which frequently have involved the use of recently developed materials and techniques, as well as new concepts of the role of both the artist and his art in the contemporary world.

In planning this complete, fully illustrated catalogue of the Gallery collections for those three decades, we have attempted to increase the general usefulness of the book by the addition of eight essays written by leading authorities on the major art movements of the period. Each essay is followed by illustrations of the major works in the particular group with which the essayists are concerned, augmented by additional information related to the specific works and brief biographies of the artists. An appendix supplies auxiliary information on the 153 major paintings, sculptures, and constructions. The final portion of the book lists all 535 works of art in the Albright-Knox Art Gallery collection, dated 1942–72, excluding works on paper.

In the introduction to the companion volume to this catalogue, the Gallery collections of works dating from 3,000 B.C. through 1941, a more complete history of The Buffalo Fine Arts Academy and the Albright-Knox Art Gallery will be included.

Briefly, the Academy was the fourth public museum to be founded in the United States. In 1905, the Albright Art Gallery, a Greek Revival building, was completed, the gift to the Academy of John J. Albright, and it became the first permanent quarters for the Academy collection, as well as its special exhibitions and other activities. In 1962, Seymour H. Knox provided an adjacent building of contemporary design, and the name of the institution was amended to Albright-Knox Art Gallery.

Also in the companion catalogue, the significant role of A. Conger Goodyear in the formation of the collection will be elaborated, as will the many contributions of other donors, Boards of Directors, and Directors of the Gallery. Related to this volume, however, is the establishment of the Room of Contemporary Art in 1939, during the Directorship of Gordon B. Washburn. Originally, eighteen donors were involved in this unusual project in which contemporary works of art could be purchased and either retained or sold at the discretion of the administrators. A number of these works are included in this catalogue. After the original funds were depleted, Seymour H. Knox and members of his family became—and have remained—the major donors to the collection.

Andrew C. Ritchie, Director from 1942 to 1949, also contributed valuably to the Gallery and published the only prior collections catalogues, completed in 1949.

Mr. Knox, President of the Academy since 1938, has been the uniquely generous donor of 362 of the total of 536 works of art in this catalogue.

We are deeply grateful to the New York State Council on the Arts for grants that provided the funds for the extensive research and preparation of all text material in this volume. The publication of the book was sponsored by The Seymour H. Knox Foundation, Inc., and a grant from the Ford Foundation.

To the authors of the essays, our thanks for their informative and interesting commentaries.

I express my particular thanks to Ethel Moore, Editor of Publications of the Gallery Staff, who edited the catalogue, wrote substantial portions of the text, and supervised the project from its inception.

Gordon M. Smith, *Director*

Acknowledgments

I would like to express my appreciation to both Mr. Smith and Mr. Knox for their invaluable encouragement and support throughout the two years of preparation for the publication of this catalogue.

My deepest thanks to the researchers: Kathryn Kline, Charlotta Kotik, and Emese Wood, assisted by Barbara Lewczyk, Betty Muzzey, and Marianne Sprague.

Also, my thanks to Robert T. Buck, Assistant Director, and James N. Wood, Curator, for their contributions, and to the many other Staff members, far too numerous to list individually, for their aid.

Matthew Held, Brenda Gilchrist, Ellyn Childs, and Gilda Kuhlman of Praeger Publishers, Inc., have been most helpful and cooperative.

Ethel Moore, *Editor*

Contemporary Art 1942-72

Collection of the Albright-Knox Art Gallery

Abstract Expressionism

Irving Sandler

Tendencies in modernist American painting since the end of World War II are entirely too diverse to categorize. Yet there appears to be an underlying sensibility—an appetite of artists (and their audience) for pictures that are open, all-over fields, frequently composed of close-valued, amorphous areas. This appetite may be contrasted to a taste for relational designs of clearly articulated, discrete components, knit-together, balanced, and contained within the picture limits. The taste for openness can be characterized as "impressionist"; that for the building of pictorial structures, "cubist." The prototypes of the one are Monet's late fields of light and Matisse's fields of color; of the other, Mondrian's architectonic scaffolds. Indeed, Mondrian can be considered the ultimate "cubist" since he focused on the structure of Cubism (in its time, the latest variant of the classical tradition central to Western art) and carried it to a purist extreme.

During the 1930's, the American vanguard was not at all impressionist in disposition. Then, its art generally was geometric composed of clearly defined forms, flatly painted in clear colors, derived primarily from Picasso's Synthetic Cubism, Mondrian's Neo-Plasticism, and Miró's flat-patterned biomorphism. The trend toward geometric abstraction, with its stress on nonobjective structural and pictorial values was motivated partly by a rejection of the social realist and regionalist styles that dominated art during the Great Depression. These styles aimed to communicate social dogmas to a mass audience and consequently favored an easily understood figuration, literary, illusionistic—and retrogressive—prompting Arshile Gorky to deride them as "a poor art for poor people."

In America, the geometric abstractionist's self-image was essentially that of a picture-maker, the designer of pictures whose primary purpose was design itself. However, there was implicit—at least in the thinking of many —a social attitude, Neoplatonic and utopian. Such an outlook was generated by the social consciousness of the 1930's and by the rationales given geometric abstraction by earlier European adherents, particularly the Neo-Plasticists, Constructivists, and Bauhaus associates. They proposed that their art was the herald of a brave new world. Believing that man (and society) was perfectible, that his irrationality was a passing aberration whose signs should be suppressed in their work, they called for an art in keeping with man's future: rational, constructivist, and idealistic, aspiring to universals, essentials, and purity.

Geometric Abstraction and the ideologies that supported it lost credibility during World War II. The war threw into sharp relief the dark side of man, and intellectuals increasingly came to believe that human nature was unregenerate. Any art that aimed to feel real had to be open to man's irrationality, because that was inherent in his being. Geometric Abstraction, moreover, had become too commonplace, too outworn, to inspire artists to creation.

Unwilling to accept any received system of ideas, a small number of artists later to be labeled the Abstract Expressionists, including Gorky, Jackson Pollock, Mark Rothko, Adolph Gottlieb, William Baziotes, Robert Motherwell, Hans Hofmann, were forced to rely on their own experiences and visions. They assumed a romantic stance, valuing the personal and the subjective. Their problem, as they saw it, was *what* to paint rather than *how* to paint. Indeed, they believed that they faced a "crisis in subject matter" (their term for content).

It is not surprising that they began to reevaluate Surrealism, a task facilitated by the arrival in New York of a group of leading Parisian Surrealists who had fled the Nazis during World War II. Drawn to Surrealism's stress on content, the Americans adopted its technique of automatic drawing and painting as a means of plumbing psychic depths to discover fresh images, composed of biomorphic shapes (in contrast to the rectilinear of Mondrian and his school) that suggested anthropomorphic sources, life both inner and outer in all of its rich, changeable, and ambiguous variety.

However, the Americans refused to accept the academic mainstream of Surrealist art, as typified by Dali. For them, its reliance on literary themes, outworn old masterish rendering, and deep illusionistic space did not entail new ways of seeing. They recognized that automatism, which was Surrealism's most liberating innovation in that it enabled the unconscious mind to speak directly and freely, tended to yield abstract images. Thus they ventured boldly in a fresh and viable direction that the Surrealists had only tentatively explored. (For similar reasons, Gorky, Pollock, De Kooning, and others reevaluated Kandinsky's spontaneous improvisations of 1910 to 1920, those which in the 1930's Alfred Barr had called "abstract expressionist.")

The Americans also differed from the European Surrealists (with a few exceptions such as Miró and Masson) in their concern for the traditions and values of modern art. Indeed, the Surrealists thought of art as a means of provoking psychic and social revolution, an aim they deemed more important than the pursuit of aesthetic quality. To Gorky, Pollock, Hofmann, Motherwell, Baziotes, Rothko, Gottlieb, and De Kooning, the creation of art was primary. The problem for them was to paint directly and spontaneously and, at the same time, to cultivate the pictorial values threatened by automatism—the masterliness that they admired in the canvases of Picasso, Matisse, Mondrian, and Miró, from whom they also derived their conceptions of a modern picture and the sense of how it should project.

Arshile Gorky's career typified the change in attitude of the New York vanguard from the 1930's to the early and middle 1940's, the shift in interest from an architectonic, flat-patterned, abstract Cubism to an automatist, biomorphic, and atmospheric abstract Surrealism. In canvases executed from 1942 to 1948 (the year of his death), Gorky improvised in a free-associational manner to invent a new order of organisms that André Breton called "hybrids," amalgams of human, animal, and plant parts. Gorky's flowing lines, which suggest rather than define soft, visceralike areas and hard, skeletal or thorny protuberances, evoke the poetry of sex, his essential content.

Gorky's abstract Surrealist painting was advanced in its time, but it was not innovative. It retained references to observable phenomena; an air of fantasy; and small scale—and so stayed in the realm of the familiar and the known. Moreover, no matter how fluid Gorky's imagery was, it remained tied to a readily discernible infra-Cubist structure.

12

It was Jackson Pollock who, in 1947, broke through to an unprecedented style by using an automatist "drip" technique to pulverize all but the most remote vestiges of Synthetic Cubist design and to create an all-over single or mass image—an open field composed of interlaced linear details lacking focal points—that resembled, if anything, Monet's late *Nymphéas* (although Pollock was not influenced by them).

The lines comprising Pollock's all-over configurations functioned differently from all previous drawing, particularly Synthetic Cubist. They did not delineate images or outline discrete planes—the two traditional functions of drawing. Instead, they trajected freely, more like traces of energy than elements from which a design could be built. Indeed, these linear forces are interlaced to create a single field or continuum of energy, so charged that it seems to expand beyond the picture limits, evoking a sensation of boundlessness—and this even though the image rarely breaks the canvas edges. Pollock's dynamic field is poles apart from Mondrian's relational design. Where the geometric painter focused on the structure of Cubism and carried it into nonobjectivity, Pollock used automatism to disintegrate pictorial architecture into nonobjective energy.

Just as extreme as his field composition was the method adopted by Pollock in 1947 to paint it, the so-called "drip" technique. He began to dribble, pour, and fling pigment to bring more of himself, of his entire body rather than just his wrist and elbow, into contact with the canvas, to "literally be in the painting," as he said. It was his desire to more *directly* register his creative experience that led him to substitute for the slower handpainted brushstroke the swifter, flowing, "dripped" line.

Moreover, the scope needed by his bodily gyrations prompted Pollock to work on a large scale. His wall-size (or environmental) canvases, each containing a single image infused with surging energy, made a sudden impact on the viewer. They possessed the kind of immediacy that a Cubist picture, which requires a slow part-to-part-to-whole reading, could not impart.

Pollock's aim was not shock or novelty for its own sake. Rather, his art was shaped by an urgent vision, mythic in nature. During the early and middle 1940's, he, along with Gottlieb, Rothko, Baziotes, and Stamos, looked to mythology and primitive art for inspiration. They employed automatism to reveal what they believed to be the residues of universal myths, tragic and timeless, that "lived" in the unconscious mind, an approach anticipated by Jung (and it is noteworthy that Pollock underwent Jungian analysis). This orientation differed from that of the Surrealists-in-exile who were influenced by Freud and who, in the main, depicted psychological experiences, such as dreams and hallucinations.

Pollock's earlier mythic pictures alluded to animal sexuality, nocturnal rites, and Greco-Roman legends—violent themes that were embodied in tempestuous painting. However, in time, he increasingly suppressed literal references and focused on the expressive properties of the biomorphic forms in themselves. Motivated, it seems, by what Newman called a "ritualistic will," Pollock concentrated on the process of painting as a ritualistic act. In 1947, he eliminated all recognizable symbols and signs and began to rely exclusively on impetuous gestures—"dripped" marks of paint. Pollock no longer illustrated, interpreted, or symbolized myths, yet his content remained mythic in spirit, the abstract painting becoming a kind of total, private ritual made visible.

Among the other American myth-makers during the 1940's was Adolph Gottlieb, who executed a series of Pictographs, each of which was sectioned into an all-over rectilinear grid, reminiscent of Mondrian's. Within the compartments were painted flat, cryptic images that ranged from schematic anatomical segments, fish, reptiles, birds, and animals to abstract signs—subjects meant to recollect man's prehistoric past. Mark Rothko also combined biomorphic motifs from diverse sources, but he invented hybrid figures engaged in contemporary reenactments of Greco-Roman myths. William Baziotes and Theodoros Stamos employed doodling to reveal the fantastic creatures that haunted their inner worlds. The images of these four artists often suggested underwater life, becoming metaphors for an "other" realm of the imagination, whose strangeness and amorphousness indicated an extreme reaction against the rational and willful character of classicizing art.

In a similar vein, Richard Pousette-Dart depicted magical abstract images suggestive of astral bodies and bejeweled totemic beings embedded in a curvilinear grid—like stained-glass leading—and paint-encrusted surfaces. Clyfford Still also painted images with mythic connotations—horizontal, female, dark earth juxtaposed against vertical, male, light suns. Barnett Newman's biomorphic abstractions, although shown somewhat later than the other myth-makers, were also akin in meaning.

During the late 1940's, Still, Rothko, and Newman "universalized" their subject matter. They had come to believe that any reference to finite and familiar imagery, either in nature or in earlier and contemporary art, conflicted with the evocation of the universal spirit of myth. Consequently, their own semifigurative inventions began to appear too ordinary and limiting. The need was for pictorial means of such dramatic immediacy as to suggest what Newman called the "sublime," Rothko, the "transcendental," and Still, "revelation." Indeed, these painters (and Pollock) tended to see themselves as shamans—as against the geometric abstractionists' self-image of the artist-as-picture-maker.

With visionary intentions in mind, Still, Rothko, and Newman began to explore the expressive possibilities of color in itself, painting fields of chromatic expanses that saturate the eye. To maximize the visual (and emotional) impact of color, they eliminated figuration and symbolism; simplified drawing and gesture; suppressed the contrast of light and dark values, and enlarged the size of their canvases—striving to literally inundate the viewer with color by situating him in an environment of color.

Working more or less exclusively with color, the three artists who have come to be called the color-field painters avoided the gridlike design found in Picasso and Mondrian. Indeed, Still sharply repudiated Cubism in all of its figurative and abstract manifestation, so much so that in 1955 Clement Greenberg asserted that he had "resumed Monet." Still rejected the parlor paraphernalia that was the subject matter of Cubism's innovators and the geometry of later nonobjectivists; its relational design contained within the canvas rectangle; its implied horizon line, shallow depth, and small scale; and its well-made qualities.

Instead, Still painted vertically directed expanses of color whose edges are organic or flamelike. This kind of drawing unlocks the areas, causing them to appear to expand up and out, conveying an immediate sensation of upward aspiration and boundlessness, attributes of the sublime. At the same time, the paint is troweled on with palette knives, producing a muscular and earthy quality.

Still considered Cubism the nadir of Old World culture, its final decadence. Thinking in a similar vein, Newman, in a 1948 article entitled "The Sublime Is Now," expressed his dissatisfaction with the desire for perfection, for beauty. This desire had motivated art, representational and abstract, painterly and geometric, from ancient Greek classicism to Mondrian's Neo-Plasticism, and Newman considered it responsible for the decline of European art. As against "notions of beauty," he posited a "desire for sublimity," which prompted "a desire to destroy form: where form can be formless."

His own abstract paintings each consist of a field of a single, almost matte color cut by one or more narrow vertical bands of contrasting colors. In the geometricity of the linear elements, Newman seemed to veer toward Mondrian—but only to challenge him. Instead of criss-crossing verticals and horizontals to produce a scaffold of separable, finite forms, causing the viewer to focus on interactions, Newman limited himself to vertical bands that function as accents energizing the whole color field, preventing it from becoming amorphous and inert. The stripes are varied in color, width, and placement so as to clarify scale, but they do not constitute a structure. The emphasis is on the open chromatic field graspable immediately in its entirety—and it is this color field that fulfills Newman's visionary intention.

Like Newman's design, Rothko's verges on Neo-Plasticism. However, his abstractions, composed of softly painted and edged, horizontal rectangles of luminous colors placed symmetrically one above the other on a somewhat more opaque vertical ground, are far different from Mondrian's since it is the field of volatile atmospheric color rather than the stable design that arouses the primary visual and emotional response. The dark tinted aura that envelops the viewer evokes intimations of a suprapersonal order.

Akin to the color-field painters was Adolph Gottlieb, but his abstractions executed after 1957 are not as limitless in effect. The bursts of color in them are symbolic shapes that evoke duality: earth and sun or moon, the tactile and the immaterial, the explosive and the calm, the gesturally free and the controlled. In a similar vein, Richard Pousette-Dart during the 1960's condensed the intricate linear symbolism of his earlier works into circular symbols on fields of pigment, the symbols celestial both in their physical and spiritual connotations.

Robert Motherwell was also an abstract symbolist. Central to his body of work after 1949 was an open-minded series entitled Elegies to the Spanish Republic, each composed of simple, roughly oval and rectangular, black vertical planes that loom large on white horizontal grounds. In these stark, funereal friezes, Motherwell symbolized his private responses to a political event, but on an epic mural scale. Indeed, it was part of Motherwell's artistic strategy to monumentalize the symbols of his intimate experiences.

Ad Reinhardt's Black paintings, a series begun in the middle 1950's, are an almost uniform gray, and thus are related to the fields of Still, Rothko, and Newman. However, in every other respect they are different. Each of his pictures is trisected on the vertical and on the horizontal to create nine equal squares—a geometric design that looks back to 1930's purist abstraction. However, the darkened tones of the squares are so close in value as to

Hofmann's dissonant yet opulent, variegated colors do not serve primarily as adjuncts to compositions, but in their own right, they strain to burst their rectangular containers.

De Kooning, Hofmann, and other gesture painters such as James Brooks, Bradley Walker Tomlin, Philip Guston, and Jack Tworkov faced a common formal challenge: If they eliminated representation and refused to design compositions of discrete forms in the Cubist manner, how were they to create coherent paintings? Their solution generally was to build images of free, painterly marks, every detail of which would be painted with equal intensity, tending toward a field configuration.

This kind of direct painting would embody an artist's particular creative experience. As Meyer Schapiro remarked: "The consciousness of the personal and spontaneous . . . stimulates the artist to invent devices of handling, processing, surfacing, which confer to the utmost degree the aspect of the freely made. Hence the importance of the mark, the stroke, the brush, the drip, the quality of the substance of the paint itself, and the surface of the canvas as a texture and field of operation—all signs of the artist's active presence." Shaping forms dictated by what Kandinsky called "inner necessity," the gesture painters could not help achieving individual styles.

De Kooning was the most complex of the gesture painters, his pictures both figurative and abstract marked by a rich and suggestive ambiguity. They are composed of vehement slashes of fleshy pigment that carve out muscular shapes that interpenetrate, overlap, and collide, opening up space and generating energy. De Kooning's images take on multiple meanings, changing as the eye picks up different relationships. They can simultaneously evoke scrawls on tenement walls, landscape and still-life motifs, or flattened anatomical segments, opulent as a Venetian Venus or tortured in their dislocation. De Kooning's painterly drawing is virtuoso, but it is also raw and indeterminate, calling to mind the squalor, violence, and restlessness of urban life.

In contrast to De Kooning—and to most other gesture painters—Hofmann's pictures are rarely scarred by anxiety. The push and pull of hefty, richly textured color planes generates a sense of physicality, an exuberant robustness. Franz Kline's bludgeoning black-and-white swaths allude to the ever changing city—to massive sections of partly demolished or constructed skyscrapers and bridges. There are other kinds of drama in the slash of oppressive blacks that hurtle in off the canvas edges and threaten to swamp the equally assertive whites that struggle to be free—the two forces held in precarious equilibrium. Kline's blacks and whites do not read as figures on grounds, as in Oriental sumi-ink calligraphy, but are charged equally with energy. The starkness and dynamism of these abstractions cause them to project with a rare immediacy.

In contrast to the assertiveness of Kline's pictures, Guston's after 1951 appear tentative in the extreme. The images in them are composed of tremulous short strokes, partly erased, clotted near the centers of the canvases, groping tortuously toward the edges, but rarely breaking them, as if lacking the resolution to do so. The colors are grayed, suggesting that once Guston asserted a hue, he nervously took it back. Guston's pictures are about the difficulty of making felt decisions in the process of painting. But they possess other meanings; the painterly nuances and the half-tones, produced by the grayed colors, generate an amorphous, shadowy atmosphere that evokes a Neo-Romantic mood of brooding melancholy.

Because they are composed of dabs of pigment and infused with atmosphere, Guston's works seem related to Monet's, although the American's images are also influenced by Mondrian's "plus and minus" pictures, are contained well within the picture limits, and do not record the movement of light in nature or any other visual phenomena. Like the Impressionist's pictures, however, they are "lyrical" or nonaggressive, at least in comparison to De Kooning's. To differentiate Guston and other older gesture painters of quieter temperaments such as Brooks, Tomlin, and Tworkov from the Abstract Expressionists, critics called them Abstract Impressionists.

This label was popularized in 1956 in an important article by Louis Finkelstein in which he discussed a younger generation of artists who tended to paint fields of painterly marks in a lyrical manner and who, on the whole, were more explicitly representational than their elders. Significant in the development of this trend was the impact made by a large *Nymphéas* by Monet purchased by The Museum of Modern Art in 1955. Finkelstein opposed Impressionism to Cubism, maintaining that for artists to achieve "continuity of space," they would have to abandon their "previous habits of construction." Abstract Impressionism also involved a "growing towards rather than receding from reality," focusing "on the field of luminous atmosphere suggestive of nature," the "discovery of nature in the course of painting."

Even at times when it was unintentional, as in the case of James Brooks, lyrical gesture abstractions prompted viewers to think of nature. For Brooks, however, Pollock's "drip" paintings were the point of departure and the liberating influence. In 1949, he began to pour thinned pigment onto the back of absorbent canvas and to use the hints of forms that showed through to begin with; unlike Pollock, however, he worked and reworked his chance shapes, thoughtfully shaping and relating them—somewhat in the spirit of Cubist picture-making. Brooks's painting is also far different in feeling from Pollock's—the one is measured, nuanced, and slow in tempo; the other is paroxysmal, raw, and fast in tempo.

Like Brooks, Tomlin built spontaneous gestures into clearly articulated patterns. In his late abstractions, he improvised with free brushstrokes to form roughly rectilinear grids contained within the picture limits (carryovers from Cubism). The colors that Tomlin favored—tans, browns, olives, off-whites—are as restrained as his calligraphy, producing an effect that is at once elegant and elegiac.

Tworkov once wrote that the Abstract Expressionists broached "the possibility that painting can be non-representational and non-geometric and still be expressive, that is, reflective of experience, insight and awareness." More than most of his contemporaries, Tworkov at different times during his career approached both poles—figuration and geometry. In many of his pictures, there are suggestions of figures found in the free brushwork from which they emerge as enigmatic presences. Other works, particularly the more recent, veer to geometry, each based on a rectilinear design, but the grid becomes a foil for what remains essentially painterly painting.

A younger generation of artists who emerged in the 1950's, including Helen Frankenthaler, Sam Francis, Joan Mitchell, Norman Bluhm, and Paul Jenkins, extended the vein of gesture painting opened up by their elders but, on the whole, in a more lyrical manner. Frankenthaler's fields strewn with stained areas are influenced by Pollock, but where the older artist relied mainly on "dripped" calligraphy, Frankenthaler focused on the interaction of fluid color expanses, buoyant and delicate. In a related manner, Jenkins found iridescent images in the flowing together of pools of thinned paint that he pours on the surfaces of his pictures.

Francis's canvases prior to 1952 are each composed of a luminous, monochromatic curtain of loosely painted, ovular cells. In later works, the cells, singly or in clusters, are multicolored and isolated against fields of white. During the sixties, the forms become sparer and are located near the picture edges, framing the central expanses of limpid white. Mitchell and Bluhm were related more to De Kooning than to any other first-generation painter. Mitchell's images—interlaces of arm-long, swift, arcing strokes—are lyrical and energetic evocations of landscape. Bluhm's paintings, composed of sweeping swaths of pigment, are more muscular and assertive.

A number of younger artists who matured in the environment of Abstract Expressionism took as their subject the human image. This was a natural step since Hofmann, with whom many had studied, taught that artists should begin by observing nature. Moreover, such older gesture painters as De Kooning and Pollock painted figurative pictures in the 1950's.

For younger representational painters, the central problem was to combine close scrutiny of the subject with gestural brush handling, producing "images in the making." Artists could emphasize either, focusing on the observable, on the process of painting (as did Grace Hartigan and Richard Diebenkorn), or remain in between.

Larry Rivers pushed to extremes in both directions. On the one hand, he painted his sitters literally—nakedly, as in his notorious portraits of his mother-in-law—but he also did near-abstract gesture paintings. Throughout much of his career, however, Rivers synthesized the two, spotlighting details of factual rendering ("purple patches," as Parker Tyler called them) against "unfinished" areas—all painted with virtuoso aplomb.

During the 1950's, De Kooning's pictorial ideas were the most influential on younger artists and even on members of his own generation. Augmenting the impact of his ideas was the appeal of his existentialist stance—the intention attributed to his painting that the artist had to discover the image in the struggle of creation, an image that would embody his authentic being. The artist conceived of himself as an existential hero whose direct process of painting was a search, an action opposite to that of picture-making, in which an image was *made* rather than *found*.

This existential attitude came under increasing attack as the 1950's progressed, particularly from John Cage and younger artists influenced by his thinking, among them, Robert Rauschenberg, Jasper Johns, and Allan Kaprow. Cage had no sympathy for the idea that an artist or his art deserve to constitute a center of special interest. Indeed, he challenged the importance of the artist's psychological makeup and existential condition as a source, or mainspring of art. He denied the value of an artist's struggling to forge an image of his own identity in the anxiety-provoking act of creation.

Instead of focusing on the revelation of the artist's private experiences and visions, artistry and taste, Cage emphasized what was experienced through the senses. The "use" of art was to "change ways of seeing," to open one's eyes to "just seeing what there was to see." "I wanted to change my way of seeing, not my way of feeling. I was perfectly happy about my feelings."

Although Cage's attitude was opposed to that of the Abstract Expressionists, he admired their pictures when each constituted "a surface which in no sense has a center of interest. . . . The individual is able to look at first one part and then another, and insofar as he can, to experience the whole. But the whole is such a whole that it doesn't look as if the frame frames it. It looks as if that sort of thing could have continued beyond the frame." Hence Cage described his ideal Abstract Expressionist picture in "impressionist" terms.

In 1958, Jasper Johns began to exhibit a series of pictures whose subjects were commonplace objects or symbols—flags, targets, letters, numbers—but whose designs were filled in with free paintings, resembling that of the gesture painters. In their literalness, his themes constitute a departure from those of the older artists, but his painting technique seems to be related to theirs. However, it actually calls their romantic premises into question. Johns's brushwork is not as impulsive as it appears; rather, he "crafted" the look of De Kooning's and Guston's facture in a dispassionate and detached manner, elevating once again the ideal of the well-painted picture as a major end in art.

Robert Rauschenberg combined found material of city origin—newsprint, billboard fragments, scraps of debris—with gestural painting reminiscent of De Kooning. His work, more explicitly than the pictures of the older Abstract Expressionists, expresses the welter of the urban environment, catching its spectacle with verve, irony, and artistic finesse. Rauschenberg called his works "combines" because he so blurred the boundaries between painting, collage, and sculpture that these traditional headings become meaningless.

Many other artists during the fifties, among whom were the sculptors Richard Stankiewicz and John Chamberlain, explored the possibilities of assemblage. A number attempted to break down the barriers between art and everyday life, creating an art of environmental field. Abstract Expressionist canvases, particularly Pollock's, were influential in this development. Their huge size stimulated Allan Kaprow, Claes Oldenburg, Jim Dine, and others to turn actual spaces into works of art called Environments, and then to stage events in them labeled Happenings. These artists transformed commonplace surroundings into theatrical events—a kind of collage-theater in which are superimposed simultaneously improvisational drama and dance, electronic music, noise, silence, and audience participation.

Such events in time became too impermanent for Oldenburg and Dine; instead, they created paintings and sculptures of mass-produced objects that symbolize the contemporary environment. These artists have been called Pop artists, but they differ from Andy Warhol and Roy Lichtenstein, also categorized under this label. The latter duplicated advertisements, comic strips, and commodities literally—with a minimum of interpretation. Oldenburg and Dine expressed a personal vision of everyday phenomena, thus continuing the romantic spirit of Abstract Expressionism.

During the late 1950's and the 1960's, many young artists extended color-field abstraction in fresh ways. Raymond Parker spread colors on white grounds until each in itself and in relation to the others was ample—visually and emotionally. The process entailed working from within color; the outline of a form (or drawing) was what remained when the colors achieved their fullness. Morris Louis, Kenneth Noland, and Jules Olitski stained areas of thinned paint into unsized canvas. The pigment fuses with the fabric, producing a textural uniformity akin to that created by the Impressionists with their all-over brush dabs. But stained color is "optical" —disembodied—swiftly inundating the eye. In their manner of applying paint, the three artists just mentioned took their cues from Pollock's "dripped" calligraphy and from Frankenthaler's stained areas of color. In the resonance produced—a vibrance that animates the polychromed and bare canvas alike—their work resembles the field painting of Newman, Rothko, and Still.

Although their pictorial ideas were similar, Louis, Noland, and Olitski developed highly individual styles. In his canvases of the late fifties, Louis painted diaphanous veils whose pale and flowing colors call to mind Art Nouveau. In later works, he abridged these open areas into pulsating shafts of multicolored ribbons that thrust across white fields, conveying a strong sense of color compression; in other works, he confined drawing activity to the vertical edges, transforming the canvas white into an expansive color.

Noland's designs—symmetrical patterns of concentric rings, chevrons, and horizontal stripes—also tend to be expansive, reverberating beyond the picture limits. Olitski carried the effect of openness to a greater extreme than Louis or Noland in his recent abstractions, each of which is an atmospheric field of drifting zones of sprayed pigment. The edges are occasionally punctuated by painted lines, for if drawing is kept close to the frame of the canvas it need not destroy the sense of field. The pictures of Louis, Noland, and Olitski are also akin in spirit; they are sensuous and hedonistic, certainly when compared to Still, Rothko, and Newman. The bright palette favored by the younger artists, their soft and buoyant, dyed surfacing, has resulted in works that are decorative in a grand style.

Developing the color-field vein, particularly in the direction of Olitski, are a number of still younger artists generally called the Lyrical Abstractionists, among them Larry Poons, who have resumed 1950's painterly abstraction but with a greater emphasis on the effect of field.

Somewhat related to the stain painters is Ellsworth Kelly, notably in those works, each composed of a separate canvas of a different, single color, but with the significant difference that each of his fields is a shape. Indeed, Kelly's concern with shape led him to construct free-standing, polychromed flat sculptures. However, Kelly also cultivated optical effects that dissolve form. In many of his pictures, simple, matte, hard-edged forms are all positive, in the manner of some of Matisse's late collages, forcing the eye to skim swiftly over them, unable to focus.

Field painting has been so pervasive during the past fifteen years that at this moment, it seems to have become tired, outworn through overuse. Artists increasingly are turning to pictorial construction, resuming a "cubist" impulse, but without repeating the look of earlier styles and thus lapsing into staleness. Foremost among these artists is Al Held. In his monumental black-and-white abstractions of the last few years, he has composed relational structures of massive geometric volumes, impacted like masonry, and paradoxically ambiguous in their interactions. Held muscles his bulky cubic volumes about to create a quality of robustness lacking in field abstraction.

It has been fashionable for more than a decade to proclaim the demise of Abstract Expressionism, as well as romanticism in general, ignoring its unfolding in the works of Frankenthaler, Louis, Noland, Olitski, Oldenburg, Held, and many more of the best of contemporary artists. To be sure, several of the tendencies that emerged during the 1960's were counter in spirit to Abstract Expressionism (but not its thrust to "impressionist" field). At certain moments, such movements as Pop art, Op art, Minimal art, Conceptual art, appeared to signal the end of romanticism, but not for long, for the romantic impulse in art soon reemerged as strong and viable as ever.

GORKY *The Liver is the Cock's Comb* 1944. Oil on canvas, 73¼ x 98 in. (186 x 249 cm.)
Gift of Seymour H. Knox K56:4

POLLOCK *Convergence* **1952.** Oil on canvas, 93½ x 155 in. (237.7 x 393.7 cm.)
Gift of Seymour H. Knox   K56:7

Arshile Gorky

The Liver is the Cock's Comb, 1944, was recognized at an early date as a key work in the development of Gorky's style. André Breton wrote on seeing the work in 1945: "*The Liver is the Cock's Comb* should be considered the great open door to the analogy world. Easy-going amateurs will come here for their meager rewards: in spite of all warning to the contrary, they will insist on seeing in these compositions a still life, a landscape, or a figure instead of daring to face the *hybrid* forms in which all human emotion is precipitated. . . . Here is an art entirely new."*

Despite the orthodox Surrealist insistence on spontaneous expression and the appearance of impulsive laying down of paint and forms, Gorky carefully plotted every aspect of the composition, as a preparatory drawing for the painting reveals.†

The primary of the hybrid forms to which Breton refers is the spongy reddish mass in the lower right, simultaneously liver and cock's comb, opened to reveal a variety of fleshy viscera. According to Julien Levy, Gorky's close friend and dealer, the Greeks considered the liver to be the seat of the soul. It is here "seen erect, proudly touched by rays of the rising sun as the cock crows." ‡ A rich assortment of other suggestive shapes: genitalia, sacs, tumors, organs, and tendrils against a warm earth-brown background all convey the sense of a ravenous optimistic virility, a paean to human and animal fecundity.

Born Vosdanig Adoian in 1905 in Turkish Armenia, Gorky emigrated to the United States in 1920, settling first in New England. He studied art for brief periods in Providence and Boston, but was largely self-taught. In 1925 he moved to New York, where he studied and later taught at the Grand Central School of Art. About 1930 he took the name Gorky after the Russian writer (in Russian, Gorky means "the bitter one") and Arshile, perhaps after the mythical Achilles.

In 1927 he began to imitate Synthetic Cubism as formulated by Picasso, Braque, and Gris. In the late thirties, he added an element of dark fantasy based on freely rendered, symbolic organic shapes, inspired by the Spanish Surrealist Joan Miró.

The arrival of the refugee Surrealists brought Gorky face-to-face with a living European tradition, and he was encouraged to give freer rein to his subconscious. Even more important, his marriage in 1941 coincided with a new era of stability after years of poverty and neglect. Beginning in 1942, he spent considerable time in the country, particularly Virginia and Connecticut, where the scrutiny of natural forms contributed to his use of highly personal symbols that evoked specific incidents from his childhood and expressed the sexuality that he saw as the fundamental undercurrent of nature.

The period of Gorky's mature and original production was tragically short-lived. A succession of disasters, a studio fire, cancer, a disabling auto accident, and a broken marriage led him to commit suicide in 1948, at the age of forty-three.

* *The Eye Spring/Arshile Gorky* (New York: Julien Levy Gallery, 1945), p. 2.
† Collection of Frederick Weisman, Los Angeles.
‡ *Arshile Gorky* (New York: Abrams, 1966), p. 20.

Jackson Pollock

Prior to painting *Convergence* in 1952, Pollock had begun to rely less on his drip technique, to reintroduce suggestions of mythic shapes in his paintings, and to limit his palette to black and white. In *Convergence*, he added the primary colors, red, yellow and blue, and—unlike his earlier drip paintings in which a space existed between the painted area and the canvas edge—he extended the loops and spots of paint over the entire surface, creating an intense activity and virtually eliminating any sense of depth.

Convergence demonstrates Pollock's revolutionary and influential approach to the act of painting. He was one of the first to use line as an independent image rather than to define forms or planes, and to distribute paint equally over the picture surface. This lack of central focus and the related monumental scale of his canvases particularly impressed younger painters. Of equal significance is the importance given to process: the painting constitutes an instantaneous record of the particular creative act, the encounter between painter, his subconscious, pigment, and chance. The uniform and high-keyed color of this painting has been especially influential on later color-field painting.

Jackson Pollock was born in Cody, Wyoming, in 1912 and grew up in Arizona and California. He first studied painting in high school in Los Angeles, but followed an older brother to New York in 1929 to study with the regionalist painter Thomas Hart Benton at the Art Students League, 1930–32. Pollock was employed, with occasional interruptions, on the WPA Federal Art Project from 1935 to 1943. Though his early paintings, dark and dramatic genre scenes from the thirties and primitive totemic images of the early forties, demonstrate great expressionistic individuality, it was not until 1947 that he arrived at his drip and spatter technique. It has been conjectured that Pollock's experience in 1936 of working in the New York studio of the Mexican muralist David Alfaro Siqueiros, who was using spray guns, air brushes, and other unusual methods of spontaneous paint application, proved fruitful to Pollock's later development. Placing his canvas on the floor, then moving around it and occasionally onto it, Pollock flung skeins of heavy pigment from brushes, sticks, and trowels, using the energy generated by his entire body to give free expression to his subconscious. This controlled frenzy, derived from Surrealism's interest in automatism, defined the gestural branch of Abstract Expressionism and proved enormously influential to subsequent painting.

Pollock was killed in an automobile accident in 1956.

BAZIOTES *White Bird* **1957**
Oil on canvas, 60 x 48 in. (152.4 x 121.9 cm.)
Gift of Seymour H. Knox   K57:13

STAMOS *Levant for E.W.R.* **1958**
Oil on canvas, 80 x 70 in. (202.5 x 177.8 cm.)
Gift of Seymour H. Knox   K58:19

William Baziotes

"The things in my painting are intended to strike something that is an emotional involvement—that has to do with the human personality and all the mysteries of life, not simply colors or abstract balances." *

Baziotes's strange and delicate biomorphic images are often suspended in a partially translucent atmosphere, painted in small touches of soft color. The major shape in White Bird, 1957, is composed of irregularly angled and soft-edged projections, representing no specific bird, but conveying the idea of slow levitation and weightlessness. Around this ghostly form, two sharp linear patterns appear, curved horizontal filaments below and a fragile, stylized organism above.

Although his often-quoted statements—"what happens on the canvas is surprising and unpredictable to me" and "to some of us the act of doing [painting] becomes the experience"—seem to ally Baziotes with the gestural branch of Abstract Expressionism, his preoccupation with fanciful imagery remained closer to Surrealism, and his color is muted and subtle in comparison to the more vibrant chromatics used by most of his contemporaries.

William Baziotes was born in 1912 in Pittsburgh and grew up in Reading, Pennsylvania. After working briefly for a newspaper and in a stained-glass factory where friends encouraged him to develop his interest in art, he moved to New York in 1933. For the next three years, he studied at the National Academy of Design under Leon Kroll. He taught in the WPA Federal Art Project, 1936–38, and worked in the Easel Painting Project, 1938–41. In the early forties, he was profoundly affected by the expatriate European Surrealists, who convinced him that abstract painting should both draw from and evoke forces deep within the subconscious. At the same time, friendships with other New York painters, among them Robert Motherwell and Mark Rothko (with whom he founded the Subjects of the Artists School in 1948), led him to be frequently exhibited and associated with Abstract Expressionism. He died in New York in 1963.

* Lawrence Alloway, Baziotes: A Memorial Exhibition (New York: The Solomon R. Guggenheim Museum, 1965), p. 42.

Theodoros Stamos

"The painting *Levant for E.W.R.* was conceived after a trip to Iran. I have for many years been interested in that part of the East, where the sun rises. From Greece eastward, from the Levantine to the 'lever.' *Levant for E.W.R.* was painted in memory of Edward Wales Root [former Curator at the Munson-Williams-Proctor Institute in Utica, New York], a dear friend and collector." *

Rich tones, reminiscent of Near Eastern decoration, contribute a chromatic intensity to this broadly impressionistic landscape. The brown earth mass, blue water, and vivid green vegetation are depicted beneath a brilliant orange sky, suggesting dawn. Energetic paint strokes and smears evoke barely contained natural forces that threaten to disrupt the rectangular zones that structure the surface.

Theodoros Stamos was born of Greek immigrant parents in New York in 1922. After studying sculpture for three years at the American Art School in New York, he turned to painting in 1939 and in this medium is self-taught. Like many other first-generation Abstract Expressionists, his work during the forties was concerned with myth. By the fifties, however, symbolic shapes gave way to the large expanses of dissolved light that have characterized his later paintings.

* Letter from the artist, July 9, 1968.

Willem de Kooning

Gotham News was painted in 1955, one of several abstract landscapes in which dissolved fragments of the female form from the immediately preceding Women series can occasionally be discerned. In the spring of 1955 De Kooning, "moved into a new series of abstractions that relate to earlier black-and-white pictures in the complication of their shapes and to the Women in their heavy, rasping colors and textures. . . . There is a proliferation of images, a piling of ambiguity on top of ambiguity. Sometimes the paint is pushed into wrinkles and folds, like dead flesh. It is as if all the despair in Woman, I [The Museum of Modern Art, New York] and in the black-and-white pictures was heaped together in a gesture of defiant exaltation." *

The newspapers that De Kooning laid directly onto the wet pigment to hasten the drying process have left traces of printed words and images along the edges of the painting. These subtle disjunctures in depth, scale, and reference, together with the crowded confusion of brushstrokes, convey the dizzying disorientation of the contemporary city, as the title discreetly implies.

A tension is generated by the conflict between De Kooning's approach and traditional painting and drawing. Line occasionally models and defines edges and yet, in an ambiguous manner, loses touch with form. Color areas move back and forth so that spatial relationships are never clarified.

Willem de Kooning was born in 1904 in Rotterdam. He left school at twelve and was apprenticed to a commercial art company, where his precocious talent was recognized and he was encouraged to attend evening classes at the Academie voor Beeldende Kunsten en Technische Wetenschappen, 1916–24. After brief periods of study in Antwerp and Brussels, he immigrated to the United States in 1926, settling first in Hoboken, New Jersey, where he supported himself as a housepainter. A year later he established his studio in New York and worked as a commercial artist until 1935, when a year with the WPA Federal Art Project allowed him to concentrate full-time on painting.

Throughout his career, De Kooning has oscillated between a dominant interest in the figure against a ground and a more abstract distribution of fragmented lines and planes. His abstractions from the late twenties and thirties gradually gave way to figure studies in the early forties. These in turn were supplanted by the bold black-and-white enamel abstractions that constituted his influential first one-man show in 1948. In 1950 he embarked of his Women series, which, with abstract landscapes, have continued to occupy him up to the present.

* Thomas B. Hess, Willem de Kooning, (New York: The Museum of Modern Art, 1968), p. 102.

DE KOONING *Gotham News* **1955.** Oil on canvas, 69 x 79 in. (175.2 x 200.6 cm.)
Gift of Seymour H. Knox K55:6

33

Bradley Walker Tomlin

In *No. 12—1952*, spontaneous brushstrokes show the influence of Abstract Expressionism while the orderly design of the painting gives evidence of Tomlin's earlier interest in Cubism. It is the remarkable fusion of these two styles, theoretically opposite, that characterized Tomlin's mature work. Color in his paintings is usually somewhat low-keyed, like that of the Cubists, with occasional bright accents as in this painting, where the basic gray-green is enlivened by spots of orange, unified by repeated strokes of white. In his paintings of the late forties, he frequently used a twisting, calligraphic stroke that later became more noticeably angular and positive and, often as in the white strokes in *No. 12—1952*, of an almost uniform width. Spontaneity is clearly visible in the uneven opacity of the paint that records the movement of the brush, and in the occasional drips of paint.

Bradley Walker Tomlin was born in 1899 in Syracuse, New York. He showed an early artistic talent and by the time he graduated from Syracuse University in 1921, he had won a number of awards and received several professional commissions. He immediately moved to New York City, where he became a successful designer of magazine covers while he continued to paint. In 1923 he went to England and France, studying at the Académie Colarossi and Académie de la Grande Chaumière in Paris, returning to New York in the fall of 1924.

About 1939 he changed his style abruptly from a modified realism to a somewhat decorative Cubism in which poetic symbolism is more evident than the pure relation of forms. In the mid-forties, he began to be influenced by his Abstract Expressionist friends—Gottlieb, Guston, Motherwell, and Pollock—and by 1949 he had arrived at his unique combination of Cubism and Abstract Expressionism, which he continued to develop until his death in New York in 1953.

TOMLIN *No. 12–1952* **1952**
Oil on canvas, 66 x 48 in. (167.6 x 121.9 cm.)
George Cary, Charles Clifton, and Edmund Hayes Funds   63:1

GOTTLIEB *Dialogue I* **1960.** Oil on canvas, 66 x 132 in. (167.6 x 335.2 cm.)
Gift of Seymour H. Knox   K61:1

MOTHERWELL *Elegy to the Spanish Republic #34* 1953–54. Oil on canvas, 80 x 100 in. (202.5 x 253.3 cm.) Gift of Seymour H. Knox K57:6

37

Adolph Gottlieb

Although Gottlieb's palette frequently involved delicate and sensitive color treatment, *Dialogue I*, 1960, is restricted to a severe and almost classical palette of red and black on white. Instead of his more usual vertical format, this painting retains the horizontal division into sky and earth of landscape. Unlike his earlier impasto, the paint is thinned with turpentine so that the swift and slashing brush leaves an instantaneous record of its passage in the drips, drags, and spatters. Faint turpentine halos cause the disks to appear to shift quietly in space.

Gottlieb's underlying concern is the dualism within the universe that man must resolve. "A radiant astral disc hovering over a seething earth mass is a statement of radical opposition, and these forms—one calm, defined, and tightly contained, the other undisciplined, in flux—suggest interpretations ranging from the actual to the metaphysical: male and female, sun and earth, order and chaos, creation and destruction, reason and emotion—positive and negative entities essential to one another that interact across the charged field of the canvas." *

Also in the Gallery collection is the artist's *Frozen Sounds II*, 1952.

Born in 1903 in New York, Gottlieb studied with Robert Henri and John Sloan, prominent figures in the Ashcan School, at the Art Students League, 1920. In 1921 he went to Europe, studying briefly in Paris and visiting museums in Germany. Back in New York in 1923, he was a founding member with Rothko of The Ten, a pioneer organization dedicated to the encouragement of abstract painting. He worked for a short time on the WPA Federal Art Project and in 1937 moved to Arizona for two years.

His work can be classified into three phases. His "pictographs," 1941–51, divided the canvas into unequal rectangular compartments, each containing an image derived from primitive myths or the subconscious. The "imaginary landscapes" begun in 1951, such as Frozen Sounds II, separated stylizations of sky and earth by a sharp horizon line. In the most recent "bursts," begun in 1957 and evolving from the landscapes, large floating discs appear above loosely brushed areas in the lower portions of the canvases.

* Martin Friedman, *Gottlieb* (Minneapolis: Walker Art Center, 1963), p. [7].

Robert Motherwell

Motherwell undertook what would become known subsequently as the Elegy to the Spanish Republic series in 1948 after he came upon the dominant motif while decorating a page of poetry by Harold Rosenberg. Though the series now numbers over one hundred, each painting contains the same stark black-and-white forms alternated in a ponderous funereal rhythm. The earliest Elegies exercised a considerable impact on black-and-white painting that flourished in New York about 1950.

"#34 is certainly one of the half-dozen most realized of the Spanish Elegy series, though saying this reminds me that when it was first exhibited Hans Hofmann told me that it was a great picture, but five or ten per cent unfinished. I knew what he meant, that it could have had a more 'finished' aspect, but I chose to stop at the moment that I thought the expression of feeling was wholly complete, and I do not regret it.

"It differs from many of the elegies in having more color in it (relatively speaking), though there are some even more colorful ones in the 1960's." *

Elegy #34 of 1953–54 is smaller than some of the mural-sized paintings in the series. Nevertheless, it has an imposing monumentality because of the relatively enlarged scale of the black verticals and ovoids. More important than any attempt to make the evident sexuality of the major configurations specific is the tension that exists between colors and shapes and the forces they symbolically represent. The pressures and points of tangency between ovoids and verticals and the contrast of black and white refer to life and death or, in terms of the existential philosophy that interests Motherwell, between the freedom that allows self-definition and the removal of choice that constitutes self-destruction.

Born in 1915 in Aberdeen, Washington, Motherwell spent his first twenty-five years on the West Coast, primarily in San Francisco. At Stanford University, 1932–36, he began to develop his lifelong interests in philosophy, psychoanalytic theory, and aesthetics, which he pursued in graduate school at Harvard University, 1937–38, and Columbia, 1940. In 1941, he decided to devote himself professionally to painting. Motherwell soon became intimate with the exiled European artists in New York, particularly the Surrealists. with whom he shared a deep interest in the processes of the unconscious. One of the most intellectual figures of the New York School, Motherwell has written prolifically, recording the history and defending the cause of the avant-garde.

* Letter from the artist, October 18, 1968.

Clyfford Still

In April, 1964, Clyfford Still gave thirty-one of his paintings, dating from 1937 to 1963, to The Buffalo Fine Arts Academy. Added to two important prior acquisitions, *1954* and *1957—D No. 1*, this group of works constitutes a unique record of the artist's career.

In 1959, an exhibition of seventy-two paintings by Still was shown at the Albright Art Gallery. In 1966, *Clyfford Still: Thirty-three Paintings in the Albright-Knox Art Gallery* was published, which includes full-color reproductions of the paintings, a statement by the artist, a foreword by Katharine Kuh, and biographical notes.

"I held it imperative to evolve an instrument of thought which would aid in cutting through all cultural opiates, past and present, so that a direct, immediate, and truly free vision could be achieved, and an idea be revealed with clarity. . . .

"Thus it was necessary to reject the superficial value of material—its qualities, its tensions, and its concomitant ethic. Especially it became necessary not to remain trapped in the banal concepts of space and time, nor yield to the morbidity of 'the objective position'; nor to permit one's courage to be perverted by authoritarian devices for social control.

"It was as a journey that one must make, walking straight and alone. No respite or short-cuts were permitted. And one's will had to hold against every challenge of triumph, or failure, or the praise of Vanity Fair. Until one had crossed the darkened and wasted valleys and come at last into clear air and could stand on a high and limitless plain. Imagination, no longer fettered by the laws of fear, became as one with Vision. And the Act, intrinsic and absolute, was its meaning, and the bearer of its passion.

"The work itself, whether thought of as image of idea, as revelation, or as a manifest of meaning, could not have existed without a profound concern to achieve a purpose beyond vanity, ambition, or remembrance, for a man's term of life." *

Clyfford Still was born November 30, 1904, in Grandin, North Dakota. Shortly after his birth, the family moved to Spokane, Washington and, in 1910, homesteaded in Alberta, Canada. After graduating from Spokane University in 1933, he went to Washington State University in Pullman, receiving an M.A. degree in 1935 and remaining to teach, 1935–41. From the fall of 1941 until the summer of 1943, Still worked in the war industries—aircraft and shipbuilding—in Oakland, California, and later in San Francisco. He lived in New York, 1945–46, where he exhibited at Peggy Guggenheim's Art of This Century Gallery. In 1946, he returned to San Francisco to teach at the California School of Fine Arts. In 1950 Still again moved to New York. Since 1960 he has lived and worked in Maryland.

* *Paintings by Clyfford Still* (Albright Art Gallery, 1959), pp. [8–9].

Ad Reinhardt

A tireless polemicist against excess, hypocrisy, and superficiality in painting, Reinhardt conducted a lifelong crusade for an art purified of gesture, pictorial incident, and color. From the beginning, he committed himself to the logical pursuit of a stripped-down geometry of regular flat forms placed along increasingly strict vertical and horizontal axes. In *No. 15, 1952,* against a deep-blue field, flat brick shapes of close-valued greens and brown appear to vibrate, intensifying the blue background and setting up an illusory shifting in depth. The implied space of these floating rectangles is deliberately contradicted, however, since the high-keyed greens that tend to come forward are, with only one exception, overlapped and fixed in space by the deeper, normally receding tones. The asymmetrically placed rectangles appear to be gravitating toward a central vertical axis, drawing attention to the imposing height of the canvas.

Reinhardt carried this rigid geometry progressively further. In 1953 he renounced color and by 1960 had devised his final paintings of nearly-black trisected squares. With this ultimate rejection of all but the minimum pictorial means, Reinhardt believed he had painted the last possible painting. Indeed, this format would be repeated with only minor tonal variations until his death.

Born in Buffalo, New York, in 1913, Ad Reinhardt showed a marked and precocious interest in art—drawing, copying, and cartooning prolifically. After graduating from Columbia College, New York, in 1936, he studied painting with Carl Holty, Francis Criss, and Karl Anderson. From 1937 to 1941 he worked on the WPA Easel Painting Project. The only New York School painter to begin and end his career as an abstract artist, he was a member of the American Abstract Artists from 1937, a year after the organization of the group, until 1942. During 1946–50, he continued the study of art history, concentrating on Far Eastern art. He died in New York in 1967.

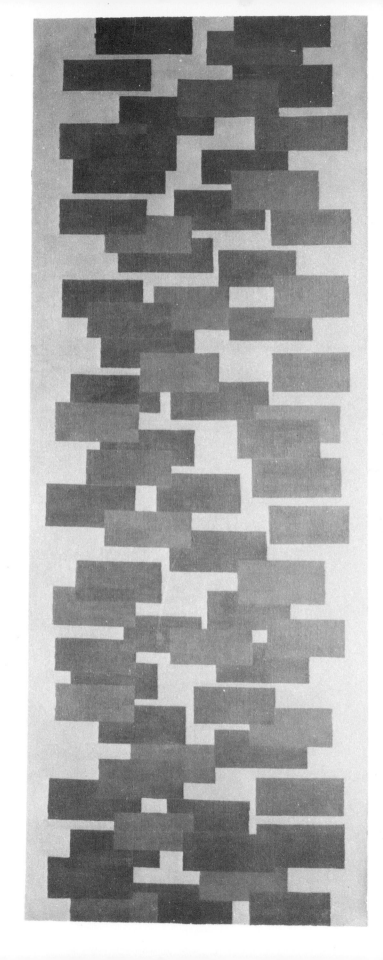

REINHARDT *No. 15, 1952* 1952
Oil on canvas, 108 x 40 in.
(274.2 x 101.5 cm.)
Gift of Seymour H. Knox   K58:42

Mark Rothko

Orange and Yellow, 1956, is representative of Rothko's work from the mid-fifties, not only in the vibrant optimistic buoyancy of the two colors, but also in their selection from closely adjacent points on the spectrum. Oil paint is thinly diffused to leave no trace of the brush or hand of the painter and to avoid any explicit edge or boundary between the various color zones. The imposing size and intensely saturated color provide the viewer with a heightened sensory experience and invite a meditative state of mind. Space and the relationship between the rectangles and the framing edges is left deliberately ambiguous. Faint halations of light appearing to emanate from beneath the surface suggest an awesome and mysterious presence.

By the 1960's, Rothko's palette and mood darkened; his earlier light-filled canvases were superseded by somber and austere paintings.

Mark Rothko emigrated to Portland, Oregon, from his native Dvinsk, Russia, in 1913 at the age of ten. He studied liberal arts at Yale University, 1921–23, then went to New York where he began painting. A brief period of study under Max Weber at the Art Students League constituted his entire formal art training.

With Adolph Gottlieb, he founded The Ten in 1935, a loose association that exhibited and encouraged advanced painting. Like most of his contemporaries, he worked on the WPA Federal Art Project, 1936–37. A one-man exhibition in New York in 1945 at Peggy Guggenheim's Art of This Century Gallery first brought him to public attention.

During the forties Rothko's imagery, like that of most of the New York School painters, relied on Surrealist-inspired myth and fantasy. By the fifties, he had simplified his approach to exclude all line and movement in a new monumentality consisting of a few soft-edged horizontal rectangles superimposed on a vertical ground.

Rothko taught during the summers of 1946 and 1947 at the California School of Fine Arts in San Francisco and later at the Subjects of the Artists School in New York, which he cofounded in 1948 with Motherwell and Baziotes. Rothko committed suicide in New York in 1970.

ROTHKO *Orange and Yellow* **1956**
Oil on canvas, 91 x 71 in. (231.2 x 180.3 cm.)
Gift of Seymour H. Knox K56:8

Franz Kline

His paintings of the fifties, such as *New York, N.Y.*, 1953, and *Requiem*, 1958, have been described by Katharine Kuh:

"[Kline inflated] a few heavy black lines to monumental proportions. However he did not merely paint black lines on a white background; the white is equally important structurally and is often superimposed over the black. Dashing on pigment with great spontaneity, he suggested the undecorated brute force we tend to identify with urban America. Our national dependence on the "loud speaker" possibly grows out of the same need for amplification. If Kline tended to negate traditional form, there is no doubt that his aggressive, jagged, open designs describe an illimitable space. His work has hypnotic immediacy; one feels projected directly into the picture, recapturing each brushstroke as it was painted. By blowing up only one structural unit, Kline was often able to describe a whole metropolis—not how it looked to him but how he felt about it as he painted." *

Franz Kline was born in Wilkes-Barre, Pennsylvania, in 1910. He studied painting at Boston University, 1931–35, and at Heatherly's Art School in London, 1937–38. Returning to the United States, he settled in New York in 1938 and soon became interested in the work of the artists who were to become the Abstract Expressionists. His own painting during the thirties and forties, however, consisted of melancholy portraits, landscapes, and city scenes in which, as with his later work, line plays an important role. Although he painted occasional abstractions during the late forties, the dramatic conversion to his mature style dates from 1949, when a friend placed several of his small sketches in a projector, throwing boldly magnified linear strokes upon the opposite wall. The new approach required new tools and he soon replaced artists' brushes and pigments with wide housepainters' brushes and quick-flowing enamel. Kline first came to public attention when these early black-and-white abstractions were shown in New York in 1950. Although he subsequently reintroduced color toward the end of the fifties, black and white remained his characteristic idiom. After a long illness, he died in New York in 1962.

* *Break-up: The Core of Modern Art* (Greenwich, Conn.: New York Graphic Society, 1969), p. 101.

KLINE *Requiem* **1958**
Oil on canvas, 101½ x 75 in. (257.8 x 190.5 cm.)
Gift of Seymour H. Knox   K59:4

48

Hans Hofmann

During the mid-1930's, Hofmann's landscapes and interiors had attempted to combine brilliant Matisse-inspired color with Cubist structure. Under the impact of Surrealism, his work became freer and his imagery more fantastic and increasingly schematic until finally, about 1944, he developed a new, totally abstract approach.

The title of *Exuberance*, 1955, seems to describe the expressionistic manner of the painting's execution, rather than the subject. Hofmann always maintained that he based his pictures on nature and, indeed, one can discern references to a studio interior behind the active surface. His characteristically vivid colors, blue, green, orange, and yellow, are applied in long, slashing strokes, the disintegrated edges of his Cubist-inspired planes.

His slightly later *Summer Night's Dream*, 1957, replaces the active surface with a more restrained though equally dynamic balance of opposing forces: thinly painted or bare canvas areas versus thick impasto, hard edges versus irregular broken contours, oppositions of intense hues and all tendencies toward deep space constantly pulled back to the surface. "Hofmann saw the picture surface consciously as a responsive rather than inert object, and painting itself as an affair of prodding and pushing, scoring and marking, rather than simply inscribing or covering." *

Hofmann's charged surfaces and active, inventive paint application (he dripped and spattered paint several years before Pollock) had an important impact on the first and second generations of American Abstract Expressionists. His celebrated "push and pull" theory, which acknowledges the overwhelming significance of the picture surface, and his selection of the rectangle or plane as the configuration best adjusted to the over-all shape of the canvas and the framing edge proved influential to the ideas of a younger generation.

Born in 1880 in Weissenberg, Germany, Hans Hofmann showed a precocious interest in music and science and began to study art in 1898 in Munich. He spent ten years in Paris, 1904–14, during the critical period of the development and the major statements of both the Fauves and Cubists. There he met Picasso, Braque, Matisse, and Robert Delaunay whose investigations of the properties of pure color particularly impressed him. Caught in Munich by the outbreak of World War I, he began an influential teaching career by founding his own art school, which flourished until 1932. After spending the summers of 1930 and 1931 teaching at the University of California at Berkeley, he immigrated permanently to the United States and soon opened art schools in New York and Provincetown, Massachusetts, where an impressive number of painters were trained. He died in 1966, in New York.

* Clement Greenberg, *Hans Hofmann* (Paris: Georges Fall, 1961), p. 24.

HOFMANN *Exuberance* **1955**
Oil on canvas, 50¼ x 40 in. (127.6 x 101.6 cm.)
Gift of Seymour H. Knox   K55:8

HOFMANN *Summer Night's Dream* **1957**
Oil on canvas, 52 x 60¼ in. (132.1 x 153 cm.)
Gift of Seymour H. Knox K58:4

Jack Tworkov

"*East Barrier*, 1960, is one of a series of paintings all called *Barriers*. It is especially related to a painting in Mr. Donald Blinken's collection in New York called *West Barrier*. The two paintings are approximately the same dimensions and were at one point considered a pair. . . . All of the *Barrier* series stressed large, looming, perhaps threatening masses entering the canvas usually from the top and side. These masses or formations avoided hard outlines and were the result of an accumulation of rather long strokes, which served as a basic structural element akin to the dot in a Seurat painting. The color in these paintings was more tonal, more naturalistic and tended towards the monochromatic.

"The *Barrier* series as well as the new paintings which I have been engaged in since about 1965 derive from some dense and rather moody pencil and charcoal drawings which I began making as far back as 1954. I believe that the rather black conté drawings of Seurat had some influence on me. I came to appreciate these drawings not as sketches for paintings, but for the quality of monochromatic gray and black and for the role stroke played in building up masses. I conceived the desire to carry over these qualities into the material and scale of paintings. My recent paintings go much further in approaching this point of view." *

The color in *East Barrier* is black and white, with a red section at the right, and strokes of blue and some brown within the black area.

Jack Tworkov was born in Biala, Poland, in 1900 and immigrated to the United States at the age of thirteen, to live in New York. He studied at Columbia University, 1920–23, majoring in English, but left to attend classes at the National Academy of Design, 1923–25, and the Art Students League, 1925–26. His still lifes, landscapes, portraits, and figure studies of the twenties and thirties reflected his enthusiasm for modern European painting and his particular interest in the work of Cézanne. From 1935 until 1941, he worked with the Easel Division of the WPA Federal Art Project. By the late forties, he was deeply involved with Abstract Expressionism; he was an original member of The Club, where many of the principles of that movement were formulated, and for several years rented a studio adjoining that of De Kooning, a friend from the WPA days. His work until the mid-sixties is characterized by broad, spontaneous brushstrokes, limited palette, and, frequently, a grid—implied, visible, or partially visible. In the paintings of recent years, the grid-patterning is more dominant, the size of the brushstrokes is much reduced, and his palette, while still limited, is more low-keyed in color. Except for periods when he has taught in other parts of the country, Tworkov has continued to live in New York and Provincetown, Massachusetts, where he began spending the summers in 1923. He was Chairman of the Art Department, Yale University, 1963–69.

* Letter from the artist, July 26, 1968.

TWORKOV *East Barrier* **1960**
Oil on canvas, 92 x 81 in. (233.7 x 208.2 cm.)
Gift of Seymour H. Knox   K61:7

GUSTON *Voyage* **1956**
Oil on canvas, 72 x 76 in. (182.9 x 193 cm.)
Gift of Seymour H. Knox   K57:4

BROOKS *Cooba* **1963**
Oil on canvas, 80 x 74 in. (203.2 x 188 cm.)
Gift of Seymour H. Knox   K64:1

Philip Guston

"This picture has a special importance for me—it is a culminating point of a period of my work." * In Voyage, 1956, the movement toward a more massive solidity that would characterize the later development of Guston's painting can be seen in the gradual coalescence of the irregular color forms. The creamy pinks of the earlier years give way to sharp oranges, greens, and, most significantly, to the grays and blacks that would dominate his later work. Despite the often fairly heavy impasto that draws attention to the surface, the smudges, intermediate tones, and eroded edges create the impression of an amorphous mass suspended in indeterminate space.

The tremulous color strokes appear to convey a high-pitched emotional state, which led Sam Hunter to observe that these paintings "are not so much demonstrations of some 'action' principle as they are luminous signs of moments of consciousness, moments which have their source in great depths and bear their own mysterious charge of poetry." †

Also in the Gallery collection is the artist's painting Morning, 1959.

Philip Guston was born in 1912 in Montreal, the son of Russian immigrants. He grew up in Los Angeles, where three months at the Otis Art Institute constituted his only formal art education. In 1934 he went to Mexico to study contemporary murals, an interest that he pursued as a mural painter for the WPA Federal Arts Project in Los Angeles, 1934–35, and in New York, 1936–40. In 1941 he turned to easel painting, frequently producing somber studies of children in desolate surroundings which shortly established his reputation as a leading American figurative painter. He taught in the Middle West, 1941–47, and in 1948 returned to New York, where he soon became involved with Abstract Expressionism and changed his painting style completely. By 1950 all traces of landscape and figures were eliminated, replaced by abstract compositions of overlapping flat planes. Although closely related to action painting, his canvases were less violently gestural than those of Pollock and De Kooning; instead of an over-all treatment of the canvas, Guston tended to retain a central focal point. Because of the particularly luminous quality of his color, critics have called his paintings Abstract Impressionist. In the sixties, his palette and forms became increasingly dark and dense, and he reintroduced figures, now broadly caricatured.

* Letter from the artist, March 16, 1960.
† Art Since 1945 (New York: Washington Square Press, 1962), pp. 317–18.

James Brooks

"*Cooba* [1963] . . . is in oil, but has characteristics (blotting of areas, washes) that caused me to turn thereafter mostly to acrylic emulsion, a water medium that accomplishes these more readily. Paintings at this time were occupied with breaking through the linear continuum by isolating forms of a shape that would repel each other, then relating them to a slightly felt scaffolding and an irrational meandering line." *

The adjustment of opposites in the painting—closed form versus open line, clear definition versus ambiguity and, most significantly, chance versus deliberate manipulation—constitutes the core of Brooks's art. It is in this deliberation, whose underlying presence always makes itself felt in spite of the obvious incidence of chance and accident, as well as the cool palette and thin, restrained paint application, that Brooks distinguishes himself from the more violent gestural painters.

James Brooks was born in St. Louis, Missouri, in 1906. He moved frequently as a child throughout the Southwest, but settled long enough in Dallas to attend Southern Methodist University, 1923–25, and the Dallas Art Institute, 1925–26. In 1926 he moved to New York, taking night classes at the Art Students League, 1927–30, while supporting himself as a commercial letterer. From 1931 to 1934, he roamed throughout the West and Southwest, sketching and painting in a social-realist manner. He abandoned easel painting to work on murals for the WPA Federal Art Project, which occupied him exclusively from 1936 until 1942. He served in North Africa as an army artist during World War II.

In 1949, closely observing Pollock's drip paintings, Brooks experimented with pouring pigment on the back of unsized canvas, letting the configurations that stained through suggest points of departure and elaboration. This simultaneous balance between spontaneity and control is one of the key elements of his achievement. About 1953 he abandoned fluidity in favor of a densely packed structure. Gant, 1955, is an important example of this technique. In the early 1960's, he added a sharp, linear calligraphy to his flat, irregular forms.

* Letter from the artist, July 17, 1968.

MARCA-RELLI *Odalisque* **1957.** Oil and collage, 66 x 83 in. (167.5 x 211 cm.)
Gift of Seymour H. Knox   K58:7

OKADA *White and Gold* **1961.** Oil on canvas, 93 x 118 in. (236.2 x 299.7 cm.)
Gift of Seymour H. Knox K61:22

Conrad Marca-Relli

Odalisque, 1957, as the title indicates, makes explicit reference to the pictorial tradition of the reclining female nude. Anatomical fragments whose contours suggest muscular thighs, calves, and shoulders, appear to undulate in shallow depth across the canvas. At the same time, the insistent tactility of the collage fragments emphasizes the flatness of both the individual elements and the canvas as a whole. Despite the complex layering of the painting, Marca-Relli's working method allows for a good measure of spontaneity. Fragments of raw and painted canvas, cut with a razor blade, are coated with black paint and glue and pinned, often several layers deep, to the supporting canvas. The shifting and rearranging of shapes allows the glue to seep out from behind, providing irregular, dark linear accents to the muted blue-brown palette derived from earlier Cubist collage. Unlike both Cubist collage, which exploited a variety of independent shapes and textures, and Dadaist collage, which sought a multitude of extra-pictorial associations, Marca-Relli alone has used canvas as the primary collage material.

Conrad Marca-Relli was born in 1913 in Boston. He began his frequent travels to Europe as a child and received his first drawing lessons in Italy, where the classical tradition impressed him deeply. He returned to New York to finish high school and then studied for one year at Cooper Union. He worked on the WPA Federal Art Project, 1935–38, which permitted him to devote himself exclusively to painting for the first time and brought him in contact with De Kooning, Kline, and others who were to become major figures in the New York School. During the forties, he painted abstract cityscapes, circus scenes, and landscapes with flattened, stylized shapes within a dreamlike space, such as Beach Stand, 1941, in the Gallery collection.

In 1953 he traveled to Mexico, where he was impressed by the sharp contrasts between the flat white of adobe buildings and the black shadows cast in the brilliant sun. When he ran out of paint, he began to experiment with collage whose immediacy and tactile quality provided the weight and materiality he had always sought in his painting. He continued to develop and extend the range of collage, more recently to metal, to a point beyond its original associations with a careful and refined European tradition to fulfill the demands for scale, expressionism, and ambiguity of avant-garde American painting.

Kenzo Okada

Onto the heroic scale of Abstract Expressionist painting, Okada super-imposes a distinctly Oriental sensitivity. In *White and Gold*, 1961, the muted elegance of the ocher, buff, and off-white palette is modulated only by the two wide intersecting bands of gray and red. A suggestion of a close-up view of two vertical screen panels at the right and the contradiction of depth through the distribution of flat shapes recall devices of traditional Japanese design. Crisp linear ridges of paint left by the spatula and overlapping layers of color create delicate textural interest and activate the broad white expanses.

An earlier painting in the Gallery collection, *Dynasty*, 1956, appears to illustrate Okada's reverence for nature. The cool tones and the composition suggest a fraction of bank beside a pool, seen in the shortened and abrupt perspective of a Japanese print.

Kenzo Okada was born in 1902 in Yokohama, Japan. After a year and a half at the Tokyo Fine Arts University, he studied in Paris, 1924–27. Returning to Japan, he exhibited widely, taught, and gained prominence as a leading realist painter. In 1950 he moved to New York City, where he adopted an abstract approach. Okada believes that the process of painting should be spontaneous. Unlike the emotional gestures of other Abstract Expressionists, however, he proceeds from a state of emptiness induced by meditation, creating "without knowing." He has coined a term for his approach, "yugenism," from the Japanese word yugen, meaning cryptic or mysterious. Okada now lives and works near Albany, New York.

Grace Hartigan

"I was interested in how to present an inner emotional state, in abstraction but related to nature. I painted *New England, October* in East Hampton [1957] after an autumn trip to Maine. I was especially moved by Castine, the yellows of the trees in the rain, the glimpses of white colonial doorways. I think I am being objective when I say I think the color in the painting is quite beautiful. . . . I was (and still am in another way) interested in my kind of an 'all over' painting. At that time I used thrusting planes against more organic forms. Also apparent is that none of these forms had any reference to the look of the visual world." *

In *New England, October*, interwoven planes and twisting lines in the upper half of the canvas are in sharp contrast to the broad ocher of the lower portion. The paint was vigorously manipulated, recording swift brush and knife strokes, and leaving areas of impasto.

Grace Hartigan was born in Newark, New Jersey, in 1922 and lived as a child in Bayonne and Millburn. After high school, she moved to California, where she began to attend drawing classes. In 1943 she returned to the East, where she worked in a defense plant as a draftsman and painted during the evenings and on weekends, studying with Isaac Lane Muse, who encouraged her to continue painting. In 1949, after a year in Mexico, she joined a group of young artists in New York who met for discussions at Studio 35 on Eighth Street, where they also exhibited. Strongly influenced by the older generation of Abstract Expressionists, particularly De Kooning and Pollock, Hartigan has continued to preserve a quasi-representational, freely brushed approach, but with a more limited palette and an increased emphasis on linearity in her recent work.

* Letter from the artist, July 12, 1968.

HARTIGAN *New England, October* **1957.** Oil on canvas, 68¼ x 83 in. (73.3 x 210.2 cm.)
Gift of Seymour H. Knox K58:2

63

Richard Pousette-Dart

"My intention is never the surface but always the inner expression. I strive for the poetic, musical spirit of form through line. All of my work is an attempt to make a structure which stands up by the presence and significance of its own mystical meaning. It is a thing within itself, mirroring different things to different minds." *

Pousette-Dart's characteristic vocabulary of repetitive symbols—ovals, circles, and diamonds—hints at highly stylized totemic figures frozen in postures of ritualistic significance. Paint is applied in numerous, small heavily impastoed daubs rather than in the broad, sweeping gestures of many other Abstract Expressionists. Although the dominant tone of *In the Forest*, 1957, is white, a variety of rich blues, greens, yellows, and browns is imbedded in the spaces between the linear shapes, testifying to Pousette-Dart's reputation as an accomplished colorist. Shapes and structure appear to be struggling to emerge from the densely packed and crumbled surface and provide a metaphor for the artist's conviction that the mysteries of life are hidden and that the act of painting consists of their gradual revelation.

Richard Pousette-Dart was born in 1916 in St. Paul, Minnesota. His family moved to the East when he was two. Though he is completely self-taught as an artist, he acknowledges the important influences on his development of his mother, a poet, and his father, Nathaniel Pousette-Dart, a painter and noted writer on art. Beginning in 1936, he worked in New York and painted at night until he decided in 1940 to devote himself exclusively to art. Pousette-Dart considers himself a religious painter attempting to uncover the fundamental nature of existence. Like Pollock, Gottlieb, Baziotes, and a number of other painters, his work of the early forties consisted of a variety of evocative linear shapes and totemic symbols, often within a grid design. Unlike the other Abstract Expressionists, however, Pousette-Dart has maintained this interest in myth and mystery as a key to experience throughout his career. Although he is known primarily as a painter, he has also made collages and constructions of painted wire and scrap metal. Since 1950, he has lived and worked in Rockland County outside New York City.

* *Art News*, April, 1961, p. 34.

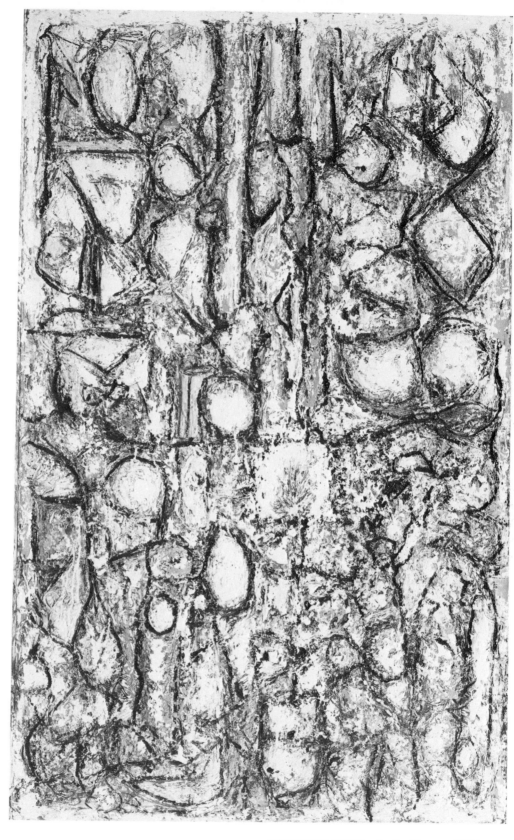

POUSETTE-DART *In the Forest* **1957**
Oil on canvas, 72½ x 43¼ in. (184 x 110 cm.)
Gift of Seymour H. Knox   K58:41

65

Sam Francis

Despite his reputation as a sensuous colorist, Francis's earliest paintings were practically monochromatic, often in blacks, grays, or tinted whites and composed of densely packed vertical flakes. By 1952, as with his *Blue-Black* (also in the collection), the dark areas were broken up to reveal a field of luminous color. Although an affinity has been noted between these early works and the style of Jackson Pollock in the distribution of emphasis over the canvas and the apparently random blurs and drips, it should be remembered that the paths of the two artists never crossed.

The Whiteness of the Whale, 1957–58, is a key painting in Francis's concern for the tension between white and the opposing forces of color. The title is taken verbatim from a chapter in Herman Melville's *Moby Dick* that consists entirely of a disquisition on the "elusive something in the innermost idea of this hue [white] which strokes more panic to the soul than the redness which affrights in blood." The white field, far from being empty and uninflected, is composed of a richly textured welter of daubs and appears a subtle yet powerful counterforce to the stream of brilliantly colored cells.

In some of Francis's more recent work, the white fields that Melville had equated with "the heartless voids and immensities of the universe," have continued to expand, relegating the vestiges of color to the farthest extremes of the edges.

Also in the collection is an untitled painting of 1956.

Born in San Mateo, California, in 1923, Sam Francis studied medicine and psychology at the University of California at Berkeley. A severe spinal injury incurred in 1943 during an air force mission resulted in an extended period of hospitalization during which Francis began painting in watercolors. After leaving the hospital, he studied briefly at the California School of Fine Arts in San Francisco and enrolled again in 1948 at Berkeley, where he received an M.A. degree in 1950.

In 1950 he went to Paris and immediately became acquainted with a small group of North American expatriate painters, particularly the Canadian Jean-Paul Riopelle. Francis remained in Paris, with few interruptions, until 1957, when he undertook a lengthy journey around the world, stopping for several months in Japan, where the culture and artistic tradition impressed him profoundly. After a second world tour in 1959, he returned to Paris and began to make lithographs, which have since constituted an important part of his production. Since 1961 he has lived in Santa Monica, California, though he continues to travel widely and maintains studios in several parts of the world.

FRANCIS *The Whiteness of the Whale* **1957**
Oil on canvas, 104½ x 85½ in. (265.4 x 218.2 cm.)
Gift of Seymour H. Knox   K59:2

Richard Diebenkorn

Although *Woman in a Window*, 1957, is a figurative painting, it is tightly structured in an abstract sense—the horizontal, vertical, and diagonal elements converge at the center, focusing on the figure of a woman who is looking out the window at the horizon and the sea. The contrasts between closed and open spaces, as well as constraint and freedom in approach, are reflected in the relationship of the figure to the landscape, both formally and psychologically. The evocative treatment of color and light establishes a strong sense of place while conveying a mood of reverie and solitude. Diebenkorn's bold handling of paint, reminiscent of the Abstract Expressionists, serves as a reminder of the picture surface. As he wrote in 1957, "One wants to see the artifice of the thing as well as the subject. Reality has to be digested, it has to be transmuted by paint." *

Born in 1922 in Portland, Oregon, Richard Diebenkorn studied art at Stanford University and the University of California, Berkeley, 1940–43. He enrolled at the California School of Fine Arts, San Francisco, in 1946; the following year he joined the faculty there, which also included Clyfford Still and Elmer Bischoff. In 1949 he received a B.A. degree from Stanford University and in 1952 an M.A. from the University of New Mexico.

Until the early fifties, Diebenkorn painted in an Abstract Expressionist style with frequent references to landscape in his work. In 1955 he began to distrust the "super-emotional" approach to painting and started to apply the working method of Abstract Expressionism to more explicitly figurative subject matter, usually the genre subjects of his home and studio. In his recent paintings, representational subjects have been eliminated again and the emphasis placed on areas of rich color in quasi-geometric compositions.

Except for brief periods in the East and abroad, Diebenkorn has continued to live and work in California.

* *Contemporary Bay Area Figurative Painting* (Oakland, Calif.: The Oakland Art Museum, 1957), p. 12.

DIEBENKORN *Woman in a Window* **1957**
Oil on canvas, 59 x 56 in. (149.8 x 142.2 cm.)
Gift of Seymour H. Knox K58:32

Helen Frankenthaler

Although the title of *Round Trip*, 1957, makes no explicit reference, one senses, as with most of Frankenthaler's paintings from this period, an abstract landscape, derived not so much from the memory of a specific moment or location as from the nature of her technique. The canvas, both the unpainted areas and those reflecting through the thin color stains, conveys an atmospheric luminosity. Working on the floor from all four sides, and making decisions by cutting away at edges rather than proceeding according to a preconceived plan, she carefully manipulates analogous colors and forms to complete the composition. In 1963 she began to use acrylic paints that permitted her to achieve more opaque and intense color fields, often covering larger areas, which have characterized her more recent work.

Born in New York in 1928, Helen Frankenthaler first studied with Rufino Tamayo at the Dalton School. At Bennington College, 1945–49, she received a disciplined grounding in Cubism from Paul Feeley, though her own instincts lay closer to the linear freedom of Gorky and the color improvisations of Kandinsky's early work.

In 1950 the critic Clement Greenberg introduced her to contemporary painting. During that summer, she studied with Hans Hofmann in Provincetown, Massachusetts. In 1951 Adolph Gottlieb selected her for an important New Talent exhibition, and she had her first one-man show in New York later that year.

The work of Jackson Pollock proved the decisive catalyst to the development of her style. Immediately appreciating the potential, not fully developed by Pollock, of pouring paint directly onto raw unprimed canvas, she thinned her paint with turpentine to allow the diluted color to penetrate quickly into the fabric, rather than build up on the surface. This revolutionary soak-stain approach not only permitted the spontaneous generation of complex forms but also made any separation of figure from background impossible since the two became virtually fused—a technique that was an important influence on the work of other painters, particularly Morris Louis and Kenneth Noland.

FRANKENTHALER *Round Trip* **1957**
Oil on canvas, 70¼ x 70¼ in. (178.5 x 178.5 cm.)
Gift of James I. Merrill   RCA58:1

71

Joan Mitchell

In *George Went Swimming at Barnes Hole, but It Got Too Cold*, 1957, a remembered landscape initiated the impulse to re-create both the scene and the state of mind of a sultry, late summer afternoon in the company of George, a favorite dog. In an article on the genesis of this particular painting, Irving Sandler has written that it "began as a lambent yellow painting, but during the second all-night session, the work changed. The lustrous yellows turned to opaque whites, and the feeling became bleak; therefore, '*but It Got Too Cold.*' The artist did not carry her buoyancy any further; the beach was transposed from summer to fall. It seemed as if the hurricane that struck East Hampton in the autumn of 1954 invaded the picture. Since her early childhood, lake storms have been a frightening symbol of both devastation and attraction, and the sense of tempestuous waters appears frequently in her work. Miss Mitchell painted four hurricane canvases based on this experience in 1954. *George* is a return to this series, the realization of what was attempted then. This picture is less linear than her work in the intervening years. The contrast of the happy heat of the multicolored central image, the shimmering water, and the sun-streaked atmosphere with the fearful suggestion of the impending hurricane creates a remarkably subtle tension." *

In some of her recent work, such as *Blue Territory*, 1972, Joan Mitchell has divided her canvas into rectangular areas of color reminiscent of the work of Hans Hofmann; but unlike Hofmann's primarily plastic paintings, *Blue Territory* remains essentially a landscape. Displaying mastery of a style originally derived from Abstract Expressionism, Mitchell builds up areas of sumptuous color, some applied in a lustrous impasto, others dissolving in thin veils and drips of pigment. In spite of the richness of her brushwork, the gravitational pull of the drips lends the painting a stable, rather serene air. This painting, one of the Fields series of 1971–72, was inspired directly by the French landscape of Vétheuil, where Claude Monet painted in the late 1870's.

Joan Mitchell was born in Chicago in 1926, studied at Smith College, 1942–44, and the Art Institute of Chicago, where she received a B.F.A. degree in 1947. A travel fellowship in 1948–49 made possible the first of several extended visits to France. In New York in the early 1950's, studying at Columbia and New York University, she was impressed with the dynamism of Abstract Expressionism, then at its height. She especially admired the vibrant palette and powerful gestures of De Kooning, which she adapted to her own work. Joan Mitchell now lives in Vétheuil outside Paris on property formerly owned by Monet.

* *Art News*, October, 1957, p. 70.

MITCHELL *George Went Swimming at Barnes Hole, but It Got Too Cold* **1957**
Oil on canvas, 85½ x 78½ in. (216 x 198 cm.)
Gift of Seymour H. Knox   K58:11

MITCHELL *Blue Territory* **1972**
Oil on canvas, 102⅜ x 70⅞ in. (260 x 180 cm.)
Gift of Seymour H. Knox   K72:7

Cubist and Abstract Sculpture

Edward F. Fry

Of all the artistic styles that have played a role in twentieth-century sculpture, the Cubist-Constructivist tradition seems thus far to have been the most influential and long-lasting. Since its pre–World War I Parisian origins, Cubist sculpture and its immediate offspring, the Constructivism of Tatlin, Rodchenko, Gabo, Pevsner, and other Russian pioneers, have together exerted a continuous and central force in the development of modern sculpture. Although sometimes overshadowed and temporarily disregarded, this tradition has been active even in periods when the artistic climate has been hostile to its forms and values, as during the height of Surrealist activity in the 1930's or the Tachisme and Abstract Expressionism of the 1940's and 1950's. During the 1960's, partly as a reaction against the romantic modes of the previous decade, the Cubist-Constructivist tradition resurfaced and again played an important role, although Constructivism was more openly acknowledged than was Cubism. American artists in particular were willing to reconsider and to use Constructivist ideas more than Cubist space or composition. These Constructivist ideas were, in fact, often used or even enunciated as new without the awareness that they had already appeared in Europe two or three decades previously. Conversely, the Cubist style was openly rejected during the 1960's, especially by painters, who believed that it could only act as a brake on their own thinking and who also associated it with a European, French tradition that they consciously wished to rival and to supersede. Ironically, it was as much a Cubist as a Constructivist heritage from which was derived much of the most important sculpture of that same decade.

Before one can assess this aspect of post–World War II sculpture and situate it within the dual tradition of Cubism and Constructivism, a review is necessary of the history and aesthetics of both styles. Cubist sculpture began in Paris in the years immediately before 1908, by which time the painters Derain and Picasso and the sculptor Brancusi had discovered a means of discarding the canons of classical representation yet of remaining representational. Freed from the anatomical restraints of classical style, sculpture could now be used not only for purposes of representation but also for the creation of new and autonomous plastic structures, beyond the classical limits imposed by the medically conceivable poses which can be taken by the human body. This one act of achieving a formal, plastic freedom underlies all subsequent developments in modern sculpture. Following it in 1912, however, was a second discovery of almost as great an importance, when the Cubists realized that in sculpture solids and voids could be treated as interchangeable with respect to the representation of an image. Of equal importance was the realization at this same time that, as in Cubist collage, any material was suitable for making sculpture. Thus by 1912 three fundamental innovations had appeared in sculpture: formal plastic freedom; the equivalence of solid and void; and freedom in choice of materials.

By 1914 two separate directions were already apparent in Cubist sculpture. The first was a purely plastic attempt to reduce all the signifying information about a subject to be represented to as concise, pure, and unitary a form as possible; a course pursued by the sculptors Duchamp-Villon and Brancusi. Although no Cubist sculptors ever crossed the fine line from this position into pure abstraction, certain works of Brancusi and others did at a later date approach a condition of pure volumetric abstraction, almost but not quite comparable to the biomorphic abstractions of Arp. The entire aesthetic ideology of nonobjective art during the early years of the twentieth century must be seen against the foil of the generalizing and abstracting yet representational function of the Cubist style. The formal innovations of the Cubists, from which other artists would draw their abstract conclusions, were in fact part of a representational style.

The second course taken by Cubist sculpture was more pictorial and more closely related to the parallel developments in Cubist painting itself. By 1915 Picasso, Archipenko, and Laurens had exploited the equivalence of solid and void to the point of making open constructions. Made of various materials, these three-dimensional collages, depicting heads, still life, or figures, were, like their counterparts in Cubist painting, composed primarily of planes in space accompanied by geometrical volumes of either solids or void. Again like Cubist painting these sculptures were organized around some sort of central axis or focus; and as an entity the single sculpture was contained within either the implicit contours of the subject represented or more rarely, within the confines of a sculptural substitute of the picture frame, such as a sphere, pyramid, or rectangular solid. Such open constructions in three dimensions were nevertheless usually made so as to be viewed and best perceived from a single vantage point, a pictorial use of sculpture seen in more extreme form in the high or low Cubist relief sculptures by Lipchitz, Laurens, and many others from 1916 through the mid-1920's.

The first consequences of this Cubist sculptural revolution were the early works of the Russian Constructivists Tatlin and Gabo, the former of whom had by 1914 assimilated the Cubist syntax of planes interwoven in either real or pictorial space supposedly after a visit to Lipchitz and Picasso in Paris. Tatlin almost immediately discarded the representational function of Cubism and, in a series of wall and corner reliefs, produced some of the first abstract modern sculpture. Gabo retained a representational image in his sculptures almost until 1920, relying heavily on the Cubist principle of the equivalence of solid and void.

By the early 1920's, however, Gabo, Tatlin, Rodchenko, and nearly all of the other Russian Constructivist sculptors were purely nonobjective, i.e., they conceived their works on strictly formal principles. In most instances the Cubist heritage survived, if in sometimes residual fashion. The Cubist liberation of sculpture from dependence on traditional materials fell on particularly fertile soil in Russian Constructivism and was intensified by the Constructivists' involvement by 1922 with industrial design and production, art centers for factory workers, ambitious architectural and monumental projects, and the over-all will to turn away from all the previous history of art. Interest in machines and production also coincided with the Constructivist romantic desire to wipe clean the slate of art and art history; and with Rodchenko and others of the most radical artists one sees the desire to make art or to design objects by starting from first principles, be they geometrical, functional, or mathematical.

76

It was this latter development in Russian Constructivism that marked a real break with Cubism and a transcending not only of French Cubism or Italian Futurism but of much of the previous history of art. Formally, it gave rise to compositional devices that Mondrian had independently developed following his own evolution out of Cubism at about the same time, including composition based on a module or other mathematical scheme, composition by an over-all unified field, controlled use of symmetry and asymmetry, and the insistent use of visual fundamentals—line, plane, Euclidian solids, pure primary colors—as the basis for art, whether fine or applied. When codified during the brief existence of the Bauhaus, this formal heritage of Russian Constructivism and of Mondrian later became the basis for art education in art academies and colleges throughout the United States, particularly in those institutions where former Bauhaus teachers became faculty members. The fatal destiny of the Bauhaus ideals was that the highly effective codification of principles arrived at by Mondrian and the Constructivists became all too easily communicable as a kind of formalist syllabus for the teaching of art. What had begun as the hard-won inventions of individual artists ended some thirty years later as a pervasive orthodoxy and one of the recognized academic styles of modernism. In retrospect, the sources of this modern tradition appear today as inevitably more radical than their numerous latter-day offspring, a phenomenon not entirely to be explained by the self-conscious historicism of the modernist sensibility and its preoccupation with innovational priorities. A revealing example is that by contrast with their own early works and those of their Russian Constructivist colleagues during the peak years of the early 1920's, the subsequent and well-known sculptures of Gabo and Pevsner partake far more of an abstracted and modified Cubist formal syntax than is usually acknowledged, despite the use of industrial materials and techniques and the superficial impression of being derived from mathematical formulae.

The subsequent history of the Cubist-Constructivist tradition leads us rapidly to a point just prior to the current situation. The Cubist heritage was developed beyond its original tenets in the sculpture of Gonzalez and Picasso during the late 1920's and the 1930's. Both artists were in turn major sources for the work of David Smith and a host of lesser sculptors. A Cubist-derived style based on the intersection of planes in space became an academic cliché of post–World War II European sculpture. Cubism today, long after its original invention and the subsequent development of its sculptural possibilities by Picasso, Gonzalez, and Smith, may properly be considered to be a truly completed and therefore academic style, as can be seen in countless examples of the 1950's and 1960's, ranging from the paintings of Poliakoff to the sculptures of Lardera.

The Constructivist tradition found brilliant support in the career of Max Bill, who has lived and worked in Switzerland since the 1930's. During the 1950's, Bill's influence reached international proportions, principally through his role in the founding and directing of a Neo-Bauhaus art and design school at Ulm in Germany. During the 1950's, Bill's influence extended to South America also, beginning with an exhibition of his works at São Paulo in 1950 and continuing through the decade with visits and lectures. His activities in South America have contributed to the rise of an entire Neo-Constructivist regional movement, primarily but not exclusively centered in Argentina. A younger generation of South American artists includes such men as Soto and Le Parc, who with others have gone to Paris and during the 1960's received prominent recognition for works in a Neo-Constructivist tradition. While Bill continues to work in Switzerland, Vasarely in France has performed the function of promulgating Constructivist principles in ways comparable to those of Bill, though at a more decorative and far lower intellectual level. Through his activities and his relationship with the Galerie Denise René, Vasarely has made Paris a major center for Neo-Constructivism. The additional presence in Paris during the postwar years of the veteran Constructivist Pevsner, as well as Nicolas Schöffer (who, along with Vasarely, is of Hungarian background and who, also like Vasarely, had been exposed to the ideas of a Bauhaus-oriented art academy in Budapest during the 1920's), made it almost inevitable that Paris should be the principal center of European postwar Neo-Constructivism.

In America, Burgoyne Diller, as both painter and sculptor, was possibly the most gifted among a large number of Constructivist practitioners active as early as the late 1930's; somewhat less well known, but influential as much for his writings as for his art, is Charles Biederman. Such artists represent the survival of an original Constructivist tradition. Beginning at the end of the 1950's, a Constructivist revival appeared in New York, primarily but not exclusively among artists born during the 1930's. Ad Reinhardt, Frank Stella, Dan Flavin, Carl Andre, Darby Bannard, Donald Judd, and many other New York artists active during the late 1950's and the 1960's have all drawn upon a prior Constructivist heritage, be it with conscious acknowledgment or through a process of unconscious recapitulation. Since Constructivism is in many ways a predictable stylistic consequence of Cubism in any situation of formal self-consciousness, and since New York was not only such a self-conscious artistic milieu but also had been during the 1950's the center of a late Abstract Expressionist style heavily indebted to Cubism, it should not be surprising that New York in the 1960's should witness a Constructivist revival. This revival included long overdue scholarly accounts and exhibitions of Mondrian, the Bauhaus, and the Russian Constructivists. It was accompanied by strong assertions on the part of critics and practicing artists that American optical, hard-edge, and shaped-canvas painting, as well as optical, kinetic, and "primary structure" sculpture, was independent of, and owed no historical debt to, European Constructivism. It is, of course, not true; the denial of a previous tradition is at best a sign of antihistoricism or of historical ignorance, a by no means uncommon American phenomenon in which the rediscovery or recapitulation of previous developments is seen as a fundamental innovation of world importance. At worst it is a sign of chauvinism and cultural insecurity, in itself a species of cultural colonialism. By such a denial of the past and of history American art does itself a great injustice. It is by their transformation of earlier twentieth-century traditions that sculptors in America have made exceptional works. One can comprehend that which is genuinely new and therefore of importance for the present and the future only by separating out that which is derived from the past.

There are aspects of the Constructivist tradition, and more specifically of its later Bauhaus formulation, which led almost inevitably to its taking root in a fertile and receptive American cultural environment. As recast by the Bauhaus, Constructivism can be taught as a more or less complex set of principles; it is therefore preeminently the egalitarian style, for with application anyone can gain a competent mastery of it. Its forms are easily relatable to industrial processes, and indeed from architecture to the "well-designed" consumer product it lends itself equally well to both fine and applied art. This universality of application also consequently breaks down any barriers between vernacular culture and culture or art which is dependent upon privileged knowledge and education: thus, again, as for the egalitarian artist, Constructivism is a style eminently suitable for the egalitarian consumer. It is basically an austere and puritanical aesthetic, qualities which greatly helped it to gain wide acceptance in America. As opposed to its politically charged initial appearance in revolutionary Russia, Constructivism now has no ideological content, and can be used by corporations as much for its political neutrality as for its susceptibility to cost accounting. At the deepest cultural level, however, the Constructivist tradition is aligned in startling coincidence with a fundamental value of American life: the belief in the possibility of escaping from history, especially European history. The Russian Constructivist attempt to make a fresh start, to break free from the accumulated history of art and culture, found its counterpart in an American society based on a rejection of European mores, political structures, and the tragedies of history. Both represent a desire to step out of time and, as with most revolutionary events, to build an ideal world based on eternally constituted principles. Time and history eventually catch up even with eternally constituted principles, however, and encapsulate them in their larger context. For Constructivism, this has meant that, once there have been definitive solutions to artistic problems, the artist must either cease to work or be condemned to repeat the solutions as clichés. Constructivism in its revival during the 1960's reached this point; and the most ambitious of the artists involved in that revival have either resigned themselves to repeating their ideas, have turned to an eclectic revival of other styles, have attempted mixed eclectic combinations of Constructivism and Cubism, or have resorted to entirely new premises for making art.

An analytical review of sculpture in the Albright-Knox collection will illuminate the preceding general statements. Beginning with the Cubist tradition, one may see in Reg Butler's *Torso* of 1950 all the attributes of the style: representation, nonclassical figure proportions, a primarily frontal view, the free use and mixture of materials and working methods, and the equivalence of solid and void. Almost identical elements were used by David Smith in his vertical figure *Tank Totem IV*, 1953. A variant of the equivalence of solid and void, namely the use of concavity for convexity, figures prominently here, as does another Cubist device—the "found object" used in an alien context. Descended from its original appearance in Cubist collages, the found objects in this instance are the steel ends of boiler tanks, cut in half and used as signs for the head, breast, and hips of a human figure. Here as elsewhere the effectiveness of Smith's late Cubism lies in his ability to reinterpret Cubist methods, to invent new means of carrying out those methods, and to do so with surprising directness and force.

Compared to its lingering survival in post–World War II Europe, as is seen in Butler's *Torso*, late Cubism was a minor component of American sculpture during the 1940's and 1950's. It did survive, nevertheless, as an important element in the formal syntax of Abstract Expressionism, which received the Cubist tradition both directly and from the Cubist residue in such Surrealists as the later Picasso, Miró, and Masson. More important to the American sculptors of the period was an amalgam of Cubist methods and Surrealist intentions, as is well demonstrated by David Hare's *Sunrise*, 1954–55. At first glance this work is an abstraction, combining in Cubist fashion diverse materials and methods; the over-all effect is that of a dream image, allusive yet incomprehensible. In a letter (see page 92), however, the artist describes his use of what are in fact Cubist signs to indicate the earth, rain, clouds, sun, stars, and moon in this dream landscape.

Eduardo Paolozzi's bronze *Japanese War God*, 1958, is rather blatantly Cubist, updated with a new set of cultural references and artifacts. Using a large number of discarded objects (the Cubist "found object"), the artist built up a frontal, representational collage that was then cast in bronze. The very wit achieved here and elsewhere by Paolozzi, through his borrowing of common and often popular objects, has its own precedent in the *papiers-collés* of Picasso and Gris.

The varieties of Constructivism are as numerous as the combinations of possibilities offered by the varieties of formal Constructivist elements and principles themselves. As was mentioned above, two pioneers of the movement in Russia, Gabo and his recently deceased (1962) brother Pevsner, developed later styles which, though essentially Constructivist, reveal affinities with Cubism. Gabo's *Linear No. 2, Variation*, 1962–65 (based, however, on similar compositions much earlier in date), is nevertheless characteristically Constructivist in its use of modern industrial materials, a repeated modular form, and cross-axial symmetry in three dimensions. The interpenetration and interweaving of planes, however, is far closer to abstract Cubist planar syntax than to any other twentieth-century style. Pevsner's *Construction in the Egg*, 1948, is a more intuitive and biomorphic version of Constructivism, as indicated by its title. Instead of his brother's use of plastic, manufactured filaments to generate surfaces, Pevsner resorted to the somewhat more artisanal method of cutting bronze rods to size and brazing them in position.

Max Bill has long been a master of an unusually elegant yet austere version of Constructivism, of which he must be numbered among the outstanding living practitioners. His *Construction from a Ring*, 1942–63, with its self-explanatory title and simple but faultless use of inversion and bilateral symmetry, shows Bill at his usual level of purity and cool logic. His *Continuous Surface in Form of a Column*, 1953–58, again with a self-explanatory title typical of the artist, is an example of Bill's personal, topological contribution to the range of Constructivism; and like the previous work, it shows no trace of the maker's hand but rather suggests the instantaneous generation of a form from an a priori conception—a quintessentially Constructivist approach. Such definitive clarity and logic pose difficulties, especially for an artist of Bill's integrity, for his definitive solutions of formal problems preclude any subsequent refinement or variation: a new work must be based on a new idea, not on what has already been realized.

The English Constructivist Robert Adams's *Triangulated Column*, 1960, shows the typically Constructivist use of a geometrical module, here a pyramid of struts which when repeated generates a curving column. That this modular concept has a multitude of applications is seen in Milkowski's *Diamond*, 1967, where four identical solid rhomboids are combined in a composition of strict symmetry. A more sophisticated use of modules is evident in the works of Tony Smith, whose *Cigarette*, 1961–67, like virtually all his sculpture, is based on the unexpected configurations resulting from polyhedrons joined together in sequence. The Constructivist module can also lead to results which, though pleasing, are essentially decorative, as may be seen in Bertoia's repetition of vertical rods in his sculptural screen, 1961. The repetition of a modular element, usually in combination with one variety or other of symmetry, is so common a Constructivist approach as to be almost a sign of the style; thus Ogden's *Three Loops*, 1966, and Nassos Daphnis's *4-J30-63*, 1963, employ essentially identical formal means and an architectonic undertone. Very similar to this last sculpture is Kipp's *Flat Rate II*, 1969, where the same elements of modular repetition, symmetry, and an aura of impersonal, industrial fabrication are joined by explicit post-and-lintel architectural imagery. It is instructive to compare this work with a sculpture by the same artist done seven years previously. Kipp's *Directional I*, 1962, is cast in bronze, the traditional material of sculpture. It betrays no elements of the Constructivist style; instead, with its empirically composed intersecting planes, this work is a characteristic example of Cubist formal syntax. A development such as that of Kipp from a Cubist to a Constructivist orientation is a frequent and significant pattern among artists during the 1960's that was seen by no means only among young artists evolving their personal styles. The most prominent example among artists of the New York School is Louise Nevelson, whose monumental *Sky Cathedral*, 1958, as well as *Royal Game I*, 1961, are superb instances of Cubist-derived collage. Frontally orientated, wholly composed of found objects, and heavily dependent on the Cubist syntax of overlapping planes, these and similar works of Nevelson nevertheless show a considerable reliance on an approximative modular and symmetrical balance. Within six years, however, Nevelson had adopted an industrial material—plastic—and industrial fabrication, as well as a strictly Constructivist modular composition, as is evident in her *Transparent Sculpture I*, 1967–68, and *IV*, 1968. A transition from Cubist to Constructivist orientation much like that of Nevelson may also be seen in Alexander Liberman during the 1960's, whose *Bond*, 1969, is orthodox Constructivism but whose sculptures of the earlier 1960's were eclectically Cubist. (Liberman's paintings of the later 1950's and 1960's, however, were pioneering landmarks in the Constructivist revival of the 1960's.) Much the same shift is evident in Robert Adams: *Tall Spike Form*, 1957, has strongly Cubist properties; while *Column*, 1961, is, as its name indicates, a pure geometrical form despite its Cubist use of welded steel collage. Similarly, Rosenthal's *Jericho II*, 1963, is basically Cubist, while his more recent works are orthodox Constructivism.

Constructivism in recent sculpture has undergone eclectic cross-fertilization with other styles and intentions. The purity of Bill's ideas or of Olle Baertling's demonstrations of lines and angles in space, as in *XIH* of 1966, is found in a majority of Constructivist works and is a normal accompaniment of the style; but divergences from the norm are by no means uncommon. The clarity of conception that is so essential to Constructivism does not mix easily with styles of lesser rigor. It is therefore somewhat astonishing to see incursions of vitalism in which the elements of time and organic process are as far removed from the Constructivist ethos as is possible. This admixture can be seen in Hans Uhlmann's *Growth*, 1952, where the explicit images of the human figure and of organic development belie the artist's later and more orthodox Constructivism. The imagery of an organic unfolding, as of the petals of a bud, in Karel Malich's otherwise Constructivist *Black and White*, 1964–65, was obviously used by the artist to display the inner and outer structure of this work simultaneously. Such an intention is only partially Constructivist at best and results in a conflict within the sculpture that is neither resolvable nor totally successful in itself. Beverly Pepper, however, in her sculpture *Zig-Zag*, 1967, has more successfully fused the Constructivist and vitalist aims; as she herself recognizes (see page 104), this work combines pure geometry with the sense of movement. In comparison to a full-blown example of vitalism, however, such as Seymour Lipton's *Sea King*, 1955, Pepper's sculpture is obviously Constructivist. James Rosati's *Big Red*, 1970–71, at first glance seems closer to the late Cubist style in which he has long worked. His shift to a Constructivist point of view in this and other recent works is partially masked by the strong intrusion of vitalism, here in the guise of the potential motion indicated by an apparently inevitable collapse of his irregular archlike structure at some moment in the near future. Despite this vitalist element, Rosati has used modules, repeated in inverted symmetry, as end supports for his arch; and the arch itself is made up of units which, if not identical modules, at least appear as such to the viewer.

As was discussed above, the Cubist style emerged early in the twentieth century as the first viable successor to classicism in form, content, and a representational function. Cubism was an omnipresent way station through which countless modern artists have passed before reaching their own mature styles, as can be seen in Malevich before 1914, Gabo before 1918, or Giacometti before 1930. The survival of Cubism after 1945 has already been described. It has assumed guises and appeared in contexts which are not easily recognizable, as in the highly symmetrical representations of the standing figures by Hoflehner (compare his *Archon*, 1956, and *Agon*, 1959). David Smith remained faithful to his own version of Cubism as late as the 1960's in his Cubis; *Cubi XVI*, 1963, like several other works in this series, is an amalgam of Constructivist method—industrial materials and methods, the repetition of standardized units—and the Cubist elements of frontality and of advancing and receding overlapped planes, in order to represent a standing, leaning figure.

It was the fate of Cubism in the 1950's and 1960's to survive not as an integral style, but, with the rarest of exceptions, as the formal remains of a style, the essentials of which were discarded. David Smith was probably the last artist of importance to have worked successfully with Cubism, and Smith himself frequently blended Cubism with aspects of Surrealism and Constructivism. The formal vocabulary of Cubism survived in post–World War II painting and sculpture as the structural component in the Cubist-Surrealist fusion underlying Tachisme and Abstract Expressionism. Surrealism itself during the 1930's had retained much of the Cubist system of representation, as is notably evident in Picasso and Miró—two artists who strongly influenced the American Abstract Expressionists. Shadowy reminiscences of Cubist representation persist in Abstract Expressionism, although inconsistently and often with a heavy baggage of rhetoric and romantic mythology; it is more usual to find only the Cubist formal and structural syntax, without the Cubist representational function.

This eclectic mixture of Cubism, Surrealism, and often Constructivism as well, characterized much of the sculpture of the 1950's. It continued, surprisingly, in the sculpture of the following decade, though with diminishing force. Thus Herbert Ferber's *Green Sculpture II*, 1954, incorporates the modular repetition of a pointed, angular compositional motif and a

Cubist interweaving of lines and points in space. Similarly, Ibram Lassaw's *Theme and Variations #1*, 1957, is dependent on a small, rectangular module in a composition which is formally Cubist in its frontality, the equivalence of solid and void, its vocabulary of overlapping planes, and an implicit anthropomorphic image. In Lassaw's *Cytherea*, 1964, the anthropomorphic image is no longer implicit, and the figure is depicted in eminently Cubist fashion through the use of planar areas functioning as representational signs, the whole composed of diverse metals and oriented toward a frontal, pictorial viewpoint.

Richard Stankiewicz's *Our Lady of All Protections*, 1958, an ironic treatment of a Catholic theme,* is based on the Cubist principles of collage and the found object. Several details, such as the umbrella-like overhang, were intended by the artist to function as representational images, or at the least to evoke the suggestion of images.

The residue of Cubist planar syntax, left behind by the retreating and decaying rhetoric of Abstract Expressionism, is nowhere more apparent than in such works as *Mars and Venus*, 1959–60, by the veteran American sculptor Reuben Nakian. The romantic mythology remains in the title and in a suggested contrast between masculine solid forms and feminine fluttering planes; but the entire work is a monumental exercise in frontally orientated, interwoven Cubist planes. In the hands of a younger and more vigorous artist, this approach was still capable of yielding interesting results in the early 1960's, as may be seen in such works of John Chamberlain as *Kroll*, 1961. Here the interwoven planes are discarded sections of automobile bodies (Cubist found objects), welded together into a compact collage. Generally, however, this Cubist technique, when attempted in recent years, has led to decorative and inconsequential effects; as is demonstrated all too clearly by Robert Jacobsen's feeble exercise in Cubist composition, *Taha*, 1961, Ian Stuart's abstract collage landscape, *Pastoral*, 1962, and James Wines's *Metro*, 1962. When frontal, pictorial effects, derived from European Tachiste painting, are attempted in sculpture, the results are all too often hopelessly weak and decorative, as in the collage relief *Color-Sadness*, 1960, by Zoltan Kemeny: the artist, using a tubular module assembled in irregular clumps on a flat surface, has succeeded only in echoing the decorous insipidness of the style of painting upon which he depended. Pietro Consagra's *Transparent Iron, Lilac*, 1966, clearly indebted to the same Tachist source used by Kemeny, is at once the beneficiary and victim of his own vigorous and elegantly mannered borrowings; but his monochromed metallic equivalents of overlapping brushstrokes cannot transcend the weakness of their origins.

The most interesting and certainly the most important sculptor to appear thus far in the late eclectic phase of the Cubist-Constructivist tradition is Anthony Caro, whose works are in effect a final summing up of the remaining artistic potentialities of this tradition. Caro before 1960 was an Expressionist figural sculptor who, largely through the influence of David Smith, abandoned his earlier style in favor of a nonobjective sculpture incorporating aspects of both the Cubist and Constructivist traditions; he has in effect *revived* these styles, though for his own use, in his own way and in a highly selective fashion. The specificity of this personal revival is demonstrated by the inability of his many students and followers to achieve results of comparable interest. Caro owes little directly to Constructivism,

* Letter from the artist, August, 1968. See p. 278.

although like David Smith he makes extensive use of standard, industrially fabricated steel units such as "I" beams, struts, and even airplane propellers on occasion. He incorporates them into his sculptures, however, not as Cubist found objects but as integers that have neither greater nor lesser importance than any other part in a composition. From the beginning of the 1960's, Caro has been a totally nonobjective artist. Elements of his sculptures never assume any signifying function nor even call particular attention to themselves as having been borrowed from an industrial source: they become "idealized" as integrated members of a stylistic performance. Caro ensures this idealized, nonobjective quality in his works by avoiding anthropomorphic verticality and by usually painting a sculpture with a single unifying color, in many cases the primary hues—a Constructivist practice.

In all other respects, Caro works as a Cubist, while at the same time subverting Cubist intentions. Technically he is a sculptor of welded and bolted assemblage of found objects, yet he juxtaposes irregular planar forms against regularized industrial shapes. Like a Cubist he composes empirically and avoids predictable relationships; yet just as he avoids representation so does he also suppress any consistent Cubist interweaving of plane. Particularly in his works of the late 1960's Caro has also assured the non-Cubist quality of his compositions by avoiding any suggestion of a potentially frontally orientated pictorial plane; in such sculptures as *Georgiana*, 1969–70, he has in fact worked on two horizontal axes of composition which intersect almost at right angles.

With his borrowed industrial materials, Caro thus uses Constructivist modules without acknowledging their modular relationships, and often without acknowledging their material qualities or their mass; he uses Cubist empirical working methods without arriving at Cubist results; and he so organizes his sculptures that they demand a continuously renewed sequence of perceptual acts. He thus stands at the end of two long traditions of which the intertwined paths have determined the course of much of twentieth-century sculpture, and the continued existence of which have acted as decisive influences through the recent past.

NEVELSON *Royal Game I* **1961**
Wood, painted gold, 90 x 55¼ x 10¼ in. (incl. base) (218.6 x 140.3 x 26 cm.)
Gift of Seymour H. Knox   K62:9

Louise Nevelson

Sky Cathedral, 1958, consists of thirty-eight boxes of different sizes, arranged in a careful balance of symmetry and asymmetry, the whole painted matte black. The individual found objects (sometimes not "found" but made to order for the artist) are arranged in a seemingly endless variety of combinations. The oblong boxes vary in size, and the content of each has a completely different character and is sufficiently complex to exist as a separate entity. In some cases, the objects are openly revealed; other boxes are closed or partially closed, the contents remaining concealed.

The construction has a strongly architectural aspect and exists less as a sculpture than as a whole environment of a particularly poetic character. The multitude of objects are arranged in a carefully controlled "disorder," and a strong tension is created between the various elements. *Sky Cathedral* is more starkly expressionistic and less romantic than many of the artist's constructions of the period.

Royal Game I, 1961, painted gold, is less complex and more open to the viewer. While *Sky Cathedral* is dark and majestic, *Royal Game I* is ceremonial and voluptuous, recalling the festive golden atmosphere of late Italian baroque art. The design is more obvious, based on the number *three*. The construction is composed of three rectangular units, almost identical in size. Within each unit, an oval element and an open rectangular box, filled with vertically arranged objects, are repeated. The theme of three is repeated in the three flat circles and the three groups of equilateral triangles.

Following her "gold" period, Nevelson turned from found objects and wood to create sculptures in metal and plexiglass. Two of the plexiglass constructions, dated 1967–68 and 1968, are in the Gallery collection.

Louise Nevelson was born in Kiev, Russia, in 1900. Her family moved to Rockland, Maine, in 1905. In 1920, she went to New York, where she studied music, acting, and philosophy before attending the Art Students League, 1929–30. She was a student of Hans Hofmann in Germany the following year, and after returning to New York she worked as a mural assistant to Diego Rivera.

During the fifties she developed her wooden constructions, largely composed of found objects, the first of which were painted matte black, followed by a series in metallic gold paint, and another in white. She has made sculptures in metal also, and during the late sixties she completed a number of plexiglass constructions. In her recent work, she has returned to the use of black.

Basically Constructivist, Nevelson's work is also poetic and has elements of Surrealism. Within the various boxes that are component parts of most of her sculptures, she usually arranges a variety of objects of different shapes and sizes. The individual boxes are then placed to create a tension and design within the finished work and are unified by a single color.

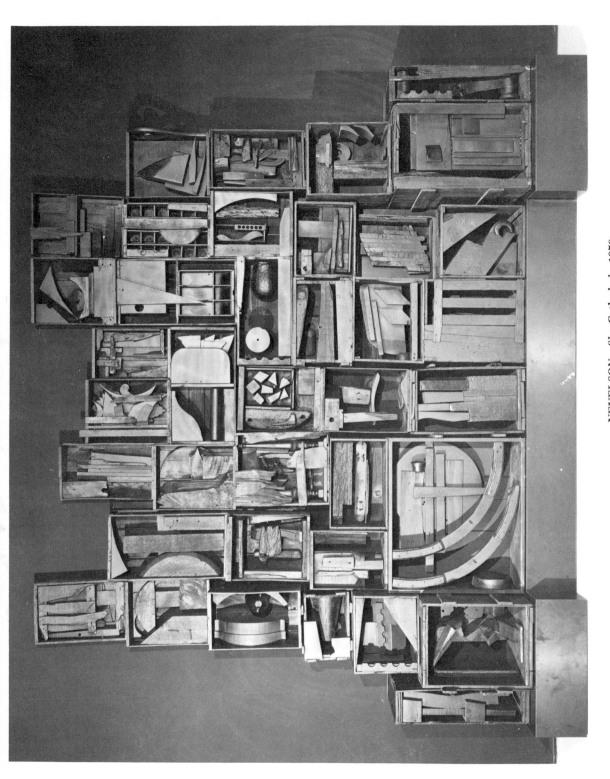

NEVELSON *Sky Cathedral* 1958
Wood, painted black, 115 x 135 x 20 in. (incl. base) (298.4 x 342.9 x 50.8 cm.)
George B. and Jenny R. Mathews Fund   70:1

David Smith

Tank Totem IV, 1953, is one of ten sculptures David Smith produced between 1952 and 1960 that have the same title, referring to the ends of steel boiler tanks he incorporated in their construction. His use of industrial materials and working methods increased during the last decade of his career as his work became more monumental and prolific. In *Tank Totem IV*, two tank ends were cut in half to become component parts of an anthromorphic structure. The half-circles are joined by narrow metal strips; a kite-shaped section at the middle is visible from the sides. The figure, poised on three curving legs, is roughly finished and the surfaces of the tank ends were incised with a calligraphic pattern.

The twenty-eight monumental sculptures of the Cubi series, dated 1961–65, constitute Smith's most important work as a sculptor. In each of the Cubis, he attempted to solve a separate sculptural problem for which a sequence of works was often required in order to reach a solution, resulting in an extraordinary variety within the series. As a whole, he developed within the group the final versions of ideas he had been exploring for twenty years.

The material Smith chose for the sculptures, stainless steel with the surfaces polished in a pattern, was of primary importance. He wrote, "I like outdoor sculpture, and the most practical thing for outdoor sculpture is stainless steel, and I made them and I polished them in such a way that on a dull day they take on the dull blue, or the color of the sky in the late afternoon sun, the glow, golden like the rays, the colors of nature. And in a particular sense, I have fused atmosphere in a reflective way on the surface. They are colored by the sky and surroundings, the green or blue of water. They reflect the colors. They are designed for outdoors." *

In *Cubi XVI* the steel was formed into hollow boxes, square and rectangular and organized into a Cubist frontal plane. The structure embodies the artist's personal reevaluation of the Cubist-Constructivist tradition as a major organizational principle of sculptural parts in space.

Cubi XVI has an anthropomorphic quality—the frontality and the vertical composition suggest a standing figure of heroic proportions.

David Smith was born in Decatur, Indiana, in 1906. After his family moved to Paulding, Ohio, in 1921, he studied art by correspondence at the Cleveland Art School, 1923, attended Ohio University, Athens, 1924–25, and studied briefly at Notre Dame University, South Bend, Indiana, in 1925. During the summer of 1925, he worked as a welder and riveter at the Studebaker plant in South Bend. After a brief stay in Washington, D.C., he moved to New York in 1926, where he studied painting at the Art Students League from 1927 to 1932. Although he continued to paint and draw throughout his life, in 1932 Smith turned to sculpture as his dominant interest after he saw reproductions of the welded metal constructions of Picasso and Gonzalez. By 1934, he had rented working space at the Terminal Iron Works in Brooklyn where, using the practical experience gained at the Studebaker plant, he began to make metal constructions. In 1940, he moved his studio to his farm at Bolton Landing, New York.

* Thomas B. Hess, *David Smith: The Secret Letter* (New York: Marlborough-Gerson Gallery, 1969), p. [7].

Smith's early work was based on an assimilation of European twentieth-century styles—Cubism, Constructivism, and Surrealism. Beginning in 1939–40 and until around 1950–52, he developed a symbolic and expressive style, derived from images drawn from within, added to the lessons learned from European art. From 1950–52 until his death in 1965, "he drew upon the combined resources of both his own previous work and whatever ideas, materials, and examples he found useful to his purpose, to create a public, increasingly monumental sculptural style, discarding and sublimating in the process his previous symbolic interests in favor of formal plastic innovation." *

By the late 1930's, Smith had completed the fifteen Medals for Dishonor, in which he achieved a personal statement largely independent of exterior influences. After two years during World War II (1942–44) of working as a welder making army tanks, he began to develop his symbolic works, employing both easily identifiable images and those which had a personal and private meaning. By around 1952, these relatively small-scale sculptures were replaced by larger and less subjective works, often anthropomorphic, and frequently produced in series. During the early 1960's, Smith began to use stainless steel and reintroduced color in some of his sculptures.

In June, 1962, Smith went to Voltri, Italy, near Genoa, where he produced twenty-six large sculptures within thirty days, which were shown in Spoleto that summer at the Festival of Two Worlds. In the remaining years before his death, Smith produced two major series, the celebrated Cubis and the polychromed Zig sculptures. Smith was killed in an automobile accident near Bennington, Vermont, in 1965.

* Edward F. Fry, *David Smith* (New York: The Solomon R Guggenheim Museum, 1969), p. 10.

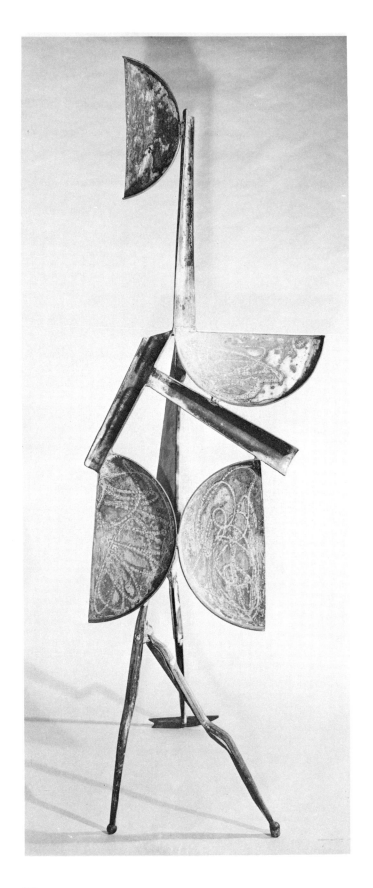

DAVID SMITH *Tank Totem IV* **1953**
Steel, 92⅝ x 29 x 34 in.
(235.6 x 73.6 x 86.3 cm.)
Gift of Seymour H. Knox   K57:15

DAVID SMITH *Cubi XVI* **1963**
Stainless steel, 11 ft. x 5 ft. x 33 in.
(335.3 x 152.4 x 83.8 cm.)
Gift of The Seymour H. Knox Foundation, Inc.
68:3

David Hare

"*Sunrise* was one of a series done in 1954 and 1955. They consisted of approximately fifteen sculptures. At the time I was living in Cannes in the south of France, the Mediterranean in front, the Maritime Alps behind. The series is all of the sea and the sun, the mountains and sun, the rain and the sky. . . . The idea of trying to make sculptures with landscape as their subject appealed to me partly because a large proportion of landscape material is not actual in the sense of being solid; there is cold, heat, rain, air, water, light, etc., all things better expressed in paint than in solid form. Sculpture classically dealt with volume. To break away from such a conception by refusing to use volume would be an act with little reason, except that of doing something different. To do so by using landscape as a subject seemed more legitimate, since a landscape itself has no volume, or to be more accurate, it is not so much made up of a series of volumes as it is only a fraction of some larger volume." * The artist has stated further that the upper portion of the sculpture represents the sun above a horizontal cloud; the construction at the right is a star; and the vertical rods simulate rain, the round object at the center the moon, and the rock at the bottom the earth.

Also in the Gallery collection is *Seated Woman*, 1958.

*David Hare was born in New York, in 1917, and moved to California as a child. He graduated from the University of Colorado, in 1936, with a degree in chemistry. For several years, he worked as a photographer, and, in 1940, he photographed Indians in New Mexico and Arizona for New York's Museum of Natural History. He began to work at sculpture in 1942, creating works that were primarily Surrealist. During the 1950's, he lived both in the United States and in France. His sculptures from this period were abstract but derived from nature until the late 1950's, when he turned to a figurative style, using simplified volumes and planes. In 1965, he began to paint with the intention of creating works combining the two media. In 1968, he wrote: "I have for the last three years been painting. I know a little about sculpture and less about painting; one must be brought to the same level as the other before there can be any real possibility of combination. I have no wish to make bumps sticking out of canvases, nor colored areas applied over forms. I want the work to be like the torso of a man on that of a horse, a centaur. Like feathers sheltering coals, a Phoenix. Close and interchangeable, like body and spirit—the human being." **

* Letter from the artist, August, 1968.

92

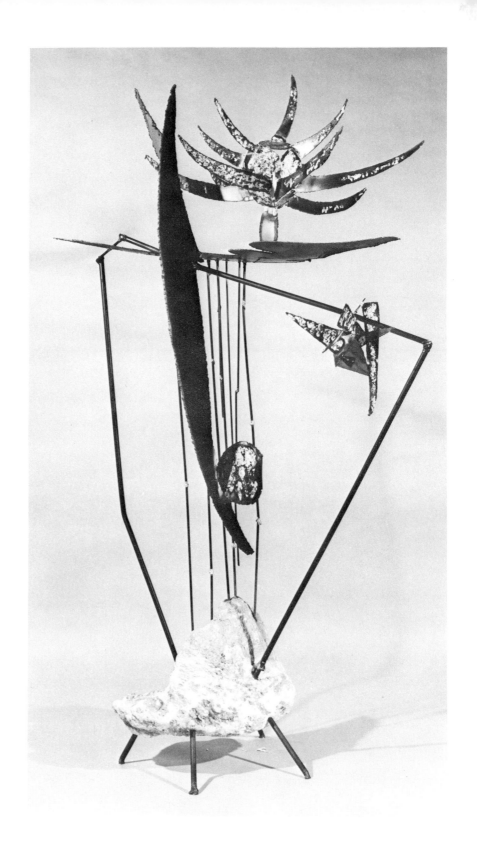

HARE *Sunrise* **1954–55**
Bronze and steel, 71 x 42 x 22 in. (180 x 107 x 68½ cm.)
George Cary Fund   55:9

Tony Smith

A thirteen-inch-high maquette for *Cigarette* was made in 1961; a full-size model and another one-half size, both of plywood, were executed in 1966, followed by the Corten steel version, 1967–68, in an edition of three.

Of this sculpture, Smith wrote, "I had set out to make a serious piece of sculpture, and thought I had done so. Upon seeing the smooth plaster model, I realized that I had been taken in by the irregularities of the paper one. The piece was redundant, and had the look of a war memorial. Stripping away everything but the spine, I wound up with a cigarette from which one puff had been taken before it was ground out in the ashtray." *

As is the case with many of the Minimal sculptors, Smith plans his work with drawings and models; the final sculptures are commercially constructed. The material used for *Cigarette* is a rust-resistant steel originally of an orange color that changes over a period of months to a warm brown.

Of the edition of three, one remains in the artist's collection and the other in The Museum of Modern Art, New York.

Anthony Smith was born in South Orange, New Jersey, in 1912. He began to study at the Art Students League, New York, about 1931, and attended night classes there regularly while working as a toolmaker and draftsman during the day, 1933–36. He studied at the New Bauhaus, Chicago, 1937–38, and then began working as a laborer and later clerk-of-the-works for several Frank Lloyd Wright buildings, 1938–39. Between 1940 and 1960, he worked independently as an architect, designing a number of houses and unexecuted monuments. During these years, he was closely associated with the artists of the Abstract Expressionist movement and was an influential teacher of a younger group of artists.

In the early 1960's, Smith ceased building and began to concentrate on his sculptures. Based on variations of polyhedra, they are related to his architectural concepts, usually monumental in size, and are frequently painted black or executed in dark metal.

* *Tony Smith/Two Exhibitions of Sculpture* (Hartford: Wadsworth Atheneum; Philadelphia: The Institute of Contemporary Art, 1966), p. [24].

TONY SMITH *Cigarette* 1961–68
Corten steel, 15 x 18 x 26 ft.
(457.1 x 548.6 x 792.4 cm.)
Gift of The Seymour H. Knox Foundation, Inc. 68:4

Antoni Milkowski

Diamond-I of III, 1967, is one of three handmade editions of the sculpture constructed in Corten, a noncorrosive steel with a protective patina that produces a rich brown surface color. The composition, basically frontal and two-dimensional, consists of the repetition of a rhomboidal module, the resulting diamond shape poised in such a manner as to minimize the tremendous weight of its components. The structure is bilaterally symmetrical, with the over-all shape repeated in the form of the void in the center of the piece, and suggested in the open forms at top and bottom. These produce the impression that the unit is actually a part of a larger whole; similarly, there is an implication of infinite repetition in a vertical direction, which is strongly reminiscent of Brancusi's Endless Column. The scale, however, is massive and impersonal, related more to the modern skyscraper than to human proportions.

Antoni Milkowski, one of the Minimal sculptors, was born in Evanston, Illinois, in 1935. He attended Kenyon College, Gambier, Ohio, and Hunter College, New York, where he obtained an M.A. degree. In 1964–65, he received a Fulbright fellowship for study in Poland, where he taught at the Academy of Fine Arts in Warsaw. His works, constructed from steel units, result in the dramatic juxtaposition of void and solid parts, or are created by the intersecting solids. His works are usually handmade and the color is that of the rust-resistant steel, Corten.

MILKOWSKI Diamond—I of III 1967
Corten steel, 16½ x 13 x 4 ft.
(502.9 x 396.9 x 121.9 cm.)
Gift of The Seymour H. Knox Foundation, Inc. 68:1

Anthony Caro

Georgiana, 1969–70, is composed of a construction beam, tank sections, and plow blades, chosen for their forms rather than as commentary on an industrialized society and welded together in a strict, rectilinear arrangement. Perpendicular to the beam, which is parallel to the floor, are two similar, but not identical, rectangular blocks, each pierced by a rectangular void; a single large circle; and six twisting blade-shapes. Caro was one of the first contemporary sculptors to use over-all color to unify the various elements incorporated in his sculptures. Georgiana was designed to rest directly on the floor rather than on a traditional pedestal, as is the case with many of Caro's sculptures.

Anthony Caro was born in London, in 1924, and grew up in Surrey. He received a degree in engineering from Christ's College, Cambridge, in 1942, and spent the following four years in the Navy. He studied at the Royal Academy Schools, 1947–52, and from 1951 until 1953, he served as a part-time assistant to Henry Moore. His work during this period consisted of single figures modeled in clay or plaster and cast in bronze. He gradually began to eliminate the figure, and, in 1959, he made his first abstract sculpture in plaster. After a visit to the United States in the same year, where he was encouraged by a number of younger painters and sculptors, particularly Kenneth Noland, Caro adopted a freer and more direct approach. Influenced by the American sculptor David Smith, in 1960 he began to work in bolted and welded steel and aluminum. From 1963 to the present, with occasional interruptions, he has taught at St. Martin's School of Art, London; in 1963–64, and during the spring of 1965, he was sculptor-in-residence at Bennington College in Vermont.

CARO *Georgiana* **1969–70**
Painted steel, 60 x 185 x 99 in.
(152.5 x 469.8 x 251.5 cm.)
Gift of Seymour H. Knox   K70:13

Max Bill

The concept of *Construction from a Ring* dates from 1933, when Max Bill made his first sculptures on this theme. He made numerous variations in different sizes, materials, and surface finishes, sometimes eliminating the base; the last of the series is dated 1963. The sculpture is based on the repetition of the circular motif in each of its three parts. The simple arrangement of the axes intersecting in right angles results in mathematical purity and legibility of composition.

Like the other sculptures of Max Bill, this nonrepresentational piece is created with a strict rationalism, becoming the symbol of the pure, faultless form.

Also in the collection are another sculpture by Bill, *Continuous Surface in Form of a Column*, 1953–58, and two paintings, *Field of 32 Parts in 4 Colors* (p. 237) and *Nine Fields Divided by Means of Two Colors*, 1968.

Biography of the artist, p. 236.

BILL *Construction from a Ring* **1942–63**
Granite, 55 x 48 x 48 in. (140 x 122 x 122 cm.)
Edmund Hayes Fund 64:9

Alexander Liberman

In 1959, Liberman learned to weld and frequently worked in this medium throughout the 1960's, executing large-scale constructions after 1965. *Bond*, 1969, is a steel construction painted vermilion and consisting of two welded tubes and a flat L-shaped section carefully balanced in both horizontal and vertical directions. It is not a solid sculptural mass but a sophisticated spatial displacement of the parts in which thin sheets of metal draw the contours of Liberman's construction. Circular form became important in Liberman's sculpture in the late 1960's, when he abandoned this motif in his painting and incorporated it in the arrangement of his sculptures.

Also in the Gallery collection is *Iota III*, 1961, which is an example of his exploration of the circle motif in painting.

Alexander Liberman, born in Kiev, Russia, in 1912, received his B.A. in philosophy and mathematics from the Sorbonne, Paris, in 1930, and studied painting with André Lhote, 1931–32. He also studied with Auguste Perret at the École Spéciale d'Architecture, 1930–32. During these years, he supported himself by working as an assistant to the poster designer Cassandre and did editorial and technical work for the magazine Vu, one of the first illustrated periodicals. In 1937, he won the Gold Medal for Design in the International Exhibition in Paris for a presentation of work on magazine editing. In 1936, Liberman began to paint seriously, adopting an academic style and, following World War II, a Post-Impressionistic style. He moved to the United States in 1941, becoming a citizen in 1946. In the late 1940's, Liberman turned to complete abstraction, and, in 1950, he began painting brightly colored circles on contrasting backgrounds, choosing the circle as an ideal shape.

LIBERMAN *Bond* **1969**
Painted steel, 7½ x 8½ x 18½ ft.
(228.7 x 259.4 x 563.9 cm.)
Gift of Seymour H. Knox   K69:32

James Rosati

Since 1963, Rosati has been making large-scale sculptures of sheet metal, designed, as was *Big Red*, 1970–71, to be installed outdoors, relating to the landscape, adjacent buildings, and natural light. This sculpture consists of eight irregular blocks, in which none of the straight lines or faces are parallel. The units are individually conceived and fabricated; each has a distinctive sculptural quality in addition to the over-all composition, whose shapes are interwoven—differing in this respect from many of the Minimal sculptures in which a single module is repeated. Although the variations of light on the angles of the sculpture imply color variations, the entire work is painted a single red-orange color.

James Rosati was born in Washington, Pennsylvania, in 1912. Trained as a musician, Rosati played the violin in the Pittsburgh String Symphony, 1928–29, and first turned to sculpture after seeing sculptural works at The Museum of Art, Carnegie Institute, in Pittsburgh. His early work was in organic, closed forms, mostly of bronze or stone—dense masses with vertical axes. After his arrival in New York, in 1949, he met the painters of the Abstract Expressionist group and the sculptors Pavia, Hare, Nakian, David Smith, and Lassaw. In his first one-man show in 1954, Rosati exhibited open, welded pieces, but this style was short-lived in his oeuvre, and he turned to the sculpture of self-contained mass. For most of his career, Rosati's work was related to the late Cubist style, which he has transformed into hard-edged, large-scale compositions, with some similarities to the Minimal sculptures of the 1960's.

ROSATI *Big Red* **1970–71**
Painted aluminum, 11 x 19 x 4 ft. (335.3 x 579 x 121.9 cm.)
Gift of Mrs. Wilhelmina S. Phillips, Mrs. Nell S. Miller,
and Dr. Judith A. Schoellkopf in memory of their brother
J. Frederick Schoellkopf IV   71:5

Seymour Lipton

Of *Sea King*, 1955, Lipton wrote, "The sculpture is a horizontal thrust with angular counterforms emerging up and down. Asymmetric balance was achieved by resting the object on a rounded shape. The sculptural drawing suggested a sea monster, therefore the name.

"The series of contiguous vertical forms bounded by a horizontal band merely is an example of my general view of the need for major dramatic interplay of forms. The base as a hollow curved horn, I believe, has the necessary surprise and variation against other forms.

"While making the drawings for this work I had the feeling of waves; of an object riding the waves—a sea horse, a dolphin, a Loch Ness monster. At any rate, it is an object of sculptural reality suggesting a driving power with dignity, grace and possibly evil. As an object of sculptural reality the varied forms were integrated in terms of weight, balance, spacing, tensions, inner and outer relations, etc." *

The artist made two preparatory drawings for the sculpture, one of which is in the Gallery collection.

Seymour Lipton was born in New York, in 1903. He graduated from Columbia University, with a degree in dentistry, in 1927. He was self-taught as a sculptor, and his early works were figurative, carved in wood, modeled in clay, or rendered directly in plaster. In the mid-1930's, he began to experiment with abstract sculpture and, by the mid-1940's, had expanded his themes beyond the human figure to include broader biological and organic subjects, influenced by his interest in Surrealism, mythology, history, and extinct animals. As Lipton's work changed, his materials changed, too; he replaced traditional materials with various metals, sometimes cast but more frequently cut and welded by the artist himself, who tends to retain a rough surface on his sculptures.

"My work is not literary, intellectual, nor traditional," Lipton has written. "In some way, the forms in each work come from a willful digging into the chaos of meaninglessness to extract a nascent otherness, and bring it back structured into sculpture. This becomes for me meaningful reality in depth." †

* Letters from the artist, June, 1957, and July 19, 1968.
† Letter from the artist, July 23, 1972.

LIPTON *Sea King* **1955**
Nickel-silver over monel metal
29½ x 42½ x 20 in. (75 x 108 x 50.8 cm.)
A. Conger Goodyear Fund   56:6

Lyman Kipp

Flat Rate II, 1969, is based on the modular repetition of a rectangular slab, composed on the principle of post and lintel. Though not specifically a doorway or gate, since it is not penetrable, the sculpture is scaled to human proportions in such a way as to suggest architecture. Primary colors are applied on the rather thin rectangular form, reminiscent of hard-edge painting. The form is monumental, though it is not massive. Kipp—one of the first Minimalists in sculpture—worked under the influence of Cubist sculpture before he turned to pure Constructivist principles, as embodied in *Flat Rate II*.

Also in the collection is *Directional I* from 1962.

Lyman Kipp was born in Dobbs Ferry, New York, in 1929. He studied industrial design at Pratt Institute, New York, 1950–52, and sculpture at Cranbrook Academy of Art, Bloomfield Hills, Michigan, 1952–54. His earliest works were light, linear constructions, the mass reduced almost to "drawing in space," and thus with no trace of his current monumentality. Later, Kipp became more concerned with the problem of mass, volume, and scale in his sculptural work, which was originally based on the Cubist formal syntax. He used plaster, bronze, and wood for his work until the mid-1960's when, preoccupied with principles of Minimal sculpture, he started to use brightly painted steel. During his career, Kipp also produced many reliefs, independent drawings, and drawings for his sculptures.

KIPP *Flat Rate II* 1969
Painted steel, 8 x 5 x 3 ft.
(244 x 152.5 x 91.5 cm.)
Gift of Seymour H. Knox K69:5

Herbert Ferber

Ferber has experimented with a new spatial organization in his work since 1950. The parts of his sculptures were conceived of as autonomous elements, designed into the sculptural space as a calligraphic gesture. *Green Sculpture II,* 1954, is based on the interaction of linear spikes connected to the flat rectangular base at six points. Brought into a three-dimensional arrangement, they create their own environment within the sculptural frame. Weightlessness and airiness are underlined by the autonomy of elements not directly connected—short, X-shaped forms bridge the open areas between the large spikes, replacing the direct contact of the main parts. Hard-edged and large, S-curved elements suggest the vegetative motifs of a thorny bush, an impression further evoked by the green color of the sculpture. The position of the spectator is important in viewing the piece, since the image changes as the viewer moves around it.

A copper and lead study for *Green Sculpture II* is in the Williams College Museum of Art, Williamstown, Massachusetts.

Herbert Ferber Silver was born in New York, in 1906. He studied science at the City College and received a B.S. degree in 1927 from Columbia University, followed by a D.D.S. degree from the College of Oral and Dental Surgery in 1930. While pursuing his later studies, he began sculpting, attending evening classes at the Beaux-Arts Institute of Design. In 1930, he divided his time between teaching at Columbia Dental School and painting and sculpting seriously. For the next twelve years, influenced by the sculptors Barlach, Maillol, and Zorach, as well as by pre-Columbian and African art, he produced realistic and figurative works carved directly in stone and wood. He experimented with open forms in the early 1940's. In 1945, he began working in metal and changed to an open, abstract style. His subsequent sculpture evidenced a Surrealist influence, and he became closely involved with the New York School of artists and Studio 35 activities. Interested in freeing the sculptural piece from dependence on a traditional base, in order to be able to create different kinds of gravity-defying forms, Ferber added a "roof" to some sculptures in 1954 as a new source of support and later created works with a roof and side walls. These evolved into sculptural environments and into sculptures enclosed in a cage-like framework.

During the 1950's, he received commissions from several synagogues in the United States to do wall sculptures and, in 1960–61, executed a full-scale environmental sculpture for the Whitney Museum of American Art, New York.

112

FERBER *Green Sculpture II* 1954
Copper, 40½ x 42 x 24 in. (102.9 x 106.7 x 61 cm.)
Gift of Seymour H. Knox K57:3

Reuben Nakian

"About the *Mars and Venus*, the medium one uses should dictate its style—the steel sheets demanded a contour of shapes, without the help of modeling. My large bronze abstractions are modeled in plaster; I think my steel pieces and my modeled ones related to each other. I usually begin my work from naturalistic drawings, and then work them up to abstractions." *

This sculpture of 1959–60 was constructed shortly after Nakian's work had undergone a transition from figurative to abstract. Composed of rods and sheets of welded steel, it is an open structure in which portions are raised from the base within the framework of an over-all space that is suggested but not fully rendered. During the late 1950's, Nakian made a series of spontaneous drawings; *Mars and Venus* has the lightness and grace of such a drawing transferred into a three-dimensional sculptural concept and realized on an enormous scale. The visually floating, interpenetrating planes project upward and outward in a number of directions simultaneously. The ancient and engaging mythological theme, executed in contemporary materials, results in a powerfully suggestive abstraction.

Reuben Nakian was born of Armenian-American parents in College Point, New York, in 1897, and—as a child—lived in New York City and several communities in New Jersey. He began drawing at an early age and, at sixteen, started to earn his living in New York, at advertising agencies. He attended the Independent Art School and the Beaux-Arts Academy; in 1916, he began studying with Paul Manship and his chief assistant, Gaston Lachaise. When Manship left for Europe in 1920, Lachaise and Nakian shared a studio until 1923. Deeply influenced by these two figurative artists, Nakian's work remained realistic until the mid-1930's, when he began a reevaluation of his style that was accelerated during the 1940's. At that time, he became acquainted with the Abstract Expressionists, particularly De Kooning, Kline, and Guston; his sculpture as a consequence became abstract and large-scale. He also continued to make many drawings and a number of works in terra-cotta.

* Letter from the artist, September 29, 1968.

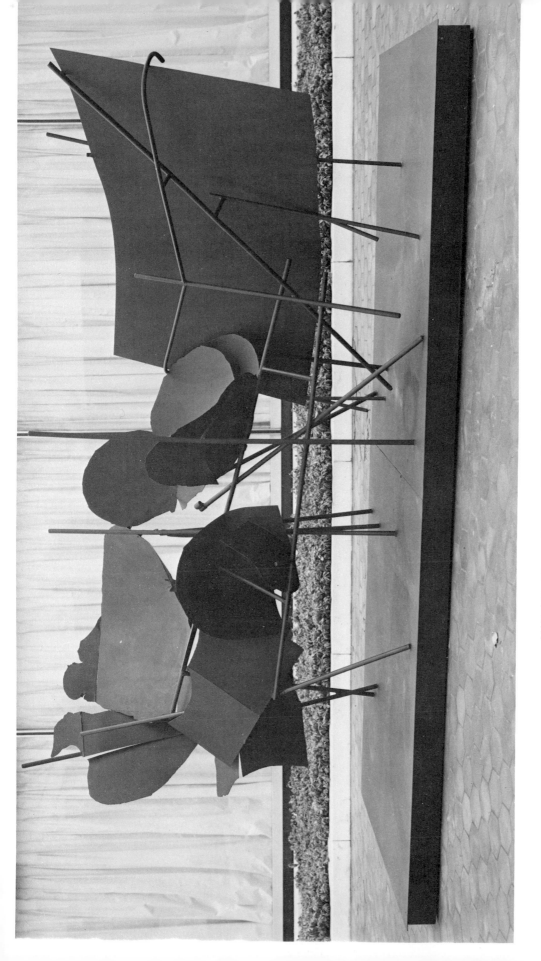

NAKIAN *Mars and Venus* **1959–60.** Welded steel, painted black, 7 x 15 x 6 ft. (213.5 x 482.8 x 182.9 cm.) A. Conger Goodyear Fund 68:2

Isamu Noguchi

Though basically an abstract design, *The Cry*, 1962, suggests an upright human figure: the head rendered as an oval, with the pierced area implying an open mouth; and the smaller, vertical section indicative of an upraised arm. The sculpture resembles a stylized and simplified version of Edvard Munch's famous painting and lithograph of the same title.

The Cry was first carved in balsa, the lightest wood, in 1959, after Noguchi's return to New York from Paris, where he designed the gardens for the UNESCO Building. At the time, he was working with untraditional materials, particularly those light in weight. This original version, mounted on a steel base, is in the collection of The Solomon R. Guggenheim Museum, New York. In 1962, the sculpture was cast in bronze in an edition of six, of which the Gallery sculpture, the third casting, is mounted on a roughly cut base of pink and gray granite.

Isamu Noguchi was born in Los Angeles, California, in 1904, the son of a Japanese poet and an American mother. At the age of two, he was taken to Japan but returned to the United States as a student in 1918. He studied medicine briefly at Columbia University, 1923–24, before turning to the study of sculpture at the Leonardo da Vinci School in New York. Noguchi went to Paris in 1927 as a Guggenheim Fellow, and there he worked with Brancusi, studied drawing at the Académie de la Grand Chaumière and at the Collarosi Academy, and experimented with abstract constructions. He returned to New York in 1929, and for several years earned his living as a portrait sculptor while continuing his abstract compositions in various materials—sheet metal, paper, wire, stone, wood, and light.

During visits to Japan, Noguchi studied brush drawing, ceramics, and Japanese gardens, which revealed to him the possibilities of land as a sculptural medium. Also, he became increasingly interested in the social uses of sculpture as relevant to everyday life and, in this connection, has designed furniture, lamps, playgrounds, bridges, and gardens, collaborating with architects all over the world. Since 1935, he has designed numerous sets for the dancer Martha Graham as well as for the New York City Ballet.

A frequent traveler, Noguchi has remained in contact with the cultures of both the East and the West, and his work incorporates influences from each.

NOGUCHI *The Cry* **1962**
Bronze, 96 x 30 x 20 in. (incl. granite base)
(44.5 x 76.2 x 50.8 cm.)
Gift of George Cary and
Elisabeth H. Gates Funds   63:2

117

British Painting and Sculpture

John Russell

The "modern British" holdings of the Albright-Knox Art Gallery cover a period of just over thirty-five years: from 1935, the date of Henry Moore's elmwood *Reclining Figure*, and from 1937, the date of Paul Nash's *Landscape of the Megaliths*, to the present day. I must at this point declare a personal interest, in that the holdings in question correspond in an almost hallucinatory degree to my own interests and experience, both private and professional. Paul Nash was the first artist whom I knew at all well, and I was barely out of short pants when his megaliths first forced themselves on my attention. I bought a drawing by Henry Moore when the asking price, with frame, was the equivalent of twenty-five dollars. John Piper is the godfather of my only child. Ben Nicholson, Henry Moore, Francis Bacon, Anthony Caro, Bridget Riley, and R. B. Kitaj are the people who in my opinion most make it worth while to live in England. It would be ridiculous to pretend that when I write about these artists there does not enter into it an element of autobiography. To come to terms with a new work of art is a formative experience, at any age; and when I go to Buffalo—which I do on any pretext, no matter how slight—I look at the modern British holdings with feelings which go far deeper than mere recognition. I say to myself what we all say on such occasions: "Because these artists were around, I am what I am."

Paul Nash gave, for instance, to young people of my generation a heightened sense of place. Thanks to him, we learned to scan the English countryside in a completely new way. This related in part to the art of the immediate past: as early as 1936, for example, Nash was inciting us to find echoes of Max Ernst's *La Femme 100 têtes* in a landscape—that of the Dorset coast—over which Thomas Hardy had long presided. But above all he taught us to look for the primeval genius of England as it was revealed in monuments most often looked at with a purely antiquarian eye. Ever since he saw the megaliths at Avebury, in Wiltshire, in 1933, he had thought of those great mysterious upended stones as the repositories of a mysterious power which predated our human arrival on the scene and was likely to outlive it. (His friend George Wingfield Digby writes that he felt the stones "as giants or heroes, as mighty forces, rugged and uncouth, but intent with potential energy emerging from chaos.") The megalith provided Paul Nash with a recurring image in the 1930's, and in the Buffalo picture it is combined with a landscape of bare conical hills; the scale of the scene is ambiguous, and we are not quite sure if the marks on the shelving fields stand for hedges—in which the stones are hundreds of feet high—or for sowings of an unexplained sort. Nash always loved the idea of flying, and in fact he once said, "Death, I believe, is the only solution to this problem of how to be able to fly"; and I suspect that the plunging perspective in the foreground of the Buffalo picture is related to the act of flying as it was experienced at that time in tiny single-engined machines, soaring and plunging at less than a hundred miles an hour over landscapes which had been seen from that point of vantage by only a very few people. It was difficult

118

to grow up in the 1930's and not be penetrated, if one cared for art at all, by Paul Nash's searching and fastidious interest in the landscape of south-western England: the fossil forests, the immemorial dead trees in the marshes, the fungi which asked to be treated as Surrealist objects, the prehistoric mounds, the castles buried beneath the grass. It was thanks to him, to pictures like *Landscape of the Megaliths*, and to the guidebook to the county of Dorset which he published in 1937, that whole stretches of England became charged with magic: a landscape beyond time was ours for the exploration.

In 1910–11, Paul Nash and Ben Nicholson had been fellow students at the Slade School in London. Nicholson's was a younger and a more restless nature, and as often as he could he used to get Paul Nash to come and play billiards with him at a pub round the corner, when they ought to have been in class. It could have been just a way of passing the time, but in point of fact Ben Nicholson is to this day an attentive student of ball games and would not at all scoff at the idea that his White Reliefs have something in common with the delicate precision of a perfectly executed cannon off the red. Between 1934 and 1939, Nicholson made a long series of these reliefs. Some people thought them a new departure, and they were certainly sparer and leaner than the witty, cross-referential paintings which he had done, for instance, in Dieppe a year or two earlier. Words like "cerebral" and "clinical" were used of the White Reliefs; but Nicholson did not so intend them. As he himself said on another occasion, "The geometrical forms used by abstract artists do not indicate, as has been thought, a conscious and intellectual mathematical approach—a square or a circle in art is nothing in itself and is alive only in the instinctive and inspirational use an artist can make of it in expressing a poetic idea."

The White Reliefs were *carved*, not built up, a fact to which Nicholson attaches great importance. In the 1960's, carving of this sort took up a great deal of his time, but at the time he was making his first White Reliefs the experience was still quite new to him. (It was Paul Nash who used the word "excavated" of the reliefs when they were first put on show in London.) In 1933 Nicholson had completed a painting called *Six Circles*, in which the irregular circles could be read (though without authority) as still-life elements: mugs or jugs such as Nicholson has always loved to draw. From pure painting of this sort to the White Reliefs was only a small step, but it was a step that took some making. It also took some understanding: the critic was rare in the 1930's who knew, as Adrian Stokes knew, that there could be discovered in Nicholson's nonrepresentational work "the slow elucidation and isolation of factors that are constant in all that is pleasurable in the process of visual perception." This was as true of the sculptural reliefs as of Nicholson's paintings on canvas; but in the reliefs there is the added element of change. This is architectural in its terms: as the light shifts, the reliefs change in relation to it. The formal statement is never the same for two minutes together; and as we confirm this in our own experience, we relive one of the decisive moments of this century—the moment at which, all over Europe, the upholstery of make-believe was questioned, in art, and people came to realize how enormous was the expressive potential of what was left when everything inessential had been cut away.

During the second half of the 1930's there was a good deal of cardboard swordplay over what was then taken to be an irreconcilable difference of position, as between the Surrealists, on the one hand, and the abstract artists on the other. But at the higher levels of activity this antagonism simply could not be maintained. Ben Nicholson could hardly bring himself to look at a Surrealist painting, whereas Paul Nash had a particularly keen interest in the subject and made some valuable contributions to it; but this did not prevent Nash from seeing the point of what Nicholson was doing and standing up for it in print. Herbert Read had the confidence of both parties; and so did Henry Moore, who was much too lively and determined by nature to get trapped in a provincial dispute. Moore showed with Paul Nash and quite a few other English artists in the International Surrealist Exhibition of 1936; but it was also perfectly possible to see him in the context of any notional international abstract exhibition that might eventually be brought into being. He has always resisted categorization; even today, when he can hardly clean his teeth without finding a television camera in the doorway of the bathroom, there are always rogue works in his oeuvre which defy us to place him once and for all.

If Moore is often misunderstood in England, as I think he is, one of the reasons is that so many of his finest carvings were bought by Americans in the 1930's and have rarely or never been seen in England again. The Americans were absolutely right, of course; and the pieces in question now seem to have gained an added immunity from the passage of time by the fact of long residence in places remote from England—Atlanta, Georgia, for the beechwood *Composition* of 1932; St. Louis, Missouri, for the carved concrete *Reclining Figure* of 1933; Narragansett, Rhode Island, for the particularly cryptic Hoptonwood stone *Reclining Figure* of 1937; and until lately the Cranbrook Academy of Art in Michigan for the elmwood *Reclining Figure* of 1945–46. (For this last, the Albright-Knox owns by the way a premonitory drawing, dated 1942, in which is foreshadowed an element to which Kenneth Clark later called attention: ". . . the pulsation of the wooden heart, like a Crusader's head, burrowing in the hollow breast").

It should also be said that Americans know very well how to position their Henry Moores. I can't think of a more inspired piece of installation than the juxtaposition in the Albright-Knox Art Gallery of Moore's bronze *Reclining Figure No. 4* (1961) with Courbet's *Source of the Loue*. This is not simply a matter of the correlation between the water-green bronze of the Moore and the glistening, weed-strewn cavern from which the river Loue starts on its journey. There is an altogether deeper affinity between the two works. Moore loves Courbet, and one of his proudest possessions is a *marine* by the Master of Ornans; and Courbet does presage, quite distinctly, Moore's preoccupation with rock-surfaces, and with rock-tunnels; and with the jut and indentation of rock which has been worked upon by water. When Moore actually placed a major bronze in water, at the Lincoln Center some seasons ago, it turned out not to work too well, for reasons quite independent of his planning and volition; but throughout his career, and notably in the huge *Reclining Figure No. 1* (1959), which is also in the Albright-Knox, there are reminders that we English are a sea people, that not one of us lives more than two or three hours' drive from the sea, and that our coast can be read as a series of climaxes in which headlands are worked on and worked over, unceasingly, by the sea. What Keats called the sea's "priestlike task of pure ablution" is actually something very much grosser and more complex: nothing less than the remodeling of the land in ways which relate to our own vicissitudes. And it is because Henry Moore's bronzes so often awake echoes of those vicissitudes that they exert so compelling a thraldom. They suggest, in other words, that human nature can survive even the most grueling of ordeals.

Albright-Knox owns, in the elmwood *Internal and External Forms* (1953–54), one of the grandest examples of an ambition which Moore first conceived in 1931. He wanted then "to get one form to stay alive inside another"; and at the start of the 1950's he did this, over and over, in a series of "helmet heads." These were characteristically ambiguous in their implications. Looking inside the fulfilled and rounded helmet-form, we found within it a form that was of quite another sort: angular, irregular, asymmetrical, unsteady. Was this form protected by the helmet, or imprisoned by it? It was always difficult to say—both at once, maybe. Nature herself, after all, has set the tone of the debate by making the skull one of the most regular and predictable of known objects, and the skull's contents so absolutely erratic and unaccountable in their activities. Moore compounded the problem by occasionally showing the interior forms on their own. Once inside the helmet, they could never be seen completely; and yet, outside it, they looked incomplete and defenseless.

Perhaps it should be written into this record that Henry Moore once commented at length on the circumstances in which the big elmwood figure was produced. The first maquette was made in 1951, and later in that same year a working model, just over two feet high, was cast in bronze. It was very difficult at that time to find a piece of wood large enough and sound enough for a carving of the dimensions Moore had in mind; he had completed a full-scale plaster model and was about to send it to the foundry when his local timber merchant came along to say that (in Moore's own words) "he had a large elm tree just come in which he thought would be exactly what I wanted. It was a magnificent tree, newly cut down, five feet in diameter at its base, and looked very sound. I bought it . . . and decided to carry out the idea as originally intended as a wood sculpture.

"I am very pleased this happened, because I am sure that elmwood, in particular, with its large-sized grain, varied, big, and bold, makes it ideal in scale for large work. It was necessary for the upright carving to be in wood, which is alive and warm and gives a sense of growth. These qualities were in harmony with the idea, which is a sort of embryo being protected by an outer form, a mother and child idea, or the stamen in a flower—that is, something young and growing being protected by an outer shell."

There is also in the Albright-Knox a small Moore bronze of 1959 which is formally quite similar to the big elmwood piece; and as that small bronze is called *Mother and Child*, there is a case for saying that the *Internal and External Forms* may also represent a mother and child. On the other hand, Moore is careful about his titles and does not give them lightly. So I incline to think that he meant us to see the piece in the context of a wider and less precise association. In fact I have partly come round, after some years of opposition, to the view put forward by Erich Neumann in his *Henry Moore und der Archetyp des Weiblichen*. Neumann likened the *Internal and External Forms* to "one of those Egyptian sarcophagi in the form of mummies, which show the mother goddess as the sheltering womb which holds and contains the dead man like a child again, as he was in the beginning." Neumann went on to say, in terms which are perhaps too grandiose for a man of Henry Moore's perfect simplicity and naturalness, that the figure was "mother of life, mother of death, and all-embracing body-self, the archetypal mother of man's germinal ego-consciousness. . . .

121

This truly great sculpture of Moore's is all these in one," he said finally. Neumann's opinion is powerfully argued, and I don't think that we should dismiss it. But it does still strike me as too explicit an interpretation: Moore has never liked either to spell out the "meaning" of his work or to have others spell it out for him. He prefers to let the work find its own echoes in the psyche of the individual spectator; perhaps we could agree to say simply that the big elmwood carving is a very fine example of Moore's ability to make visible the ambiguous and reversible nature of human relationships. The embrace which he sets before us can both protect and stifle, nurture and repress.

John Piper was responsible in the late 1930's, and during the years of World War II, for a shift in sensibility no less radical than that pioneered by Paul Nash. Through him and because of him, a whole generation looked differently not only at the masterworks of the English country-house tradition but at a whole gamut of minor vernacular buildings: Victorian churches in the north of England, Welsh nonconformist chapels, ruined cottages only fit to be pulled down and carted away. He also taught us to look at textures with a new eye, and at stenciled lettering, and at the marine sparkle of paintwork at the seaside, and at the energy and variety of post-Renaissance sculpture in English parish churches. He seemed to turn up everywhere, in those years, moving at a steady pace with an idiosyncratic loping walk and finding time to write as well as to paint. His little book on *British Romantic Artists* (1942) has given thirty years and more of unalloyed pleasure; it showed us, among other things, that the byways of art could be as rewarding as the byways of nature, and that a Victorian illustrator could be as provocative a guide to visual experience as many of the great swells of the museum and the salesroom.

Piper has always worked at a rate which would kill off a lesser man in a week: painting, drawing, making stained glass, writing, designing for the theater and the opera house, illustrating books (notably Adrian Stokes's classic writings about Venice), and latterly turning to pottery fired in his own kiln. There was a time when one simply couldn't go into his neighbor's house and pick up a pot of jam without finding that John Piper had designed the label for it. The little picture in the Albright-Knox cannot, in itself, speak for this many-sided and indefatigable artist, but it is a late and elegant example of his work in watercolor. Anyone who knows the English watercolor tradition will recognize at once certain echoes of what John Sell Cotman, for one, could do with English vernacular architecture. But the picture is also the work of someone who has looked closely at Synthetic Cubism and adapted its flat, overlapping planes to a straightforward descriptive purpose. Piper in the 1930's used collage with an effect of offhand English wit; and in his *Study for "Shobden Folly"* he brings together the ornamental battlements, the decorated archway, the man-sized wild flowers and the niched medallion with just that same deft aerial touch. It is thanks to paintings such as this one—and they must by now number many hundreds—that it is difficult for an Englishman of my outlook and generation to come upon a characterful building in any country of the world and not think of John Piper.

Piper has treated very serious subjects in his time, and I myself would rank his window on the theme of the Instruments of the Passion as one of the few really successful religious utterances in the English art of the last twenty-five years. His stage designs for *Don Giovanni, A Midsummer*

Night's Dream, The Turn of the Screw, Oedipus, and *Simon Boccanegra* were memorable on more than one count. Yet his rapid, allusive turn of mind and his delight in every kind of new adventure have made him unpopular with certain grave observers; such people feel, also, that Piper keeps back too much of himself. If he has doubts or fears, he disdains to show them, and although his likings and dislikings have changed and evolved in the forty years that he has been before the public, it is only indirectly that he allows the fact to come out.

The case is quite other with Graham Sutherland, who was born in the same year as John Piper and until 1945 was loosely allied to him in many people's minds. The alliance amounted to no more than a shared interest in the unexplored resources of English and Welsh landscape. When Sutherland decided at the end of the 1940's to spend the greater part of each year in the south of France there was no longer any reason to associate him with Piper—or with anyone else, for that matter. Sutherland since then has played only a very small part in English life, but there is no doubt that in the late 1930's and early 1940's he too was responsible for a shift in English sensibilities. He brought out an aspect of nature which, for all the hundreds and hundreds of artists who had been painting English landscape for a century and more, had never quite been brought out before. He made us realize, in a word, that nature in England could be hostile, and that fear, as much as delectation, could enter into our reactions to it. This was quite contrary to the English tradition, which had always been that our landscape is a safe place, a blessed bower, sweet-smelling and luxurious, where all is repose and refreshment, solace, and delight.

Sutherland did not see it in that way, and many of his Welsh landscapes of the late 1930's had a power out of all proportion to their size. It was not that he edited what he saw, but rather that he became a compliant part of it, reporting faithfully on nature's hidden tantrums and breaking down the unspoiled Pembrokeshire landscape in terms of tusk and crevice, mantrap and bolt-hole. These paintings raised a question never before asked in English art: What if we are not at home in the world? And because that question corresponded to unfocused anxieties of a perfectly rational sort—who among us could have felt at home in the world in 1940?—they had a long reverberation. No one could have called Sutherland a popular painter at that time; in fact, he was one of several English artists, all of them long since famous, who would have found it hard to go on working without the patronage and encouragement of Kenneth Clark. But he had made a contribution to our English consciousness, and those of us who were around at the time will never forget the impact of those little Welsh landscapes.

The Albright-Knox Sutherland dates from 1945, and it is a key picture for the English painting of its day. Sutherland at that time, and to a degree not as yet quite defined by the historians, had an influence on several younger painters, notably on Francis Bacon, on Lucian Freud, and on John Craxton. His spare, sharp, angular forms recurred constantly in the work of his friends and acquaintances; and if we note the overtones of human anatomy in the right-hand branch of the Albright-Knox tree we shall quickly relate it to the anatomies in Francis Bacon's *Three Studies for Figures at the Base of a Crucifixion,* which had been by any count the most remarkable English painting of the year 1944. Sutherland in later years became well known as a portrait painter, and he has spent most of the year in what is at first sight a more seductive landscape than that of our wet little, windy little island; but he has never lost his sense of the natural scene as a place where things may go wrong, any more than he has lost his sense of human beings as a genus to whom a great many unpleasant things can happen.

The middle and late 1940's were a great time for rumination among English artists. We had been so long cut off from the outer world, and for most practical purposes the outer world was still so inaccessible, that thoughtful people were pushed down within themselves and within the past history of English art. They thought, and they ruminated, and they wrote. I remember that in the last months of World War II, Keith Vaughan emerged not only as a good painter but as a particularly intelligent writer on art, as Patrick Heron was to do during the years when he worked as a practicing critic, week by week, for the *New Statesman*. Vaughan first came to notice, in the galleries, with small-scale paintings which derived somewhat from Samuel Palmer. Palmer's tranced visions of an England all aglisten with moonlight were just about everyone's favorite English paintings during the war, when moonlight itself had a more dangerous connotation; Keith Vaughan adapted them with very considerable skill to his own personal vision of our countryside. When the war came to an end, he began to develop a larger, barer, and less luxuriant subject matter: The human figure was still sited in landscape, but the figure itself had a gaunt and sculptural cast, while the landscape had none of the lichened crevices and soft greeny hollows which had struck us as valid emblems of a peace long vanished. These new, plain, monumental images were an act of courage at the time; we in England have no tradition of that sort. The pictures looked awkward, but they also looked *true*; and the Albright-Knox *Bathers by a Gray Sea* (1947) is a very good example of them. I never see it without remembering how English art was then recovering from the numbed state of wartime, and although it is in no way an anecdotal painting there is something in the stance of the two figures, and something in their deep and easy breathing, of the period when it was at last possible to look at the sky without apprehension.

English collectors were still dominated at that same time by French taste and French achievement, and one of the most successful exhibitions of the late 1940's was Geoffrey Tibble's, from which every painting was sold, and reviews of which in general were eulogistic. Tibble died not long after—too soon, in any case, to refute the minority of people who thought, as I did, that the paintings were too much an impersonation of Degas to hold up strongly in their own right. Seeing Tibble's *Hairdressing, No. 3* (1948) in Buffalo after more than twenty years, I found that I had underestimated the role of the spirit of the age in Tibble's work—the element, in other words, of the odd and the spiky, the jagged and the uneasy. It is as if a whole generation had been infected with the knife-like acute-angled forms which were finding their way as much into English sculpture as into English painting. Herbert Read invented the phrase "the geometry of fear" for these forms when they were apotheosized in the sculpture of Lynn Chadwick; and although nothing could have been further from a situation of fear than the scene portrayed by Tibble in the Albright-Knox painting, there is a nervous, unrelaxed quality about the drawing which speaks for England at that time. I can think of many English paintings of its date which I would rather see in a great American museum, but the Tibble is, even so, a part of history.

It is not forgotten in England that the Albright Art Gallery, as it then was, was the first museum in the United States to open its doors to a mixed show of *British Contemporary Painters* after World War II; 1946 was the well-remembered year. It was also the year of Henry Moore's first major retrospective, outside of his own country—at The Museum of Modern Art in New York. Among English artists in the second half of the 1940's, Moore was distinctly the man who most imposed himself. After he won the Grand Prize for sculpture at the Venice Biennale of 1948, the idea began to get about that English sculpture in general might be worth looking into. Veterans of the period will remember the enormous goodwill which was extended to English people of every kind at that moment in history; and that goodwill was particularly vibrant in the case of English artists who showed in Venice, and in São Paulo and in the Carnegie International in Pittsburgh. Indulgence of a kind normally extended primarily to handicapped persons, or to convalescents, became ours, universally, for a brief season. American visitors to London soon got the habit, in the 1950's, of going to Gimpel Fils to see what was going on in British sculpture. There were other galleries (Reg Butler always showed at the Hanover, for instance, just as Henry Moore showed mainly at the Leicester for many years) but Gimpel Fils had (and still has) a magic touch with transatlantics. Andrew Ritchie and other American scholars offered a most ready acceptance of what was going on in England, and by the 1950's there was, indeed, something to look at, insofar as a new generation of sculptors was coming up.

Not all of them were predestined to sculpture in the way that Henry Moore and Barbara Hepworth had been predestined to sculpture—irresistibly, that is to say, and from first youth. Bernard Meadows had been Henry Moore's studio assistant from 1936 to 1939, but Reg Butler, for one, did not take up sculpture till he was thirty-six. Lynn Chadwick was in his thirties before he found his true bent. Even those who were clearly born sculptors—Robert Adams, for instance—were likely to have had a five or six years' interruption between 1939 and 1945. So when these artists began to show their work in the 1950's they appeared to us as seasoned human beings who happened to make sculpture, rather than as professionals who might never have had a general idea or taken a look at the world outside the studio. They were considerably older than the people who now come forward as debutants, and most of them had an inner life that was both rich and wry, even if they disguised it beneath the sculptor's traditional bluffness and extroverted camaraderie.

This particular phase of English art is well documented at the Albright-Knox Art Gallery with substantial pieces by Adams, Armitage, Butler, Chadwick, and Meadows. Among them, it was Reg Butler who first made an international name. When he won first prize in the *Unknown Political Prisoner* competition in London in 1953, he was still comparatively unknown and the award caused a good deal of local exasperation. Could this be *sculpture*, people asked? Questions were put down in the House of Commons, and Winston Churchill was pressed for an undertaking that in no circumstances would a full-scale version of the prizewinning work be erected on the cliffs of Dover. There were motives both general and particular behind the uproar. People just didn't want to hear about political prisoners, known or unknown, at that time. Even in maquette-form, with the human figures only an inch or two high, Butler's evocation of *le monde concentrationnaire* made visitors uneasy. Enlarged, with the hapless prisoners man-sized and the watchtower visible from many miles away, it would have been an unwelcome and ever present reminder that there were thousands of people for whom the day of liberty was still to come.

There was also the fact that Reg Butler worked with materials like forged iron at a time when people thought of sculpture in terms of carved wood, carved stone, and cast bronze. Very few visitors to the *Unknown Political Prisoner* exhibition had heard of Gonzalez's iron sculptures or of the sculptures made by Picasso in that same material between 1929 and 1932. The battle for understanding had to be fought all over again, and on ground made all the more difficult by the alliance of unpopular subject matter with an unfamiliar idiom. (Butler had, in point of fact, been showing iron figures since 1949, though it was only in 1950 that he stopped practicing as an architect and industrial technologist under the name of Cottrell Butler.)

The Albright-Knox *Torso* is one of Butler's earliest iron figures. Anyone who knows Picasso's *Woman in the Garden* (1929–30) and his other sculptures of that period will recognize the source of the tiny circular head with its even tinier eyes. From the same great source come, equally, the pelvic platform, the freehand drawing-in-space of the legs and breasts, and the discreetly parodic air of the sculpture as a whole. Butler has here remade the human figure in a way which, though not of his own invention, was an important step toward the de-provincialization of English sculpture. (It is worth adding that D. H. Kahnweiler's book on Picasso's sculpture, with its many photographs by Brassai, was published in England in 1949.)

Robert Goldwater in his *What is Modern Sculpture?* has this to say about Reg Butler's *Unknown Political Prisoner:* "Conceived in the constructivist mode, it is open, and at first sight abstract, with a free-flowing space playing a predominant role. Only gradually do the sinister associations of the linear design become apparent. Its stabbing, encircling wires recall the electrified barriers of the concentration camp; its figures are dwarfed by the overpowering mechanical contrivance whose delicacy intensifies its menace. . . . It is perhaps ironically fitting that this monument to unrecognized heroism was never built." Butler thereafter was to work his way back toward a well-rounded naturalism: an art whose echoes were all of enjoyment. But there lingered for just a while something of the watchful stance of his prisoners, and in the other Albright-Knox piece we catch an echo of their stoical way of standing around on a rock from which there can be no escape. *Manipulator* dates from 1954; it has the transitional look of a figure midway between the opened-out and schematic iron figures of 1949–50 and the straightforward, busty young girls who were soon to follow. It is very much a cold war image: that turretlike neck, that face turned toward the sky, that precarious perch on a point of vantage are more appropriate to the prisoners of 1953 than to the avocations of a man at liberty. The generalized disquiet which Herbert Read singled out in the English sculpture of the 1950's comes out strongly here, and we do not even have to leave the Albright-Knox to find another example of the uneasy vigilance which characterized the period—Lynn Chadwick's drawing *The Watcher* (1960).

Chadwick had won the international sculpture prize at the Venice Biennale of 1956. Giacometti had represented France on that occasion, and there were a great many people who thought at the time that Chadwick was rather lucky to have come in first. The good fortune which favored him on that occasion may be said, in any case, to have turned her back on him since. Lynn Chadwick has, in fact, been penalized for having fulfilled so completely the demands, conscious or unconscious, of the mid-1950's. His *Two Dancing Figures* (1954) also in the Albright-Knox, has just the jaunty, evocative, conversational tone that people prized at that time. It could be applied to subject matter of a discreetly spooky sort (whence the "geometry of fear") but Chadwick at that time was working on ideas of balance and wing-span, tension and thrust, which may well have been an after-echo of his war service as a pilot in the Fleet Air Arm. The lean, angular, spiky form-language of the 1950's was ideally suited to him, and people all over Europe responded to it as eagerly as they responded to Chadwick's rangy, outgoing, and not seldom uproarious presence.

Fear is by its nature contagious. Once bruited, it is likely to turn up everywhere, whether intended or not. We are invited, almost, to find it in Bernard Meadow's *Startled Bird* (1955); and there is an element of unease in the sword-and-dagger slenderness of Robert Adams's *Tall Spike Form* (1957). But that particular hand can be overplayed. There is nothing in the least fearful about the reinforced-concrete relief wall which Adams made for the town of Gelsenkirchen in 1959, for instance, and Meadows has always had, and now has more than ever, a streak of raunchy humor. Even in 1951, when the news from Korea seemed to justify the most lugubrious of speculations, there were still people around who did not exclude the idea that sculpture could on occasion be funny.

One of these was Kenneth Armitage. The Albright-Knox has two pieces by Armitage, and they show how he could carry over into sculpture certain qualities of affectionate observation which are more commonly found in the English novel. Armitage has always enjoyed cutting across the traditional categories of sculpture: the totemic standing figure, on the one hand, and the no less expectable reclining figure, on the other. He knows that in life people do not fall so regularly into one or the other of these extremes; they squat, they lose their balance, they lean against the wind, they bunch themselves up in all manner of odd and unpredictable ways. Armitage brought all this into sculpture. He also provided a counter-image to the spiked and fleshless physical type which had been promulgated by Chadwick. His women, especially, tended to be chunky and bottle-shaped, with heads like knobs or stoppers, arms and legs that stuck out in an awkward, defenseless sort of way, and a deep, door-shaped indentation at the navel. If they were dressed, as they are in *Family Going for a Walk*, their clothes took on a droll character of their own. If they were undressed, as in *Seated Woman with Arms Extended*, they were nearer to the naked body as it is in life than to the naked body as we know it in "fine art."

There was in all this something anecdotal, something local and unpretentious that made no claim to be big-time sculpture. But it was not to be despised, either; and if in later years it was despised, or at best passed over in silence, the fault lay with a system that in the 1950's had empty places to fill and demanded of certain artists that they should fill them, irrespective of whether they were ready, or whether they could fill them for more than a month or two, or whether they were that sort of artist at all. The needs in question were especially imperious at a time when it was generally believed among museum directors that British sculpture had a collective stature that should not be ignored. A consecration of that kind was still quite new for England, and we wanted to hold on to it. What got overlooked was the fact that every artist's career has a natural rhythm, and that that rhythm, once lost, is very difficult to recover.

It is a fact of international art-life that sculptors hang together and have an easy community of contacts and ideas, in a way that painters do not. No one in the 1950's, or later, talked of "English painting" in the way that they talked of "English sculpture"—with a sense of specific, recognizable identity. Nor were there among painters many friendly alliances of the kind that bound Armitage to Chadwick, or bound both of them to César, for instance. There was just nothing in common between Ben Nicholson and Francis Bacon, or between William Scott and Alan Davie. And painting is, in any case, a more secretive activity than sculpture. Sculpture takes up a lot of room. It often calls for the assistance of one or more people. It may cost a great deal of money to make, and quite a bit of money to store. A painter either has none of these problems or has them in ways which impinge much less on his peace of mind. He can be, on occasion, of a delicate, aesthetic physical type that could never cope with the traditional strenuosities of sculpture. He can also be very much a man on his own and not feel diminished.

This last has been Francis Bacon's position for many years. He has one very close friend among painters—Lucian Freud—and he is on good terms with one or two others; but he does not rely on anyone for the kind of professional dialogue that many artists find indispensable. In such matters he keeps his own counsel. He does, however, go to just about every exhibition in London that is worth looking at. "I think of myself," he once wrote to me, "as a kind of pulverizing machine into which everything I look at and feel about is fed." From this there builds up "a sort of compost out of which images emerge from time to time. These are perhaps partially conditioned by the mood of the material which has gone into the pulverizer." All this is relevant to the early and very beautiful Bacon, *Man with Dog* (1953), which was not the least of Mr. Knox's many benefactions to the Gallery. Like most Bacons, this one has a compound derivation. One could say of that derivation that it is half known, half unknown, and all irrelevant. In other words it doesn't really help, in the last analysis, to know that the dog came eventually from a photograph of a mastiff by Muybridge, or that the schema of the painting relates to Balla's *Dog on Leash* (now in the Albright-Knox collection) which had been in an exhibition at The Tate Gallery in the summer of 1952. On the level that really matters, the pulverization has been too complete. As with William Blake's *Ghost of a Flea*, scholarship can suggest the "source," in scholarship's own terms; but the real source, the driving inner compulsion, will never be divulged to us. Bacon often thinks about Muybridge and very probably saw the Balla when it was at the Tate. Blake knew the redoubtable portrait of a flea in Robert Hooke's *Micrographia* of 1665. Dog for dog, and flea for metamorphosed flea, there's a resemblance—anyone can see that. But there is also a great difference between Balla's tightly drawn and mechanistically conceived portrait of a dog on the move and the spectral aspect of the dog in the Bacon. And as Bacon has got a name—not always fairly—for raucous and emphatic subject matter, it should also be said that in the early 1950's he was using paint, as in the Albright-Knox picture, with a Whistlerian delicacy. Animal movement was much in his mind at that time; he had been to Africa for the second time in the spring of 1952, and during his first visit to South Africa in the winter of 1950–51 he had looked closely at the wild animals in Kruger Park. (At the same time, it would be characteristic of his methods if he had drawn as much on the evidence of hunters' photographs as on firsthand experience.) The Albright-Knox painting is one of four dog pictures that he painted between 1952 and 1954; what we take away from it, in the end, is not the subject matter but the memory of paint used with the rarest and most delicate vibration.

In the dialectic of English taste, William Scott has played a special part since 1945. He was, to begin with, the "younger painter" who found most favor at the end of World War II with the heirs of Roger Fry. Whenever Clive Bell was pressed for the name of a young man to watch, he was most likely to say, "Well, I think William Scott's coming on pretty well." And William Scott did, in effect, satisfy a French-formed taste as well as anyone of his generation. Born in 1913, he got off the mark even before World War II and became a Sociétaire of the Paris Salon d'Automne as early as 1938. He loved French painting, and French life, but he never went in for the richly cooked and oversauced way of painting that characterized the School of Paris in its decline. He stood for a barer, more summary way of dealing with the world. He was sparing with his images and sparing with his paint, and the fundamental subjects of his art never changed. He was, and is, concerned with proportion, the division of space, relations of tone, and the management of a small number of recurring forms. As to the nature of those forms, I cannot improve on what I once wrote: that Scott "takes the traditional subjects of European art—landscape, still life, and the figure—and gradually discards those elements in the completed picture which could prompt the observer to identify its point of departure. 'Gradually' is the key-word here, for there is nothing arid or schematic about Scott's activity. He starts from palpable and often delectable fact: his harbors would really give shelter, his frying-pans would dependably fry, his women are never merely fleshed armatures."

We in England rather admire a painter who can tightrope his way through material of this sort, never quite losing the original source and never quite going over, either, into pure abstraction. But I have found that in the United States activity of this sort is ranked as at best devious, at worst epicene and untrue to history. In the United States it can count as minus, not as plus, if one and the same painting can refer back to the Cubists' upturned table-top, to the wraith of Bonnard's inhabited baths, and to the memory of broad-bottomed boats tied up beneath a Cornish harbor wall. It is a fact of history that Scott came to the United States in 1953 and was one of the first English painters to seek out Pollock, Kline, and Rothko and learn something at first hand of what they were doing; but it is a fact about Scott himself that he is every bit as interested in the strange chalky, sandy *matière* of ancient Egyptian painting and that the masters to whom he returns, after no matter how rewarding a foray elsewhere, are Chardin, Corot, Braque, and Bonnard. Scott also has ideas about what he calls "the beauty of the thing done badly." He is attentive, for instance, to the graffiti which are left behind after children have been playing in the street; and if there are loose ends and unexplained marks on the canvas it doesn't disturb him. The picture should in his view be a complete world, not a perfected one.

To all this, the two big paintings in the Albright-Knox are an ideal illustration. They are many things in one: the diagram of a children's game, the diagram of a well-stocked kitchen table, the diagram of a harbor to which the fishing fleet has lately returned. They are scored, as much as drawn; baked, as much as painted; immediate, and yet instinct with centuries of pictorial tradition. If I might quote myself again, these are paintings "in which Scott gets away from the easel tradition and turns toward that of the mural; the pictures are large not merely in the physical sense but in their indifference to momentary inequalities of execution. Where the Beaux-Arts easel painter strives to protect the paint against the roughness of ordinary life—to create, in fact, an enclosed garden in which all is perfection—Scott lets the picture take its chance, aiming to let life take hold of it, at the cost even of a few bumps and bruises and a *gros mot* or two."

Scott negotiated with conspicuous skill the gap between the aesthetic of the 1930's and aesthetic that defined itself some twenty years later. Alan Davie, only seven years his junior, came into a world in which the earlier loyalty no longer applied and could have been taken up only in affectation by an artist in his twenties. It was in the late 1940's, and when he was in Europe on a traveling scholarship, that Davie saw paintings by Jackson Pollock at Peggy Guggenheim's house in Venice. Pollock at that time was unknown in England, though it is said that one painting by him was put on view in the cathedral city of Canterbury in the year 1947. Davie showed paintings like the Albright-Knox's *Female, Male* in London at a time when social realism was the going thing and the most-approved subject matter was drawn from the minutiae of domesticity. It would be untrue to say that Davie was "made" by his first experience of Pollock; even their points of likeness were sometimes coincidental, in that for instance Davie came quite independently by his enthusiasm for Indian sand-painting; but there is an evident affinity between *Female, Male* and a Pollock, such as the *Male and Female* of 1942. What Davie got from Pollock, and what he could never have got from our local scene, was the signal to go ahead. Pollock's work encouraged him to let the images well up, rough and raw, from his unconscious; and he has been doing it ever since.

After nearly twenty years what strikes an English observer about Davie's *Female, Male* is no longer the brusque, raunchy approach to sexual imagery. Nor is it the vigor, rare in England at that time, of the marks of the canvas. It is the echoes of English Neo-Romanticism which linger on in the picture. The schema is not so far, after all, from the thorn trees of Graham Sutherland. Davie has taken the motifs of crescent and spike and slender vertical stem and transposed them, whether consciously or not, into the domain of human anatomy. There is a reckless, thrusting quality about *Female, Male* which cannot be found in the Neo-Romantic paintings of the late 1940's in England; but the recent past has its part to play in folk memory, and in this case it does seem to have intermingled itself with attitudes from across the Atlantic.

Female, Male dates from the year before the first comprehensive showing of "the new American painting" in England. That exhibition was of very great importance for the evolution of English art. It was the end of isolation, the end of ignorance, the end of the long period in which it was believed in England that English-speaking artists were lucky to be taken seriously at all. It was a difficult exhibition, and I do not think that I was the only person who got a lot of things wrong when I first went round it.

130

The attitude known to psychoanalysis as "defensive rigidity" came into play in all this. It took a long time to work one's way through so complex an experience; history—as so often—now simplifies and accelerates a process which at the time was diffuse and sometimes self-contradictory. The aftermath of that exhibition (and of its successor in 1959) would make a good subject for a doctorate thesis. Both the influence and the lack of influence—the resistance, one might say—must one day be disentangled. The Albright-Knox owns, meanwhile, two paintings dated 1958 which should feature in any such thesis: William Turnbull's *Abstract #25* and Robyn Denny's *Red Beat 6*. Turnbull was much liked, as a man, by Barnett Newman, and his *Abstract #25* is one of the acts of identification which Turnbull has used as marker buoys in the course of his career. With the Denny, as with the Hoyland of 1961, *No. 42.10.11.161*, which is also in the Albright-Knox, we come to an aspect of institutional collecting for which there is no easy solution. In other words, neither picture gives even a forecast of the artist's later stature. The Denny is, for its date, and for English art, an adventurous painting—in the alliance of the drip with big repeated stenciled lettering, for instance. Set beside one of Denny's hieratic and immaculate paintings of the late 1960's, it would make a most interesting historical point. Seen by itself, it does not come completely alive. Likewise, and even more so, with the Hoyland. So thinly and so tightly painted, it does not foreshadow in any way the glorious fatness and fullness of Hoyland's later procedures. Yet no museum today can follow up every artist it collects, in the way that Duncan and Marjorie Phillips followed up their favorites in the 1920's and 1930's.

This problem is particularly acute in the case of artists from a far country. The Albright-Knox has, for instance, a good Pasmore of 1960: *Abstract in Red, No. 3*. There's absolutely nothing wrong with it. Pasmore has judged to the smallest fraction of an inch the relationship between the ponderous, rhomboidal central form and the reed-thin black shape which so subtly leans away from it. Yet without some knowledge of Pasmore's earlier figurative work, and of the effect on the English art scene of his break with figuration toward the end of the 1940's, the experience is incomplete. Of course any painting by a good artist should be able to stand alone; but there is in the career of any such artist a moral continuum. *Billy Budd* is a great story in its own right; but if we see on the title page the words "By the author of *Moby Dick*" we focus with renewed interest and heightened appreciation on the very different qualities of *Billy Budd*: the concision, the sense of limited material completely mastered, the refusal to digress.

For this reason I welcome the presence in Buffalo of very fine examples of the way in which Ben Nicholson in 1945, and again in 1952, could adapt the overlapping planes of Synthetic Cubism to his own purposes. The up-ended table top of the Cubists find here an incorporeal apotheosis. The pictures work as abstract designs, but they also work in terms of volumes seized and set down before us. They work in terms of the pure, thin color which Nicholson has made his own; but they also work in terms of a grand, spare architecture. With these two paintings, and the earlier *White Relief*, there is a workable nucleus of Nicholson in the Albright-Knox. The museum becomes what a museum should be—a dictionary and a drawing room in one. In contrast, the representation of Eduardo Paolozzi by his *Japanese War God* (1958) would suggest that he is primarily a *bricoleur*, a man who patches his sculptures together; among middle-generation painters Sandra Blow and Patrick Heron, and among middle-generation sculptors Hubert Dalwood, are also represented in a partial, and partially misleading, way. But no museum can take out a life contract with the artists it picks out, and the important thing in these cases, from our point of view, is that the Albright-Knox was right in there, buying, as early as any of our English institutions.

Every museum of real character has its allegiances. It does not, in other words, aim to buy "a bit of everything." The Albright-Knox has so glorious a spread of works by Johns, Rauschenberg, Rosenquist, Warhol, and Lichtenstein that I sometimes groan to think that its English holdings for the relevant period—from 1959, the dates of Johns's *Numbers in Color*, to 1963, the date of Rosenquist's *Nomad*—are comparatively sparse. At such times I imagine acts of piracy by which the Albright-Knox would suddenly acquire substantial early works by Richard Smith, Richard Hamilton, David Hockney, Allen Jones, and Peter Blake. Peter Phillips's *War/Game* (1961) is a good work, for a painter aged twenty-one and still in art school; it speaks, incidentally, for the delight in the folklore of a still inaccessible America which characterized many young English painters at that time. But fundamentally there is a gap in the collection between paintings like the Peter Lanyon of 1956, *Lulworth*, and R. B. Kitaj's *Walter Lippmann* (1966). The one is concerned with an attempt to reconcile old-style nature painting with abstraction; the other comes from a complete break with traditional English picture-language.

It was at the end of the 1950's that word first went around London of an American called R. B. Kitaj who was stirring things up at the Royal College of Art and producing some very curious paintings. Kitaj has never ceased to be an American, and I shall not defend the logic which places him here in the British School. At most, I could suggest that nearly all of Kitaj's best work has been done in England, though there is a lot to be said on behalf of the mixed bag of new achievements which he brought back from a sojourn in California not long ago. Kitaj the easel painter is an English phenomenon, one might say—even if, once again, I would have to qualify the remark, remembering as I do the look of the half-finished canvas in his studio in Berkeley, California, which had on it a portrait of Francis Bacon wearing Sigmund Freud's overcoat. But certainly the initial thrust by Kitaj the easel painter was made in England in the first half of the 1960's—and the initial success also.

A comparable success has attached itself, since those first days, to Kitaj the printmaker, and it is true that Christopher Prater, in particular, has proved himself able to carry out Kitaj's complex intentions with an extraordinary readiness. There seems to be literally nothing that Prater can't do with a silkscreen. But a superior magic resides, even so, in the compound images which Kitaj lays down with paint on canvas in a painstaking and consistently ironical way. The Albright-Knox Kitaj is called *Walter Lippmann* (1966). And, sure enough, the bright-eyed sage appears on the lower right side of the picture. Kitaj is a portrait-draftsman of a most penetrating kind, and this is one of many shrewd likenesses that he has completed over the last fifteen years. The subject matter of the painting does not, however, relate directly to the matters with which Mr. Lippmann has concerned himself so deeply for the past fifty years and more. Kitaj once said that the role of the Lippmann figure in this picture was not so much that of the political journalist as that of "the explainer or whatever he was" who intercedes from time to time in Thornton Wilder's *Our Town* to make sure that we know what's going on. And what *is* going on? Well, there are some learned games with space, and with perspective; just two years earlier, Kitaj had painted a picture called *The Apotheosis of Groundlessness*, which is a purely architectural piece, a pillared and strutted interior in which absolutely nothing—floor, roof, walls—sits quite as we would expect it to sit. *Walter Lippmann* has a bit of that, too. We cannot "read" the space in any ordinary sense, and yet we realize that its very oddity and discontinuity are acts of largesse on the painter's part. They make it possible, in other words, for us to see more, in an unaccountable and inscrutable way, than we see in other pictures.

Kitaj has been unusually forthcoming about the ingredients of this picture, and has even suggested that it might be called *The Vitality of Fresh Disorder.* "That's R. P. Blackmur's phrase . . . and he goes on to say: 'Each time we look at a set of things together, but do not count them, the sum of the impression will be different, though the received and accountable order remains the same.' " The "set of things" in this case includes, on the left, a memory of Margaret Kennedy's once-famous romance, *The Constant Nymph,* with its pigtailed heroine on her way up a ladder. Just below her is a derivative of Robert Donat—was there ever a better light romantic actor?—in military greatcoat: an echo, this, of the days when light comedy was played out in uniform. Above, a classic moment from the movies: Girl in white raincoat confronts belted stranger. The material is fragmented, overlaps with itself, jumps here and there and is subject to compositional devices that don't at any point make literal sense. It has always been Kitaj's practice to pit one style against another, one objective against another, one concept of information against another. "There is no, or very little question of, *ultimate* meanings," he once wrote in response to a letter from the Albright-Knox; and there is certainly no one ultimate meaning to *Walter Lippmann.* But what we do have is a new set of answers to the question "What can a picture do?"

That question could be prefixed, equally, to any exhibition of paintings by Bridget Riley. One of the key exhibitions of the 1960's—of the whole postwar period, in fact—for English art was Riley's second show in London, in 1963. The catalogue was prefaced by Anton Ehrenzweig, not yet famous as the author of *The Hidden Order of Art,* and the show included several paintings which were soon acknowledged as classics of their date. Riley at the time was working in black and white only, in the belief that the oppositions and antitheses and confrontations with which she was to deal were too intense to allow of chromatic elaboration. (Also, she knew that Van Gogh had valued above many a more "highly-colored" ingredient of the Provençal scene the Japanese blackthorn bush, starred all over with white flowers.) This is how the pictures looked to me in September, 1963: "A Riley is about the changes—progressive, sometimes abrupt, sometimes apparently disastrous—that can take place in a given situation. . . . The changes to which that situation is subject are presented in terms of color-contrast confined to black and white; shifting, accelerating and decelerating eye-rhythms; linear movements that confound expectation; unexpected pulls and thrusts that bring the whole structure to the point, it seems, of breakdown. The paintings could be read as studies in dislocation; but their final statement is on the side of recovery and integration, and their effect for that reason is one of an intense and hard-won exhilaration."

It will be clear from this that I do not see these particular paintings in terms of "optical art," and still less in terms of trick effects or stunt attacks on the retina. They seem to me now, as they seemed then, to be late but fine restatements of the kind of existential anguish which was exemplified in the 1940's by the literature of extreme situation. That extreme situation could hardly be put more directly, in art, than in the Rileys of 1964 like *Crest* and *Intake*.

Such an intensity cannot be counterfeited. Nor can it be prolonged beyond a certain point without falling into mannerism, at one extreme, or into madness at the other. One way to modify, or to moderate, the oppositions in question was to move into color as it is normally conceived, and in point of fact Riley was experimenting with this from 1961 onward, though no hint of this was made public. The Albright-Knox painting *Drift No. 2* (1966) is one of the two paintings of its title and date in which Riley explored an intermediate stage between total black and total white, as she had used them before 1963, and the voluptuous color-mixes (cerise, turquoise, olive) to which she has since graduated. In the two *Drift* paintings she made use of polarities of warm and cold within her grays which were, in effect, an introduction to color. The contrasts were softer, more sumptuous, less needling in their approach to the observer; the "either/or" of the earlier paintings was still there, but an element of "yes, but . . ." was not excluded. Visitors to the Albright-Knox may like to note the following authorized description of what happens in the sister picture, *Drift I*; it applies with only minimal adjustment, to the Buffalo picture:

"A cold tone remains constant over the whole area, while from left to right a warm sequence moving at two rates gives rise to warm/cold contrast, gradually changing to light/dark contrast, in the central area and moving away again into warm/cold contrast. Diagonal movements at two different speeds powerfully influence the curving bands flowing from top to bottom. The climax of the tonal sequence and the climax of the curve movements are at variance."

So precise a description might suggest something merely cerebral; but we have only to compare a Riley with most of the work in the catalogue of The Museum of Modern Art's *The Responsive Eye* exhibition of 1965 to see that beneath that exact description there lies an almost frantic subjectivity and an unremitting search for truth to private feeling.

In that same year, 1963, in which Anton Ehrenzweig prefaced Bridget Riley's exhibition, Anthony Caro had a retrospective exhibition of his sculptures at Whitechapel. Americans were way ahead of us, at that time, in their understanding of Caro's work, and I often wish that the Albright-Knox had a Caro of the early 1960's to set beside its later piece, *Georgiana* (1969–70). Once again, the assured complexity of the later work is difficult to site, in historical terms, without reference to what went before it. So much happened to Caro in that decade: no English artist has had a stronger, more coherent, more highly energized evolution. Like all Caro's best pieces, *Georgiana* is impossible to photograph. (Or, rather, all photographs of it are revealing, but none is complete.) Relevant facts from the immediate past are that Caro has for several years been making table sculptures—pieces, most of them quite small, that seem to have been caught in the act of vaulting over the table-top. From this comes, I fancy, the delicate poise of the plow blades on the horizontal section of *Georgiana*. (By the way, the title refers to Georgiana Street, in which Caro has a studio, and not to a young lady; and the plow blades were bought as a job lot which was going cheap after the failure of a crack-brained agricultural scheme in what was then British Africa.)

It is also relevant that Caro likes, or liked then, to get two mutually contradictory sets of forms to live together within a single work. In *Georgiana*, for instance, he uses some soft-looking spoon- or tongue-shaped forms which seem to peel away both from the long horizontal bar and from the curious doorlike form which is upended in one part of the piece and laid down on its side in another. The piece is about unexpected relationships: forms that don't normally live together, forms that deny their habitual weight and solidity, forms that suddenly lead a completely new life. (Caro at one time had poised a monumental tank-end on top of the recumbent door-form, and the piece was reproduced in that state in *Art News* for May, 1970.) Caro is an open man; "I want my sculptures to be *true*," he once said, and he has proved that he can fulfill this ambition as much on the scale of epic as on the scale of epigram. *Georgiana* is a first-rate example of what will eventually be called his middle, or early-middle, period. Certainly there is nothing in the British section of the Albright-Knox which augurs better for the future of British art. The Caro belongs right in there with the masterpieces of modern American art, as their equal and their peer.

Ben Nicholson

"The kind of painting which I find exciting is not necessarily representational or non-representational, but it is both musical and architectural, where the architectural construction is used to express a 'musical' relationship between form, tone, and colour and whether this visual, 'musical' relationship is slightly more or slightly less abstract is for me beside the point." *

Tableform, 1952, is essentially a Cubist composition of flat overlapping planes. Nicholson avoids, for the most part, use of the right angle, and his diagonal lines create an illusion of space, as does the blue pigment along the top of the painting that suggests landscape, perhaps as seen through a window. His palette of soft blues and browns is restrained and delicate, punctuated in the upper left by a bright spot of red.

Also in the Gallery collection are White Relief, 1937–38, and a small Still Life of 1945.

Ben Nicholson was born in 1894 in Denham, Buckshire, England, son of the painters Sir William Nicholson and Mabel Pryde. He attended the Slade School of Art in London, 1910–11, followed by several years of travel, primarily in Europe. During his frequent trips to Paris, he was attracted to Synthetic Cubism and developed his semi-abstract still lifes. He met his second wife, the sculptor Barbara Hepworth, in 1931 and, probably influenced by her direct carving, began his carved geometric reliefs, often painted white, shortly thereafter. In the early 1930's Nicholson became interested in the work of Arp and Mondrian and was particularly impressed by a visit to Mondrian's Paris studio in 1934 which had a marked effect on his work of subsequent years. He was a member of the 7 and 5 group, 1925–36, of Unit One, 1933, and Abstraction-Création in Paris, 1933–35. In 1937, he was coeditor with J. L. Martin and Naum Gabo of the book Circle: International Survey of Constructive Art, published when Gabo and Mondrian were his neighbors in Hamstead. From 1940 to 1956, he lived in St. Ives, Cornwall, and since 1958 has resided in Ticino, Switzerland.

* Ben Nicholson (London: The Tate Gallery, 1955), p. [4].

NICHOLSON *Tableform* **1952**
Oil and pencil on canvas
62½ x 43¾ in. (158.8 x 111.1 cm.)
Gift of Seymour H. Knox   K56:11

Reg Butler

Of *Torso*, c. 1950, Butler has written: "Although it is abstracted it is by no means non-figurative, that is to say, *it is a torso*. Technically it is the first figure in which I used arc-welding as a means of modeling, the forms in iron in previous figures were forged only, not forged-welded-forged." *

Derived from the iron sculptures of Gonzalez and Picasso, *Torso* with its spiky, insect-like forms and blank staring eyes is a manifestation of postwar Surrealist imagery. As opposed to Henry Moore's earthbound figures, Butler's early sculpture is, in effect, a drawing in space; the linear qualities are free-flowing and expressive rather than constructivist or architectonic. Close to life size, the figure confronts the viewer head on, its abbreviated and juggled anatomy producing a curious and disquieting effect.

Reg Butler was born in 1913 in Buntingford, Hertfordshire. He trained as an architect and received his degree in 1937. Although interested in sculpture from an early age, he practiced as an architect and industrial technologist until 1950. While serving as a conscientious objector during World War II, he worked for a village blacksmith and learned the art of forging. Although he worked with Henry Moore in the late 1940's, his early open iron sculpture represents a change from the "direct carving" aesthetic of Moore and Barbara Hepworth. In 1953, his controversial maquette for a Monument to the Unknown Political Prisoner was awarded first prize, but it was never erected.

In the 1950's Butler gave up welded iron sculpture in favor of cast bronze, with a resulting shift in emphasis to mass and surface qualities rather than the linear and spatial concerns of his earlier constructions.

The Manipulator, 1954 also in the collection of the Albright-Knox Art Gallery, is representative of his work of that period. More recently, he has been making naturalistic figurative sculptures of painted bronze.

* Letter from the artist, January, 1956.

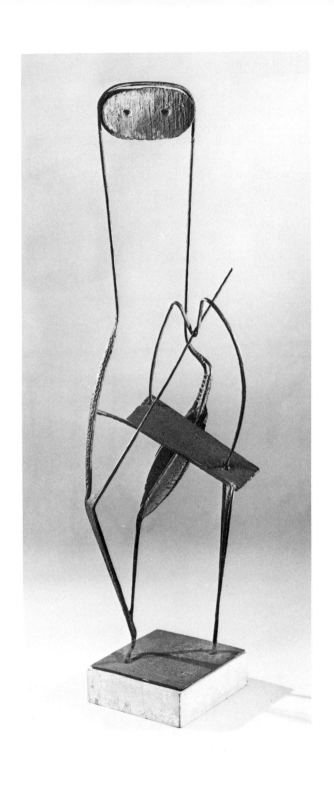

BUTLER *Torso* **c. 1950**
Iron, 56½ x 17 x 16 in.
(143.5 x 43.2 x 40.6 cm.)
Charles Clifton Fund   55:10

Alan Davie

Davie has stated that he paints to find enlightenment and revelation. His approach is essentially a romantic one, in that he seeks to reveal fundamental truths of human existence through art, a philosophy that has attracted him particularly to primitive art.

In *Female, Male,* 1955, the frankly erotic imagery is depicted with an aggression that becomes part of the content. Davie was influenced by Jackson Pollock as early as 1948, and in *Female, Male* a similar intuitive technique with emphasis on spontaneity and improvisation is evident, as well as a fascination with symbolic imagery, characteristic of Pollock's early work before 1946. Davie has written that *Female, Male* was repainted many times before its final resolution, and originally was intended to have a horizontal format.

Also in the Gallery collection is a 1960 painting by Davie, *Study for "The Key"*.

Born in Grangemouth, Scotland, in 1920, James Alan Davie began to study music as a child and to paint at the age of sixteen. While attending Edinburgh College of Art, 1937–40, he became interested in primitive and exotic art and in jazz as well, learning to play the clarinet and saxophone. These dual interests persisted—Davie had temporarily abandoned painting in favor of jazz, when he saw some of Jackson Pollock's "totemic" works in 1948 while spending a year traveling in Europe and began to paint again, attempting, as he said, to use the same extemporaneous composition as in jazz. From widely varying sources, both ancient and modern, he developed a personal mythology emanating from the subconscious. In his method of working, an image placed on the canvas calls forth another which, in turn, evokes still another until a group of associative forms fills the painting. During the 1950's, his colors were dark and somber, replaced in the 1960's by a brightly colored palette.

DAVIE *Female, Male* **1955**
Oil on masonite, 78 x 59 in. (198.1 x 149.8 cm.)
Gift of Seymour H. Knox   K56:9

141

Eduardo Paolozzi

Paolozzi has said that his aim is to achieve "the metamorphosis of quite ordinary things into something wonderful and extraordinary." * In *Japanese War God*, 1958, and similar figures of the 1950's, he used an assortment of found objects in the construction of sculptures that simultaneously suggest an injured, hollow human being and a mechanism in the shape of a man. *Japanese War God* is a frontal sculpture, animated to a degree by the placement of the legs, which implies forward movement. The circular head recalls the Japanese symbol of the rising sun.

Paolozzi constructed these sculptures from wax sheets that retained the impression of the objects and, alternatively, from negative molds into which hot wax was poured to form sheets. The sheets were then cut and shaped to form the sculptures and cast into bronze by the lost-wax process.

Born in Edinburgh, Scotland, in 1924 of Italian parents, Eduardo Paolozzi studied at the Edinburgh College of Art in 1943 and the Slade School of Art, London, 1945–47. He lived in Paris, 1947–50, where he became interested in Dada, Surrealism, l'art brut, and the paintings of Miró and Klee, and spent considerable time with Giacometti in his studio. As his works in different media reveal, Paolozzi is attracted by almost every visual image— charts, diagrams, advertisements, photographs, graphs, patterned papers, cartoons, and designs derived from nature and machines.

His early works were drawings, collages, and roughly finished sculptures, usually of concrete. After his return from Paris, he designed environmental works, collages of mural size—and the intricate sculptures utilizing found objects, based to some extent on the human figure. Although bearing a resemblance to injured men or animals, these sculptures, constructed of an elaborate collection of objects and transposed into unpolished bronze, also suggest crude robots.

In the 1960's, Paolozzi continued his assemblage technique, but selected his components from smoothly surfaced machine parts, either ready-made or manufactured according to his designs. For his earlier bronze sculptures, he used the ancient technique of cire-perdue casting; his more recent sculptures are in aluminum and steel, manufactured by commercial foundries under the artist's supervision.

In addition to his sculptures and collages, Paolozzi has become well known as a printmaker and has worked also in ceramics, film, electronic sound, and creative writing.

* Diane Kirkpatrick, *Eduardo Paolozzi* (Greenwich, Conn.: New York Graphic Society, 1970), p. 18.

PAOLOZZI *Japanese War God* **1958**
Bronze, 64½ x 23 x 12 in. (163.8 x 58.5 x 30.5 cm.)
Gift of Seymour H. Knox   K60:8

Bridget Riley

"The basis of my painting is this: that in each of them a particular situation is stated. Certain elements within that situation remain constant. Others precipitate the destruction of themselves. Recurrently, as a result of the cyclic movement of repose, disturbance and repose, the original situation is restated. . . . I want the disturbance or 'event' to arise naturally, in visual terms, out of the inherent energies and characteristics of the elements that I use." *

In some of her recent work Riley has become increasing involved with the structure of contradiction and paradox involving qualities of fast and slow motion, cool and warm colors, static and active forms, and structured or open space. Her approach to color has been initially through the development of cool and warm tonalities of gray. In *Drift No. 2*, 1966, unchanging black bands are interspersed with vertical bands graded tonally from dark to light to dark, and modulated from a cool blue-gray to a neutral light gray. The undulating curved bands precipitate wavelike diagonal motions of differing speeds, which seem to emanate from the bottom of the picture. Thus two simultaneous "events" are occurring, but instead of coinciding, they culminate in different zones of the canvas.

Bridget Riley was born in 1931 in South London and spent the war years with her family near Padstow in Cornwall. She studied with Colin Hayes at Cheltenham Ladies' College, 1946–48, and with Sam Rabin at Goldsmiths' College School of Art, 1949–52. She attended the Painting School at the Royal College of Art, London, 1952–55, where she was awarded the Diploma of Associateship. In 1957–58, she taught art to children and became intrigued with their varied solutions to specifically restricted artistic problems. She worked in the J. Walter Thompson advertising agency periodically from 1958 to 1964. In 1959 she attended summer school in Suffolk and traveled in Spain and Portugal. In 1960 she traveled and painted in Italy and was particularly impressed by the work of the Italian Futurists. While teaching part-time at the Hornsey College of Art in 1960, she experimented with "field-painting" and subsequently developed her characteristic style, working primarily in black and white. Her work became known in the United States through the exhibition The Responsive Eye, in 1965, in which two of her paintings were shown. In recent years, she has begun to exhibit paintings in which color is an important factor.

* The artist, in *Art News*, October, 1965, p. 33.

RILEY *Drift No. 2* **1966**
Acrylic on canvas, 91½ x 89½ in. (232.4 x 227.3 cm.)
Gift of Seymour H. Knox   K67:5

145

SCOTT *Blue Painting* **1960**
Oil on canvas, 71¾ x 48 in. (121.9 x 182.2 cm.)
Gift of Seymour H. Knox   K61:4

146

KITAJ *Walter Lippmann* **1966.** Oil on canvas, 72 x 84 in. (182.9 x 213.3 cm.)
Gift of Seymour H. Knox   K67:4

William Scott

A tension between logic and impulsiveness underlies Scott's approach. In *Blue Painting*, 1960, his classical attitude to composition can be seen in the approximate squaring off of circles, the straightening of curved lines, and the alignment of forms along strict horizontals and verticals. Yet the surface clearly reveals the spontaneity of the working process through scratches, blemishes, corrections, and irregular lines of paint applied directly from the tube. Although the painting is almost entirely blue, Scott used a wide variety of hues so that the effect is far from monotonal. The variations in color are further increased by the differing thicknesses of paint areas and the occasional overpainting, in which gradations of color interact.

Also in the Gallery collection is *Nile Valley: Morning*, a predominantly white painting of 1962.

William Scott, born in 1913 in Greenock, Scotland, grew up in Northern Ireland. He studied at the Belfast College of Art from 1928 until 1931, when he entered the Royal Academy Schools in London; he studied sculpture there until 1934 before turning to painting the following year. Beginning in 1937, he traveled extensively in Italy and France. During the summers of 1938 and 1939, he taught at an art school which he and Geoffrey Nelson established in Brittany at Pont-Aven, where Paul Gauguin and his followers had worked at the end of the nineteenth century. Returning to England at the outbreak of World War II, Scott painted little during four years of service in the Army, 1942–46. After the war, he took up again the traditional subjects of European painting—the figure, landscape, and particularly still life. His characteristic works of the late 1940's and 1950's were arrangements of familiar and recognizable kitchen objects on table tops, thinly painted in clear colors and defined by crisp edges. Scott then began to eliminate detail, flatten the objects into simplified, quasi-geometrical shapes, and increase the texture of the paint surface.

Ronald Kitaj

"Let me say at once that *Walter Lippmann* is just about my favorite among the very few pictures I've made which I care for at all. . . .

"The picture was painted in England, at my home at that time in Dulwich/London. What is and was important was to connect often over the weeks and months with those fugitive passions which occasion themselves and pattern themselves at the centers of one's interest. . . . There is no, or very little question of, *ultimate* meanings, as, I think, issues of meaning are far less clear than is often supposed, even in simple, abstract art. . . . While I wouldn't call this picture a difficult picture, it would seem to be a complex one. . . . Fugitive passions then . . . collected and suggested . . . does anyone remember *The Constant Nymph?* and Robert Donat, in costume, was a source or factor for the man holding a drink . . . Girl confronts stranger at lamplight and Grand Hotel and all that, ebbs into more obscene twilight than any painter could have imagined—and no one did. Lippmann has watched all through more than the two large shooting wars and he may as well stand in at stage right, name misspelled [on canvas at right], . . . elegant voyeur . . . as if the explainer or whatever he was in *Our Town* wrote for the Paris edition of the *New York Herald-Tribune.*" *

Ronald Kitaj was born in Chagrin Falls, Ohio, in 1932. In 1950, he began traveling as a seaman on freighters, visiting Europe and South America. Between expeditions and sailings he studied at Cooper Union, 1950, and the Academy of Fine Arts in Vienna, 1951. After serving in the United States Army in Germany and France, 1955–57, he studied at the Ruskin School of Drawing, Oxford, 1955–57, and the Royal College of Art in London, 1957–60. He has lived and worked in London since that time with the exception of a year in California, 1967–68.

A man of wide interests, Kitaj uses material from many sources—literature of all eras, political manifestos, economic pamphlets, current and historical events, and the various visual arts—to create his works, in a collage-like style, often including actual photographs and pages from books which are intended to elicit both an emotional and an intellectual response from the viewer. His large paintings, particularly, are composed of diverse elements which collectively assume a new, though sometimes obscure, meaning. Besides paintings and collages, he has produced silkscreen prints, drawings, and, recently, sculpture.

* Letter from the artist, July, 1968.

BACON *Man with Dog* 1953
Oil on canvas, 60 x 46 in. (152.4 x 116.8 cm.)
Gift of Seymour H. Knox   K55:3

SUTHERLAND *Thorn Trees* **1945**
Oil on cardboard, 42¾ x 39¾ in. (108.6 x 101 cm.)
Room of Contemporary Art Fund   RCA46:1

Henry Moore

Of *Internal and External Forms*, 1953–54, the artist has written: "The large wood version was started in early 1953, only about a week after the tree had been cut down. Such a piece of wood, five feet in diameter, would have taken thirty years of special care and treatment to be seasoned, as on the average, wood seasons in a natural way one inch per year. . . . But by carving it slowly over a period of two years, and because its final form has no part over five inches thick, it is now fully seasoned, and the seasoning has been less precarious, and more thorough.

"I think it may need showing in the kind of light it has had in my studio where it has been made. That is, in a top light, which does not shine too directly into the interior—a light which lets the interior look like a cave, with some mystery in it. . . . Its idea needs to be connected with the size of a human being and the spectator should be able to imagine himself standing in the place of the interior form." *

"It was in 1929 that I began to sense the reclining figure as a series of mountains." † In *Two-piece Reclining Figure No. 1*, 1959, Moore combined for the first time, in monumental scale, the treatment of the female figure as landscape, a long-time obsession, with the fragmentation of the body into two or more pieces, a concept originally developed in small carvings of 1934. Moore has acknowledged that two particular (although probably unconscious) sources for the landscape element in this piece were **Adel Crag**, a natural rock formation that Moore knew as a child which has a vertical thrust remarkably similar to the lower portion of the sculpture, and *La Bec du Hoc*, Seurat's painting of a jutting cliff on the French coast. Moore has said that he did not originally intend to make this sculpture in two pieces; the idea seems to have been a natural extension of the holes which have appeared in his figures for many years. Once it was separated, Moore was pleased with the effect, feeling that the figure, freed of naturalism, could more justifiably be made to appear as landscape and rocks. Although separate, the two pieces are interrelated and function as a single structure. Among the most three-dimensionally conceived of his sculptures, the *Two-piece Reclining Figures* (Moore created several later versions) reward the spectator as he walks around them with a changing and unexpected variety of views.

Other sculptures in the collection by Moore are *Reclining Figure*, 1935; *Mother and Child*, 1959; *Two-piece Reclining Figure No. 4*, 1961; and *Oval with Points*, 1968.

Henry Moore was born in 1898 in Castleford, Yorkshire, England. At an early age, he determined to be a sculptor, but it was not until 1919 after two years of army service that he entered the Leeds School of Art. In 1921, he transferred to the Royal College of Art in London where he studied until 1925, and remained as a part-time teacher for ten years.

Moore's early naturalistic style with the emphasis on surface carving, influenced by archaic sculpture, was replaced during the 1930's by a more abstract approach in which the solid forms were opened, frequently pierced,

* Letter from the artist, October 31, 1955.
† The artist, in *Réalités*, May, 1965, p. 50.

154

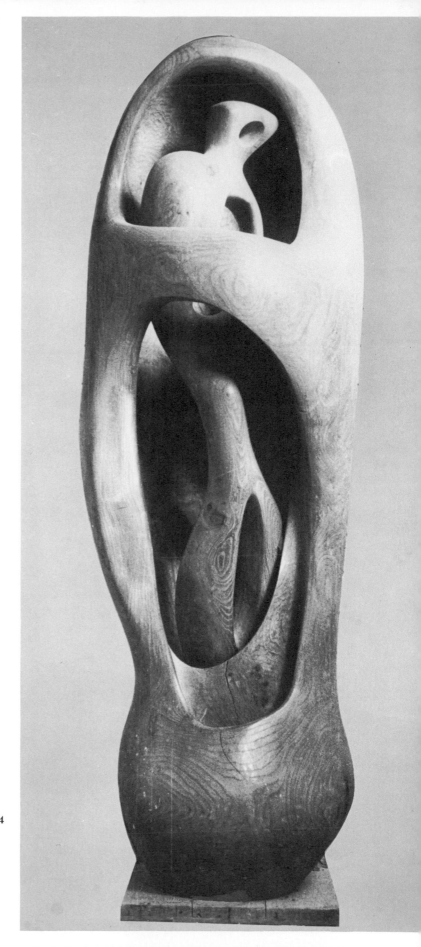

MOORE *Internal and External Forms* **1953–54**
Elmwood, 103 x 36 x 109 [circumference] in.
(261.6 x 91.4 x 276.8 cm.)
Charles Clifton, James G. Forsyth,
Charles W. Goodyear, Edmund Hayes,
and Sherman S. Jewett Funds   55:11

and the compositions became more three-dimensional and spatially dynamic. During World War II, he worked as an Official War Artist, producing the famous series of Shelter Notebooks and studies of miners at work, as well as drawings for sculpture which could not be realized during the war.

By 1946, when The Museum of Modern Art presented a major retrospective of Moore's work, he had become an internationally known sculptor.

Several recurrent themes have occupied the sculptor throughout his career—the figure, reclining, seated, and standing; a mother and child; the family group; and abstract forms, often biomorphic. He has worked in wood, stone, marble, concrete, lead, and bronze and has had a continuing interest in compositions of several component parts and in the relationship of internal and external forms.

Since 1940, when his studio in London was bombed, he has lived and worked near Much Hadham, Hertsfordshire.

MOORE *Two-piece Reclining Figure No. 1* **1959**
Bronze, 62 x 95¾ x 51½ in. (incl. base) (157.5 x 243.2 x 130.8 cm.)
General Purchase Funds 61:12

European Sculpture

R. W. D. Oxenaar

The Continental European sculpture collection of the Albright-Knox Art Gallery, dating from 1942 to the present, includes sixty works by forty-nine artists and presents a survey of what has happened in sculpture in that era since World War II.

The earliest works are Max Bill's *Construction from a Ring*, conceived in 1942, and Antoine Pevsner's *Construction in the Egg* of 1948; the most recent date from 1968—Étienne Hajdu's *Livia*, Vjenceslav Richter's *Rasver I*, and Getulio Alviani's *Structure Composed of Green/Red Square Elements*. The oldest artist represented is Picasso (born 1881) and the youngest Alviani (born 1939). Of the forty-nine artists involved, eight were born between 1880 and 1900, twenty-three between 1900 and 1920, and eighteen between 1920 and 1940. An arrangement of the artists as to nationalities constitutes a problem. Should this be done according to country of birth, or is the country where the sculptor mainly lived and worked more important? In the first case we would, for example, have only four French artists but several Eastern Europeans and a group of Argentinians. In the second case, which seems to be more true to the real situation, one finds twenty French artists, thirteen Italians, six Germans, and a scattering of others, from Danish to Spanish.

These statistics already say something about the inner structure of what is broadly called postwar European sculpture on the Continent. English sculpture is dealt with elsewhere in these texts, and when I say European it is meant to exclude Great Britain. The task given me reflects this rupture of ties, only recently confirmed politically and so dominantly maintained artistically during the period to be discussed here. Some English overtones will therefore be unavoidable in the course of what follows. The outcome of the nationality poll rightly suggests that France, and then of course Paris, was in this period the all-embracing cultural center of Europe in terms of bringing together different countries and cultures into the realm of Latin taste. It is, however, not by chance that Italian and German artists, originating from the two other main cultural spheres in Western Europe, mostly stayed at home.

In Paris one finds the Swiss (Arp, Giacometti, Tinguely), the Belgians from Wallonië (Ubac, Bury), the Russians (Pevsner, Lipchitz), the Balkanese (Schöffer, Hajdu), the Dutch (Appel), the Danes (Jacobsen), the Spanish (Picasso, Sobrino), and since the early fifties an ever growing group of South Americans (Penalba, Le Parc, Boto), who have contributed vital new ideas to the international Paris scene.

The case of the Dutch is perhaps typical concerning the motivations of certain European expatriates. The Netherlands always is on the crossroads between England, France, and Germany. The country is small, soon too small for an artist of more than local stature. A Dutch artist in that situation used to express his admiration for French art and try to go and live in Paris. Once there, however, like Mondrian and Appel, he would continue to produce work of a rather pronounced Germanic character, be it slightly

157

softened and transformed by the French atmosphere. He would find himself integrated in a network of lively cultural communication, but confronted at least in the beginning by a rather hostile local market. Both Mondrian and Appel found their clients earlier and easier in Holland, Switzerland, Germany, and the United States than in France.

Such artists made their way to international influence, understanding, and admiration from the Paris platform, but seldom directly in Paris. Others came to prosper immersed in the warm, wide, and vague climate of what can very broadly be named an "École de Paris," an international School of Paris that stylistically goes beyond and astray from the narrower French limits of the so-called École de Paris—painters like Bazaine, Manessier, Estève, and others of fame in the fifties.

The ramifications of the Paris art stream and the reverberations of its waves stand central also to the structural attitudes within this collection. However, other centers existed and grew to be of new importance. One cannot look justly at these sixty sculptures without the background of the London scene of the years around 1960, or without the widely felt impact of American developments in the sixties. Also, Italy went through a many-sided and influential revival of sculpture in the fifties, and Germany contributed a clearly defined new approach in the early sixties with the Zero movement.

While the European artist may still be conscious of his national background, he is before all European, and the growth of postwar artistic communication has made such an orientation ever more easy and self-evident. One is never really an expatriate in Europe, at least not as an artist and not in the postwar years.

Since the early sixties, however, many European artists look at the United States as a center of their world. Although only a few actually live there, many regularly go to New York or Los Angeles to try to scratch out a beachhead of appreciation for their work. A measure of esteem in the new world is now a status symbol for a European artist. The tides have turned —Europeans come to America to see, to learn, and to be seen. The time of the eleven European refugees summing up in their 1946 exhibition at The Museum of Modern Art what America had meant for them and so by comparison evaluating the impact of their guest performance is long bygone. And Americans come to Europe to be received as valued guests, to be given exhibitions and commissions. They go mainly to London, Amsterdam, Stockholm, Germany, and Switzerland—not in the first place to Paris, which in recent years has lost much of its central position by not really opening up to new developments.

The postwar period in Europe has also seen an increasingly dense pattern of exhibitions, often going from country to country in a chain of participating museums and "Kunsthallen." Amsterdam, Stockholm, Brussels, Düsseldorf, Krefeld, Leverkusen, Mönchengladbach, several other cities in the "Ruhrgebiet," Stuttgart, Nuremberg, München, Berlin, Basel, Zürich, Bern, Paris, Vienna, Milano, Torino, and of course London have been instrumental in propagating the art of our time.

The now almost defunct Venice Biennale, the many other "Biennales," active for a longer or shorter period, in San Marino and Ljubljana, in Nuremberg and Paris, in Lausanne and Zagreb, the Documenta extravaganzas in Kassel, and the large, comprehensive shows covering periods and styles that appear every so many years in one or another big European city have made it possible for everybody to see all. Since 1948, the international open-air exhibitions of sculpture in Battersea Park, London; Sonsbeek Park, Arnhem; Middleheim Park, Antwerp, and incidentally in almost any other park or city environment (Spoleto, Italy; Marl, Germany; Biel, Switzerland) available for the purpose, have focused new attention on the relationship of sculpture with landscape and architecture.

The sculptors themselves worked together in several international symposia, mostly organized in out-of-the-way places where the right materials were at hand, as in St. Margareten, Austria; Kostanjevica and Portoroz, Yugoslavia; and later in Toronto, near Los Angeles, in Japan, in Mexico, etc. It became fashionable to form "sculpture routes," and the term "symposium sculpture" clearly indicated an ambitious large work in stone or another durable material lacking the necessary refinements of detail caused by too short a period of preparation.

For years after World War II, many sculptors found a certain basic living in accepting commissions for war monuments. As a trend in sculpture, one could say that the genre culminated in the grand 1952–53 competition on the theme of the *Unknown Political Prisoner* sponsored by the Institute of Contemporary Arts in London. "This, the first International Sculpture Competition," wrote the director of the ICA, "was organized to promote interest in contemporary sculpture, and to show that it is still related, as in past ages, to our way of living, to our architecture, and to our thinking. In the minds of many people less attention and stimulation have been given to sculpture in recent years than to the other visual arts. The competition was undertaken, therefore, on a truly international scale, in the hope that it would prove to be an inspiration not only to artists, but to all those in positions great or small who may give support to the arts. On the basis of such support our age may be judged as much as on the nature of the art produced."

An idealistic, at the time almost utopian plan. There were 3,500 applications from fifty-seven countries, and the grand prize was won by Reg Butler, but the monument, intended for "a prominent situation in one of the great capitals of the world," has never been erected. The above statement now sounds as an early *cri de coeur*. It is only recently that new attention to the possible social functioning of sculpture, also through the ideas of a new generation of sculptors, begins to lead in some European countries to the development of truly integrated projects. Town planner, architect, and sculptor now sometimes come together to give form to a social environment. And the sculptor is met as an equal who is not only allowed a spot for a piece, but a place at the drawing board, a voice in the process of developing an over-all, complex form-system that includes everything from buildings to benches, with "sculpture" in the last place. Without chauvinism, it may be said that Holland is in the forefront at the moment in realizing some such projects.

Nevertheless, all through the fifties and sixties there has been a growing awareness of the role of sculpture in everyday life, and many a sculptor found—and finds—his living fully in commissioned work. Sometimes the quality of the relationship with architecture is questionable. The Institute for Social and Economic Studies at St. Gallen, Switzerland, by the architects Förderer and Otto (1965) may be mentioned as an outstanding example of the now more conservative, applicatory way of bringing sculpture and architecture together. In and around that building, one finds work by the sculptors Calder, Kemeny, Mastroianni, Penalba, Arp, Hajdu, Giacometti, Stahly, and some lesser-known Swiss artists (also painters like Braque, Miró, Soulages, Tapiès)—an unusually rich and high-quality profusion of "decoration," but only a few of the sculptors really made work to measure on the spot. The rest is well-fitting ready-made.

It is against the broad background sketched heretofore that a museum collection of sculpture should be seen nowadays. They stand there, sorely without engagement, as relics of individual emotions, which can or cannot help to change us, as signs and designs designating the ever growing urge to be understood by people, to be included in a way of living as valid, indispensable symbols of our time.

The ICA competition gave a further interesting indication of then still future developments. The organizers found it necessary to emphasize to the applicants "that symbolic or non-representational treatment of the subject will receive the same consideration as a more naturalistic expression." Such was the trend of the time that this had to be said. Nevertheless, virtually all prize winners made nonrepresentational projects.

Large-scale representational monumentality was perhaps unfeasible for this specific theme against the background of the Arno Breker colossals of Nazi fame, but the jurors, led by Sir Herbert Read, certainly made a progressive choice, and that could also have impeded execution of Butler's entry.

The Albright-Knox European sculpture collection shows a just measure of these developments. Let us have some more statistics: of sixty works, forty-two are related to organic nature in their concept of reality; eighteen to inorganic nature. Within the largest essentially representational group, seventeen sculptures are clearly anthropomorphic, five show animal figuration and twenty deal with nature in general, with vegetation and landscape, with geological formations and the elements, with celestial bodies and climate, with growth and structure. In terms of copying nature, there are gradations from strict realism in the classical sense to a seemingly fully abstract presentation. Seemingly, for abstraction is more successful as the object is less easily identified and the identity check on human and animal figuration is as unavoidable as the check on, let us say, a landscape which is almost impossible to render. Ubac's *Fields* seems almost to depict a Japanese Zen garden, but without its title it remains an artifact, a piece of beautiful material brought into human meaning by an individual and only visually readable handwriting. The balance between personal transformation and primordial form is easily disrupted. Artists can enter this field of tension from different sides and end up on the same spot. Delahaye and Somaini appear to reach a similar point of balance, but Delahaye calls his sculpture *Wing*, while Somaini describes his as *Vertical*. Uhlmann names his bronze *Growth*, but his transformation of the human figure is not essentially different from the figurine "New Man" in El Lissitsky's electro-mechanical theater piece *Victory over the Sun*.

All through the fifties, representational sculptors strove toward the non-existent point of absolute abstraction or accepted representation, but then in its most primitive form. This led to a variety of tendencies and a new interest in children's art and *l'art brut*.

There is a fairly clear-cut dividing line between the two main groups heretofore indicated, the organic and the inorganic, the warm and the cold, the subjective and the objective sculptors. Within each group, however, endless refinements of divisions and cross-references are possible because of the lack of schools and coherent movements. The period has time and again seen the beginnings of groups forming, but individual striving toward a personal, isolated statement always spoiled any attempt to coordinate. Only recently are there signs of a new approach, less concerned with personal heroics, more socially involved, and directed at anonymity and teamwork.

Both groups have their roots in the turbulent, formative years of the first quarter of the century. It had all been said already in Cubism and Futurism, in Dada and Surrealism, in Neo-Plasticism and Constructivism. It could only be further elucidated. The postwar sculptors, those who had to find their personal styles after the war, continued along the lines set out by the older generations from before the war. They found directives and turning points in the work of artists like Picasso, Pevsner, Arp, Gabo, Lipchitz, Marini, Giacometti, Wotruba, and Bill. Of those, Picasso, Arp, Lipchitz, Marini, Giacometti, and Wotruba are the important precursors and continuators in the organic group.

The work of the oldest three, Picasso, Arp, and Lipchitz, originated in the Cubist period, but only Lipchitz subsequently developed the Cubist principles into a style entirely his own. In a letter to the Director of the Stedelijk Museum in Amsterdam, published in the catalogue of his 1958 exhibition in that museum, he wrote: "It was by returning into my past, that I understood that my father, a contractor, took a brick to build a house, and not the other way around. Why don't I do the same—out of a crystal construct a man, a woman, a child." * Such "crystals" became the inner core of his work, bringing the waves of his formal ideas to compactness, to clarity of movement and structure, as illustrated in his bronze *Sacrifice* of 1948. In this sculpture, as in many older works, there are reminiscenses of his early admiration for the sculptural qualities of the small Scythian gold reliefs in the form of a panther or a stag in the collection of the Hermitage at Leningrad, which have contributed to the angular, emotional monumentality of his manner.

The versatility of Picasso's sculptural devices became fully known only in recent years and were therefore not of any great direct influence. But his work confirmed what had happened in the meantime, and his 1958 bronze *Bather Playing* is an exemplar of much that was produced by younger sculptors in the same period. In form and technique, it owes more to Dada attitudes than to Cubism. Picasso's transformations of reality are as free and uninhibited in his sculpture as in his paintings. The playful technique of assembling handmade and ready-made elements to form outrageous, absurd figures gains unexpected unity and dignity of expression by the casting in bronze.

The very direct, often almost shocking, animation and humor of his sculpture has seldom been equaled, although Robert Jacobsen sometimes came close to it. His *Taha* of 1961 owes a debt to other work by Picasso and seems related to his iron figures of the early thirties. In this context Julio Gonzalez should be mentioned as the originator of welded sculpture in iron and as an inspiration to both. The three together represent the center

* C'est alors que remontant dans mon passé, j'ai compris que mon père, l'entrepreneur de construction, prenait une brique pour bâtir une maison et non le contraire. Pourquoi n'en ferais-je pas autant, d'un cristal bâtir un homme, une femme, un enfant."

in a wide and varied field of welders and assemblers, where we will also meet Hoflehner and Tinguely, with his *Cocktail au cheval*.

The work of both Picasso and Lipchitz shows certain archaic and mythological tendencies. The legendary and the religious they brought with them from their countries of origin, mixed with the magic of the simple, expressive forms and the imaginative handling of materials in the primitive art they both learned to admire and to collect as young men, became part of their ways and means. Both also consider themselves, in the words of Lipchitz, "a link to the human past, to all its experiences in my field, to all its achievements." * They reacted to the immediate academic past but opted for a continuum. A deeply rooted cultural engagement made them find symbols of action against the threats of our time as shibboleths and warnings of war and technology.

Archaic trends run through modern sculpture in ever changing shades and blends as perhaps one of the few marks of stylistic unity in our century. Jean Arp contributed his own personal variety, more detached, enclosed in a fabulous world of Cycladic euphoria, of peacefully flowing organic life: primeval forms, pebbles rounded by water, artifacts to be forgotten in a forest and to be found as natural forms ready for a happy assemblage into sculpture. "Hans Arp was mesmerized by words. He invented words and articulated them as if he had not been taught by anyone," † wrote Max Hölzer in the catalogue of the memorial exhibition at the Erker Gallery, St. Gallen, 1966. His sculpture has the same effect. Arp, rooted in Dada, never really became a Surrealist, but in his work there always is something absurd, bordering on something childlike and germinating a wider consciousness about the nature of forms and the forms of nature.

Arp's work is inimitable, but his influence has been widely felt. Henry Moore and Barbara Hepworth admired him, and we should mention Viani, Signori, and Hajdu as sculptors seeking a similar way of expression through highly polished, simple, compact, closed or open forms, and usually a slightly more anecdotal relation to nature.

Andrea Cascella is one of the rare younger sculptors who continues a style that honors the classic craft of stone-carving. His work has a monumental quality, notwithstanding the seldom really large sizes. Its heavy forms suggest anatomical as well as machine parts and almost always show the characteristic, for him, joints of stone on stone.

Of the three younger precursors, Giacometti always was a solitary figure following a lone and narrow path. His *Man Walking* of 1960 is typical of his way of seeing space and expressing it. The elongated, compressed human figure on heavy feet, bound to the earth but soaring upward, moves in space and becomes part of it through an all-devouring process of quiet disintegration. No other modern sculptor has given such a penetrating suggestion of unlimited space by minimizing the existence of matter.

Giacometti has always been admired, not followed. This is not true for Marini. After the war he became the central figure in the great revival of Italian sculpture. His skillful, harmonious deformations paired with solid but light closed forms, a delicate feeling for detail, and a subtle painterly surface treatment gave his bronzes the Mediterranean synthesis of the

* Introduction to *The Lipchitz Collection* (New York: The Museum of Primitive Art, 1960).

† "Hans Arp war vom Wort verzaubert. Er fand das Wort vor und sprach es aus wie einer, der es von niemand gelernt hat."

162

plastic and the poetic that is one of the secrets of modern Italian sculpture. In the symbolic value of his horses and riders, the tender movement of his dancers, and the psychological insight of his portraits, he always stands above the many followers, who never really eluded the danger of mannerism that is inherent in this sort of sculpture. Both Marini and Manzù, the other great Italian innovator of his time and generation, found inspiration in the sculptural traditions of their country and continued, according to their own personalities, the work of their two great Italian precursors, Rosso and Martini.

Manzù's work always stayed closer to reality, closer to a humanist tradition, closer also to the subtle impressionistic clay-modeling of Rosso. His *Standing Cardinal* is a prominent example of his postwar productivity and stability. It has great lyrical quality and at the same time a direct and simple monumentality.

The vagaries of modern sculpture are such that this could just as well be the place to discuss the work of some younger Italians. One cannot say that Arnaldo Pomodoro and Consagra continued the Marini-Manzù tradition. They enriched the broad spectrum of modern Italian sculpture with new chapters. After the "Rotante" and the "Semi-colonna," Pomodoro also occupied himself in the late sixties with the cube as a basic form to be ruptured or split. The glyphs he traces in an otherwise perfect geometrical shape are for him the expression of an interior movement that clarifies the inner disequilibrium of "absolute form." Notwithstanding their size and presence, the highly polished surfaces and the delicacy of the minutely detailed incisions bring to mind that Pomodoro also is an outstanding goldsmith who produces some of the best sculptural jewelry of our time.

The slightly older Pietro Consagra developed a personal means of expression in the limited field of free-standing reliefs with a flattened three-dimensionality, marbled by space and seemingly shredded by the elements. He went from bronze and wood to the use of steel and so came to ever thinner and more open compositions. Since the late sixties, his sculptures are often brightly colored.

Almost no other sculptor in our time has identified himself so fully with the material stone as Fritz Wotruba, the last personality of the older generation in this group. Although he produces many bronzes, he sees, thinks, and forms in stone. Bronze is used mainly to multiply his work that otherwise would have a limited dissemination. He cuts stone in "taille directe," and perhaps also for that reason his carvings have the freshness of the newly born and the self-evidence of the archetype. The human figure, the human body one could better say, became his central theme. Within a small range of basic postures and gestures—lying, seated, standing, walking, hands high, no hands, or torso only—he finds endless variations of structure and expression. From cylindrical and still rather representational sculptures, he went to ever more softly angular and rectangular block forms, rhythmically stacked like megalithic tombs or ancient architecture, but always bound in size and scale to the measurements of the human body.

The younger Viennese sculptor Hoflehner, who worked with Wotruba in the middle fifties, seems to adhere to the Wotruba principles of handling human measurements, without ever coming close to following directly. He works in iron only, and the properties of that material bring him nearer to Gonzalez. His figures are sharp, aggressive and constructive in their articulation, practically always strictly vertical, and with an idol-like imagery.

Alicia Penalba has won a special place for herself, not only in Paris but also internationally. She is one of the purest and most forceful representatives of what I have described as organic sculpture. She finds her inspiration in nature, in animal and vegetative life, in the winds and the sea, in forms washed by memory. She began with tall, closely knit columns, totems of treelike growth. Later a diagonal flaring-up of wings and petals from a core became the mark of her style. Movement and rhythm, the balance of forms in space, the significance of light and shadow are the properties that come to life in her exotic world full of myth and magic.

Another solitary figure should be mentioned here. The former technician and fashion designer Zoltan Kemeny made a late start in sculpture but developed a rare style of his own. Through collage, l'art brut, and Tachisme he discovered the relief in metal (iron and copper, mostly) as his real means of expression. "Iron has a heart and nerves," Kemeny once said. "The respiratory system of a plant can be the same as the molecular system of steel. There are miraculous similarities between a pot filled with microbes and metal molecules." Kemeny tried to make visual and active the inner movement of matter by giving it material substance in rhythmical strings and swivels of either ready-made or self-made elements. His reliefs are meant as models for the geography of the internal forces in man and matter.

The term l'art brut refers to Jean Dubuffet's early style of painting and the enormous collection of his "Compagnie de l'art brut." His style was based on an anti-art philosophy, and he found his views illustrated in the nonintellectual, uncultivated, spontaneous creations of the naïve, the insane, and the psychic. An adult processing of such imagery and of the child's vision of reality has been used after the war as a point of return to a more free and sincere approach to art. It began in Paris, where Dubuffet in 1944 and 1946 had his first heavily criticized exhibitions and where in 1948 the Cobra group emerged from the ashes of the revolutionary Surrealist movement.

Constant, the later New Babylon town planner, wrote in the 1949 issue of Reflex, the periodical of the Experimental Group in Holland, "The E.G. [the Dutch section of Cobra] takes the point of view that improvisation is an essential condition for a vital art and therefore rejects any principle of a prioristic composition." This, in short, is the basis of Cobra philosophy.

Appel, with Jorn the most talented Cobra painter, has also made sculpture. In the early Cobra days he did painted assemblages of wood and other materials; later came the enormous, brightly colored tree trunks. Since about 1965, he has transformed his paintings into reliefs and even free-standing figures. The use of new materials such as polystyrene allowed him more freedom of form, but the style of his painting became more formalized, with some traces of Pop art. The visual impact of his newer work is as strong and immediate as ever.

The work of Jean Dubuffet went through many metamorphoses: from personages and landscapes via assemblages, Texturologies, Topographies, and Materiologies to his late style, begun in 1962 and called "l'Hourloupe," an untranslatable word of his own fabrication that could perhaps signify something like "pulling your leg." Purely abstract formal elements, fluid networks of cells circumscribed in black, red, or blue, originate from all sides and agitate to all sides. The cells seem to multiply as much according to chance as guided by an ever alert imagination and an opportunistic power to use possibilities when they arise. Within these webs, reality comes and goes. Suddenly a whole web appears to be a personage, or a group of cells condenses into a house, a tree, a utensil, a piece of furniture, only to disappear again in a fabulous landscape of rocks and grottos, or to melt into the rudiments of an unreadable sign language. There is space within, around and beyond; there is movement and action, images are born and fade away. The intricate ins and outs of such a space-structure game logically seem to lead to sculptural and even architectural ideas. The webs determine form and shape, content and meaning. Since 1962, Dubuffet has produced sculpture molded in polyester resin and covered with painted networks of cells. Small pieces first, but quickly growing larger in size to twenty-foot-high trees, personages, and towers, and finally to 1:10 scale models for architectural projects, are his Edifices. He designed castles and towers, a summer and a winter garden, forests, and apartment buildings. Of those projects, some have been executed: in 1970 the *Logological Cabinet*, the clearest expression of Dubuffet's philosophy; in 1971 the *Winter Garden*. The *Group of Four Trees*, commissioned by the Chase Manhattan Bank in New York, was completed in 1972.

In 1966 and 1967, the formative years for the more ambitious projects to follow, Dubuffet did a series of eight fairly small sculptures called "Borne au logos," of which the Albright-Knox Art Gallery owns the seventh. These sculptures are landmarks on the road to architecture and boundary stones for the "logos" that represent the essence of Dubuffet's l'Hourloupe-thinking: his logology. Max Loreau, Dubuffet's biographer, explained logology as "ramassis de ramassis," the "scratch collection of a scratch collection." The word was in the beginning and will be in the end; within reason, it signifies the universe. But in Dubuffet's language the word lives its own life. His wording can pile up into a repertory of our experience and still be a rudimentary choice. The rudiments of that choice could serve to explain the relativity of our effort. Scrap from scrap and what results is a logograph as well as a logomachy.

An attachment to the expression of different and deeper layers of human experience and perception, to be clarified by new insights into the behavior of nature and new research of space-time problems, is clearly a general quality of postwar artistic developments. Both Fontana and Yves Klein have been instrumental in furthering solutions to many facets of such problems. They have carried art to the outer edges of its domain and so explored virgin land. Their work, as represented in this collection, fits the general description of the group at hand. The three *Lecteurs* by Klein and the *Natura I* by Fontana are organically determined works, but Klein's blue and red sponges orbiting in space on long stakes and the bursting, oversized seed capsule by Fontana express an alienation from nature that goes beyond mere transformation. They do not seek a personal abstraction of nature, they use it as object to explain views about the functioning of space. Fontana's lacerated sphere, one of a series of five called "Concetto spaziale natura" is not meant to be a sculpture, is not made to show beautiful form or a nice surface. It is a spatial concept of art, a step on a trail of research, that, as in his perforations of the canvas, should open our eyes to new dimensions, to other galaxies. A fitting description in terms of his earlier constellations of stones and holes.

Yves Klein has followed Fontana in similar research to further and even more radical solutions. We shall meet both again as the inspiration of a younger generation of quite differently oriented artists.

Abstract became concrete, or, as Gabo said, "In art everything is real." It is not necessary to descend into the subconscious, nor to leave the studio to feel the breath of our universe. Art has its own ways and means separate from but equal to nature. Or, in the Szeemannian terms of a younger generation: live in your head and attitudes will become form. Those forms could be more equal to reality than others. The forms of the mind, springing from the laws of nature, went through many phases from the "absolute form" of geometrically defined objects, born out of a positivistic belief in the technology of new materials, to the "relative form" of artistic processes, born out of a speculative belief in the personal activities of the artist as a human being and new media of communications.

Some final statistics may clarify a point before we go further. Of these sixty works, nineteen are bronzes. There are seven stone carvings, seven sculptures done in iron, steel, brass, or aluminum, two in wood, of which one is a relief (Arp) and the other (Bury) not a classic woodcarving, but an object made of wood. The remaining twenty-five show varying degrees of mixed media, with stress on the new "clean" materials, plexiglass and metals, not on assemblages of waste material.

In nine pieces, color has been used as an important means of expression. Of those, the Appel and the Dubuffet are by painters interpreting their painting in three dimensions. The Arp Constellation-Punctuation and the Tinguely Peut-être No. 11 are, respectively, white and black-and-white reliefs but find their essence in a formal problem. Consagra, Klein, and Léger used color for very different reasons, but none as the starting point of their conception. Color was added to them, to enhance, or to clarify.

The forms-of-color sculptors as related to American color-field painting, like Caro, or some of those younger English artists whose work I once heard described by Bryan Robertson as "Pop-Arp," are not represented, at least not in this part of the collection. This seems to be rightly so, as Continental Europe shows many followers of the trend but very few originals.

Color frequently acts as a medium in the work of Alviani, Boto, Gerstner, Schöffer, and Sobrino, but then in terms of light, of transparency, reflection, radiation, and kinetics.

A preference for highly polished surfaces and a perfect finish that sometimes points to industrial fabrication, although it seems practically certain that all were made by the artist himself or under his direct guidance, is to be found in twenty-four of the sixty works. Of those twenty-four sculptures, nine still belong to the organic group (three by Arp, and one each by Cascella, Hajdu, Pomodoro, Signori, Uhlmann, Viani). A soft geometry brings them closer to the inorganic, away from archaic tendencies and imitative abstraction. Arp, as no other, found a balance between two worlds by merging symbol and reality. The gesture of Uhlmann's Growth seems to announce and to welcome a new freedom.

The principles of the brothers Gabo and Pevsner, as expressed in their Constructivist Manifesto, radically broke with all traditional notions about sculpture. They declared themselves in favor of space and light instead of mass and volume as the ruling qualities of a three-dimensional art. They argued for a dynamic, open, transparent form directed by linear elements as against a static, closed form determined by contours. They advocated a virtual reality in art that rejects allegory, abstraction, and illusion. They saw sculpture as directly related to architecture and thus to society. Their ideas were new, revolutionary, and projected toward the future. They welcomed new technical and industrial developments as positive contributions also to the possibilities of new ways of expression in art. For the first time there is no trace of a romantic attachment to the archaic. They broke with the past, but not with art, and by virtue of their formal rules as well as the course of their lives, the œuvre of Gabo and Pevsner stayed enclosed within the limits of sculpture in a now again more traditional sense.

Both Gabo and Pevsner developed subtle, laborious filigree techniques to visualize complicated spatial tensions, forces, and structures. Gabo, the theoretician of the two, is more delicate, immaterial, and rarefied in his work. His usually fairly small pieces always suggest a larger scale. They look like maquettes for work with an architectonic bearing. In 1955 Gabo received his most important commission to realize such a project—the eighty-five-foot-high structure in front of Marcel Breuer's department store, De Bijenkorf, in Rotterdam.

Pevsner's structures are more sturdy and severe in their limitation to the use of metal bars as a building material. His compositions are more enclosed, introvertedly seeking to clarify inner organisms as in his *Construction in the Egg*.

The Swiss sculptor, painter, architect, and designer Max Bill has been instrumental in furthering Constructivist ideas by giving them the wider setting of what came to be called "Concrete Art." He propagated and explained such principles for a younger generation. In his 1944 exhibition, *Konkrete Kunst*, at the Kunsthalle in Basel, he brought together work by Brancusi and Arp, Gabo and Pevsner, Mondrian and Vantongerloo, Kandinsky and Moholy Nagy. In the catalogue he stated his views: "We called those works of art 'Concrete Art' which were created on the basis of their very own means and laws, without outwardly leaning on the natural phenomena, but neither have they come into being through abstraction." *

This is essentially a restatement of Gabo's ideas, but Bill continues to say that Concrete Art is a form of optical perception realized by means of color, space, light, and movement. No material is mentioned, and thus points to the optical and kinetic art that would come to full development more than a decade later. He sees Constructivism as a separate section devoted to principles of "law, pre-image, order, and harmony." † His own work, produced in perfectly finished metal or stone, is always based on strict, simple mathematical formulas leading to intriguing structures in space that in their perception often have an "egg of Columbus" effect.

At the end of the emotional, organically determined fifties, many lines striving away from intuition and individual expression converge in an—as yet—complicated knot of new directions. The general tendency is toward anonymity of form, elementary research, and universal meaning; toward rationality, reduction of means, law and order on the one hand, the movement of chance and the chances of movement on the other. Some younger artists, such as several of the Parisian South Americans, were

* konkrete kunst [Bill writes his German without capitals] nennen wir diejenigen kunstwerke, die auf grund ihrer ureigenen mittel und gesetzmässigkeiten, ohne äusserliche anlehnung an die naturerscheinung, also nicht durch 'abstraktion' entstanden sind."
† "gesetz, vor-bild, ordnung, und harmonie."

167

freshly and deeply impressed by Mondrian and the Constructivists; others reached the clear sky of reason and systematic research through stages of Tachisme and informal art.

Jean Arp, restating what he had written in 1915, says in the 1944 catalogue of the *Konkrete Kunst* exhibition: "The works of Concrete Art should not be signed by their authors; these paintings, these sculptures—these objects—should remain anonymous in the great studio of nature like the clouds, the mountains, the seas, the animals, man. Yes! Man should return to nature!" * A new art moves to a new mystique in a new relation to nature.

Around 1960 the rather disparate views in this field began to be known under the vague name of "New Tendencies." The series, now four, of *Nove Tendencije* exhibitions at the Zagreb Museum of Contemporary Art, started in 1961, has been important for the crystallization of standpoints in this field, the meetings of artists organized on the side.

Under the wide umbrella of the New Tendencies, several groups and separate individuals can be distinguished. In this context we should mention Zero in Germany (Düsseldorf) and Holland, Le Centre de Recherche d'Art Visuel in Paris, and the Gruppo N and Gruppo T in Milano. All groups started around 1960; none existed more than a few years as such. Teamwork was a typical feature of all groups. In the "Acte de Fondation" (July, 1960) of Le Centre de Recherche d'Art Visuel, the eleven participating artists stated their purpose as collective research. All individual ideas had to be submitted to the Centre. In the beginning, the Italian groups exhibited under the group name without mentioning the participating artists.

The New Tendencies generally included all artists concerned with light and movement, but there always were close relations with the group of the Nouveaux Réalistes founded in 1960 at the Paris home of Yves Klein. In one of the earliest exhibitions of this younger generation in 1959 at the Hessenhuis in Antwerp, the group Zero (Mack, Piene, Uecker) exhibited together with Mari and Munari, Soto and Bury, and also the New Realists Klein, Spoerri, and Tinguely. At the third Documenta exhibition in Kassel in 1964, the attic of the Fredericianum was given to the theme of light and movement. The Zero group was included as an afterthought; Fontana and Klein were not represented. The exhibiting artists protested and at the last minute a small Fontana exhibition was presented. The Zero group showed its work under a banner with a homage to Yves Klein, who had died in 1962. Fontana's early research into spatial relationships, combining aspects of light, movement, and environment with a new interest in the object, and his charming personality made him the admired father of a younger generation. Yves Klein's new perceptive approaches to the real (the shortest definition of the aims of the New Realists) and especially his "immaterial" statements and acts made him the initiator and the theoretician—one could also say the Duchamp of his generation.

Independent of these later developments, the older Nicolas Schöffer has advanced his ideas on a synthesis of constructive, spatial, and dynamic elements in sculpture. He started around 1950 with Mondrianesque open structures built from metal strips and bars. In his earliest spatiodynamic

---

* "Les œuvres de l'Art Concret ne devraient plus être signées par leurs auteurs, ces peintures, ces sculptures—ces objets—devraient rester anonymes dans le grand atelier de la nature comme les nuages, les montagnes, les mers, les animaux, les hommes. Oui! Les hommes devraient rentrer dans la nature!"

stage, those elements became either movable by hand or mechanically driven. In later stages, he gradually added the use of light, color, and sound. The projection on surrounding screens or mirrors of moving forms in changing light is an important feature of his elaborate environments programed according to cybernetic principles.

Tinguely and Bury are central figures in the variegated pattern of recent developments, but both found a personal style entirely separate from the current vocabulary. The absurd, animated antimachines of Tinguely, made from scrap metal and useless machine parts, are a poetic, playful, but serious comment on the role of the machine in our lives. He humanized the machine, in contrast to the Russian Constructivists, who made it an idol.

Bury is the master of slow movement. Slender tentacles move like hairs standing upright under an electrical current. Balls, cylinders, and cubes very slowly change places in the narrow space of a wooden box. The mystery of such movement, so adequately expressed in the natural material wood, recalls the revelation of inner tensions as in the growth of a plant made visible on film.

The remaining artists here to be discussed could be rallied to the banner of the Groupe de Recherche on the face of their work, but only Le Parc and Sobrino were members. Modulation of the optical effect of the raster; intermittent or otherwise programmed light; impersonal, simple, geometric form; serial or chance arrangements; and virtual as well as mechanical movement are some general properties of an art basically concerned with new functions for the eye through a new approach to space-time problems.

Mack belonged to the German Zero group, and Zero was different—Zero was both less and more. It was an attitude, a philosophy, not in the first place a coherent style principle. It was a reaction to the arbitrariness of earlier explosions of emotion, a return to the "simple which is difficult to do," as Piene expressed it. In essence, Zero had to do with visualization of natural processes and structures, with the elementary order of nature. Zero could thus embrace more than Neo-Constructivist ideas; it could also welcome the intentions of the New Realists.

Mack's Dynamos and Movements refer to the movement of wind, water, and sand (see his Sahara project) and, above all, to light reflected in those ever changing structures.

The Yugoslav architect Richter, one of the organizers of the Zagreb Nove Tendencije exhibitions, is interested in random arrangements of identical form-elements. As an architect, he relates these researches to town planning and structures in building. It seems strange that his Rasver I suggests a representational accent, a figure standing or walking, that goes against his strictly systematic intentions.

The two former members of the Groupe de Recherche—Le Parc and Sobrino—are quite different in their approaches. Sobrino confines himself particularly to faceted structures of plexiglass in subdued colors. The movement of the spectator's eye multiplies the diversity of formal arrangements in a given constellation.

The activation of the spectator's eye stands central to Le Parc's conception of art, but he approaches the problem from many sides. In his Unstable-continual Light, one of a long series of similar works, the metal paillettes are so light in weight that the movement of a spectator passing by is enough to start the process of random variations of light and shadow within a strictly regular form system.

The reflection of form and color can add unexpected insights, as in Alviani's work. Mechanical rotation of form elements and the refraction of light through lenses, as in the work of Boto and Gerstner, are again another approach to light as a medium for artistic expression.

In spite of all theories, European sculpture in the fifties and sixties remained imprisoned in its own realm and, for the better part, bound to the pedestal. Size and scale usually stay within the limits of human measurements. A truly functional relation to architecture or directly to society has as yet not been found.

This has been a period of almost frantic research, of countless experiments. Everything is possible, every new idea is accepted. This sometimes leads to a desperate search for originality, but also to the discovery of uncharted territory. No style, no principle has won the race. Representational, abstract, and concrete continue to be of approximately equal importance. The newer and newest tendencies, such as Minimal Art, Land Art, Process Art, Arte Povera and Conceptual Art, have created the "Post-Studio Artist," as Carl Andre named it. They have added new formal aspects, new media, and new suggestions for a relationship with society. But the social position of the artist has remained essentially the same. One could perhaps find a common denominator by stating what most artists now reject in that status. In 1962, Le Groupe de Recherche d'Art Visuel formulated the actual relation of artist-society in the following points in their "Propositions Generales": "The artist alone and isolated, the personality cult, the myth of creation, aesthetic or anti-aesthetic conceptions overestimated, elaboration for the elite, the production of single works and the dependence on the art market." *

A real solution for these problems could lead to new unity of purpose and meaning in the arts.

---

* "L'artiste unique et isolé, le culte de la personalité, le mythe de la création, les conceptions esthétiques ou anti-esthétiques surestimées, l'élaboration pour l'élite, la production d'œuvres uniques et la dépendance au marché de l'art."

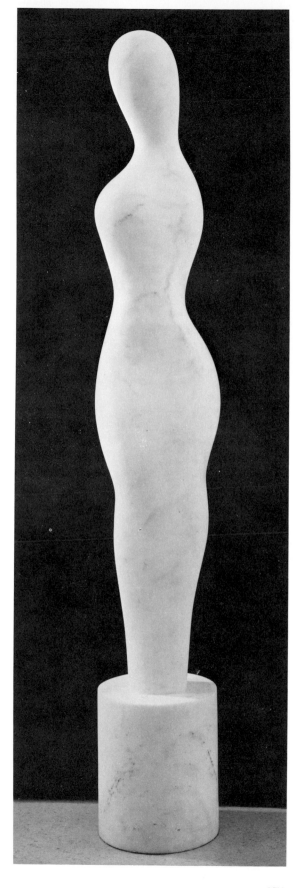

ARP *Classical Figure* **1964**
Marble, 96 x 14 x 16 in.
(248.9 x 35.6 x 40.7 cm.)
A. Conger Goodyear Fund 65:3

171

Jean (Hans) Arp

Arp's wooden reliefs derive from the assemblage-collage tradition in that they are additive and planar. The early ones of 1916–17, coinciding with Arp's Dada period, were polychrome or bare wood, often humorous or whimsical in form. By 1930 they evolved into greatly simplified white-on-white compositions. *Constellation-Punctuation*, 1956, composed of oval and teardrop shapes—or periods and commas—is a descendant of his reliefs of 1929–30 entitled *Arranged According to the Laws of Chance*, a concept which Arp originated in collage and which had a deep, almost metaphysical significance for him. Arp's forms and configurations are poetic and can be interpreted on several levels. He wrote in 1950, "At Ascona [1917] I drew in pencil and Chinese ink broken branches, roots, grasses and stones. . . . Finally I simplified these forms and reduced their essence to moving ovals, symbols of growth and metamorphosis of bodies." *

In the fifties Arp made two visits to Greece, and classical references appeared subsequently in his titles and his forms, particularly in his renewed interest in the human torso, which is related less to the organic forms of his earlier "concretions" (such as *Imaginary Animal*, 1947, and *Star*, 1956) than to the grace and harmony of proportion of the classical models. In 1960 he created a *Classical Sculpture* in both bronze and marble, a smaller version of the monumental, over-life-size *Classical Figure* of 1964. In this piece the erect female form has been reduced to gentle curves and rhythms which mark the points of articulation of the human form—shoulders, hips, and knees—with suggestions of the torsion and contraposto of classical figures. In contrast to some of Arp's sculptures which have no base, or a base of contrasting materials, *Classical Figure* is of one piece with its pedestal, emphasizing its "statue" quality. The sculpture in the Albright-Knox Art Gallery collection is the unique marble version, created after the bronze, of which five casts were made.

Jean Arp was born in 1887 in Strassburg, then in German territory. By the age of fifteen, he had begun writing poetry modeled on that of the German romantic poets. He studied at the School of Applied Art in Strassburg, 1904; at the Weimar Art School, 1905–7; and at the Académie Julian in Paris, 1908. Returning to Switzerland, he settled with his family in Weggis, where he was a cofounder of the Moderne Bund group, which first exhibited advanced art of the period in 1911. In the same year, he met Kandinsky, Klee, and other artists in the Blaue Reiter group in Munich and exhibited with them in 1912. He went to Paris in 1914, where he knew Max Jacob, Modigliani, Picasso, and the Delaunays. After he moved to Zurich in 1915 he met and married Sophie Taeuber, an artist and dancer, with whom he collaborated on collages, fabrics, and tapestries until her death in 1943. In 1916–19 Arp was a cofounder and leading activist in the Dada movement in Zurich and participated in the Cabaret Voltaire. By 1925 he became involved with the Surrealists in Paris and took part in their first exhibition in that year. He settled in Meudon, outside Paris, in 1927. In 1932 he was a member of the French Abstraction-Creation group. In addition to creating reliefs, collages, and paintings, Arp began modeling sculpture "in the round" in 1930–31. His writing has been widely published. Arp lived and worked in Soldino, Switzerland, before his death in Basel in 1966.

* Herbert Read, *Art of Jean Arp* (New York: Abrams, 1968), pp. 80–81.

ARP *Constellation-Punctuation* **1956**
Painted wood relief
21 x 34¾ x 1⅝ in. (53.3 x 88.2 x 4 cm.)
Charles Clifton Fund   69:5

Jacques Lipchitz

"The bronze *Sacrifice* has to deal with a theme which has preoccupied me for a long time. It is a theme of expiation of a victim to find a link between spirit and nature, between Earth and Heaven.

"My first sketches on this theme of prayer and expiation started, I guess, in the late twenties. I have in my Paris studio a sketch in terra-cotta from which everything that followed stems.

"In this country in 1943, I started a large statue in bronze called the *Prayer* which has to do with the same theme dealing with the consecration of the victim. After this piece, I started the *Sacrifice* itself, which is the next step or the killing of the victim. I made many drawings and two small sculptures before arriving at this stage. I worked for seven months on the plaster and made quite a few changes. Unfortunately, this plaster model perished in the fire which destroyed my studio on the fifth of January [1952].

"So the bronze now in your museum is a unique piece. However, I am planning to continue on this theme." *

Concern over the rise of Nazism and the fate of the Jewish people led Lipchitz in the thirties and forties to create sculpture with themes that were universally applicable, but also contained specific political references. *Sacrifice*, 1948, portrays a solemn figure wearing the ceremonial *tallith* while performing the ancient Hebraic rite of slaying the victim over which he has intoned, "This is my substitute, this is my expiation; this rooster will go to his death and I will go forward to a good long life and peace." A lamb sits curled at his feet, perhaps symbolizing the innocents who are saved and whose future is thus secured.

Also in the Gallery collection is a 1914 bronze, *Sailor*.

Chaim Jacob Lipchitz was born in 1891 in Druskieniki, Lithuania, the son of a prosperous building contractor. After studying engineering at Vilna in accordance with his father's wishes, he emigrated to Paris in 1909 in order to pursue his interest in art. He studied at the École des Beaux-Arts, 1909–10, and the Académie Julian until 1913. In the early 'teens he occupied a studio in Montparnasse next to Brancusi, and—through Diego Rivera— became friends with the Cubist painters Picasso and Gris, as well as Modigliani and Soutine. His early sculpture is in the Cubist style, and not until the twenties did he begin to break away from its rigorous forms with open-work bronze pieces known as "transparents." In the early thirties, the death of his parents and sister and the troubled political situation in Europe caused him to turn away from the purely formal concerns of Cubism to a more symbolic and expressive art. The advancing German Army forced him to leave Paris for Toulouse in 1940, and in 1941, with little more than a portfolio of drawings, he emigrated to America. He established a studio in New York, which together with much of the work Lipchitz had produced in America was destroyed by fire in 1952. Since 1953 he has lived and worked at Hastings-on-Hudson, New York.

* Letter from the artist, January 18, 1952.

174

LIPCHITZ *Sacrifice* **1948**
Bronze, 48¾ x 39 x 24 in. (124 x 99 x 61 cm.)
George Cary, Elisabeth H. Gates, and Edmund Hayes Funds   52:3

Pablo Picasso

An extraordinary sensitivity to materials and an inventive imagination underlie the interest in sculpture that has continued throughout Picasso's prolific career. While existing fully in its own right, his sculpture has served also as a catalyst for stages of development in his painting and at two periods, in 1909 and 1931, was a major part of his work.

Picasso's fascination with a variety of textures and the multiple associations achieved by incorporating found objects dates from his early Cubist reliefs of 1913–14. By the early thirties and even more frequently during World War II when traditional sculpture materials were scarce, he used objects as diverse as bicycle parts, sieves, toys, and springs, ambiguously transforming the original materials and setting up complicated visual puns.

Female Bather Playing of 1958 is one of two bronze casts. (The original sculpture in wood and found objects and the second bronze remain in the artist's collection.) It was made at the same time as a group of standing bathers designed to be installed around a pool. Constructed originally of wood scraps, plaster, and corrugated cardboard, the gawky figure takes on life and humor with her huge though flattened breasts, vacant eyes, secretive smile, and tubular legs, apparently submerged below the ankles. "The hands of the *Playing Swimmer*, absurdly out of scale with the rest of the figure, contain in their movement an irresistible suggestion of the childish gesture of the bather splashing herself with water." *

Biography of the artist and description of *The Artist and His Model*, 1964, pp. 248–49.

* Roland Penrose, *Picasso* (New York: Universe Books), p. [13].

PICASSO *Female Bather Playing* **1958**
Bronze, 44½ x 15½ x 25½ in. (113 x 39.4 x 64.8 cm.)
Gift of The Seymour H. Knox Foundation, Inc. 65:2

Alberto Giacometti

"I never tried to make thin sculptures," Giacometti has said, "they became thin in spite of me." * In 1935, when he went back to working from the model, he had a sudden, terrifying revelation of objects "suspended in a frightful silence . . . there was no longer any relation between objects, divided as they were by immeasurable gulfs of void." † From that time, Giacometti attempted to sculpt the visual appearance of figures in space. His sculptures, such as *Man Walking*, are personages that appear as though seen at a distance. The attenuated figures, divested of bulk, nevertheless retain a powerful presence. The roughly worked surfaces create a shimmering effect like that of a mirage—constantly shifting and ethereal. He said that one of his problems was that his vision was constantly changing; the model was never the same, not only from one day to the next, but even from one glance to another, "disappearing . . . appearing again. . . . It always finds itself between being and non-being, and that is what one wants to copy." † Giacometti has sculpted numerous walking figures, large and small, which, even when combined in groups, project a feeling of solitary activity, though the space around them is charged with their nervous energy. *Man Walking*, 1960, exists in six bronze casts.

Also in the collection is *Woman Holding a Void*, a bronze sculpture of 1935.

Alberto Giacometti was born in 1901 in Stampa, Switzerland. Son of a well-known Impressionist landscape painter, Giovanni Giacometti, he was interested in art from an early age. He attended secondary school in Schiers, 1915–18, and studied sculpture at the École des Arts et Métiers, Geneva, 1919. In 1920–21 he visited Italy and lived nine months in Rome. In 1922 he went to Paris, where he studied for the next three years with Bourdelle at the Académie de la Grand Chaumière. In 1927 he moved into a small studio with his brother Diego, which they continued to share until Alberto's death in 1966. His first sculptures were solid Cubist-derived pieces, which yielded to transparent, cage-like constructions in the late twenties. At this time he became friends with many of the Surrealists, and he joined in their exhibitions and activities from 1930 to 1935. After working for many years from the imagination in a semiabstract style, he felt the need in 1935 to return to working from the living model. This led to a lifelong involvement with depicting the human figure, which at different times varied from minuscule to monumental in scale. In the mid-forties, after his sculptures had shrunk to pin-size, he started creating the well-known attenuated figures, often combined in compositions. Parallel with his sculpture, Giacometti maintained an interest in painting, drawing, and printmaking.

* *Life*, May 29, 1964, p. 95.
† *Life*, January 26, 1966, p. 60.

178

GIACOMETTI *Man Walking* 1960
Bronze, 71¾ x 10½ x 38 in. (incl. base)
(182 x 26.6 x 96.5 cm.)
Gift of Seymour H. Knox   K61:27

179

Fernand Léger

The Walking Flower was executed in 1951, shortly after Léger started to make ceramics at Biot in Southern France. He was primarily interested in the integration of architecture, painting, and sculpture, and his deep ceramic reliefs were designed as murals. He made only a few free-standing sculptures. The Walking Flower appears with little modification in a large composition of 1951–52, Projet monumental polychrome, in which a variety of flower motifs are depicted, a subject he used frequently. A similar flower was included in a large sculptural composition, Kindergarten, which was completed five years after Léger's death in 1955.

On The Walking Flower, Léger used lustrous glazes for the colors, combined with a dull, off-white glaze. On the reverse, the basic design is repeated in high-glaze black on white. Although small in scale, the sculpture suggests monumentality.

Two oil paintings, The Smoke, 1912, and Village in the Forest, 1914, are also in the Gallery collection.

Fernand Léger was born at Argentan, Normandy, France, in 1881. From 1897 he worked as an apprentice in an architect's office in Caen, then moved to Paris in 1900, where he worked as an architectural draftsman and studied painting briefly at the École des Arts Décoratifs in 1903. Influenced by Cézanne's aesthetic, Léger reduced the shapes of objects to cubic volumes, abandoning the influences of Fauvism and Impressionism that appeared in his early paintings. In 1910 he met several Cubist artists and exhibited with them the following year in the Salon des Indépendants. He joined the Corps of Engineers in the French Army in 1914, where he was deeply impressed by the formal qualities of machines. After his discharge from the Army, he entered his so-called Mechanical period, in which the objects and figures were reduced to tubular geometrical forms, with monumental figures treated as a static sculptural mass. In the mid-twenties Léger became interested in abstraction, resulting in the series Objects in Space, in which architectural elements were replaced by an assembly of scattered objects. The paintings of the thirties and forties were less concerned with formal experimentation and mostly based on further exploration of the figurative motif. Léger spent the years 1940–45 teaching and painting in the United States, which he had visited three times in the thirties. After his return to France, Léger designed mosaics, stained-glass windows, and tapestries, as well as his first ceramic sculptures at Biot. Léger worked also as a stage designer and filmmaker. He died in Gif-sur-Yvette in 1955.

LÉGER *The Walking Flower* **1951**
Ceramic, 26½ x 20½ x 15 in. (67.3 x 52 x 38 cm.)
Gift of Seymour H. Knox K69:20

Naum Gabo

"My comment about the *Linear No. 2, Variation* . . . which belongs to the Albright-Knox Art Gallery is that it represents a unique variation of the first *Linear No. 2*. It is a variation made in a different size both in dimensions and in the thickness of the material. Secondly, the presence of a starry image in the inner structure is unique in this work. Also, the base is differently constructed from the first one." *

Linear No. 2, Variation, 1962–65, is the embodiment of the ideas formulated by Gabo in the thirties and realized in his sculptural work of the early forties, especially in the variations of *Linear Construction No. 1*. *Linear No. 2, Variation* is constructed from plastic curved-edge planes, intersecting at right angles, and covered by stainless steel wire, which shapes the body of the sculpture in space and designs the star-shaped emblem inside the sculpture. The shape of the curved-edge plastic planes is repeated in the form of the plastic base.

Naum Gabo was born Naum Neemia Pevsner in Briansk, Russia, in 1890. In 1910 he went to the University of Munich, where he studied medicine for a year, then transferred to the natural sciences and, in 1912, to engineering studies. He also attended lectures on the history of art by Professor Heinrich Wölfflin, 1911–12. Gabo visited his older brother Antoine in Paris, 1913–14; at the outbreak of World War I, he went to Scandinavia with his younger brother Alexei, where he formulated his theoretical theses and created his first constructions, signed with the name Gabo. In 1917 he returned to Russia, and in 1920 he and his brother Antoine published the Realistic Manifesto, setting forth the essentials of Constructivism, a new aesthetic in which time and space were redefined and volume and mass were given new values, as were line and color. Static rhythm was replaced by kinetic rhythm, which resulted in Gabo's first motorized constructions in 1920. In 1922 he left Russia and lived until 1932 in Berlin, where he designed sets and costumes for Diaghilev's ballet La Chatte in 1926. In 1929 he proposed a Fête Lumière, one of the earliest electric-light shows, which was to be in the center of the city, focusing on the Brandenburg Gate. During the Berlin stay, Gabo designed several large-scale monuments that were not realized; his first large construction was completed in 1957 at the Bijenkorf Shopping Center in Rotterdam. In 1932 Gabo went to Paris, where he lived until 1935, and became a member of the Abstraction-Création group. He lived in England, 1935–46, and in 1937 coedited a book with J. L. Martin and Ben Nicholson, Circle: International Survey of Constructive Art. Gabo immigrated to the United States in 1946, becoming a United States citizen in 1952. He lives in Middlebury, Connecticut.

* Letter from the artist, August 15, 1971.

182

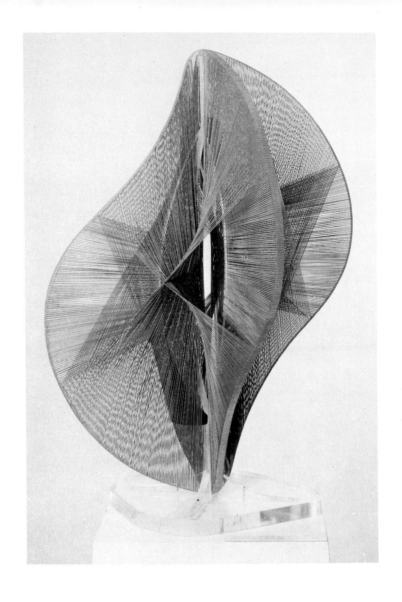

GABO *Linear No. 2, Variation* **1962–65**
Stainless steel coil on plastic
46 x 16 x 25 in. (incl. base) (117 x 40.6 x 63.5 cm.)
Gift of The Seymour H. Knox Foundation, Inc. 65:15

Antoine Pevsner

In the thirties, a new element became evident in Pevsner's work: the severity of flat, intersecting surfaces he had used in previous constructions was transformed into round, dynamically curving shapes, forming solid masses and voids. Developing the idea of curved planes became Pevsner's major preoccupation; later the shapes were structured from a dense network of interrelated lines. *Construction in the Egg* from 1948 is one of a group of Pevsner's major sculptures in which the interchangeability of solids and open space became dominant.

Pevsner, like Brancusi, attempted to limit himself to a particular elementary form. For both sculptors, the egg shape was a fundamental one, being the evocation of the origin, and both used it frequently in their work. However, Pevsner tended not to use the entire shape but to expose an inner structure, created by his imagination, within the basic form.

Construction in the Egg was executed in 1948 as a unique piece of bronze dorée rods brazed together. It was formerly in the collection of Pevsner's close friend, Pierre Peissi.

Antoine Pevsner was born in Orel, Russia in 1886. After attending the School of Fine Arts in Kiev and the Academy of Fine Arts in St. Petersburg, he went to Paris in 1912. There he became acquainted with the work of the Cubists, but their theories were not satisfactory to him and he devoted himself to the creation of a new aesthetic based on contemporary principles of science. During his stay in Norway in 1915–16, he turned from painting to sculpture in which the pure forms constructed in space and the use of the void as a formal element replaced traditional concepts of sculptural mass.

In 1917, Pevsner returned to Russia, teaching at the Moscow Academy of Fine Arts, together with Kandinsky, Malevich, and his brother Naum Gabo, with whom he prepared and cosigned in 1920 the Realistic Manifesto, setting forth the theories of their production. Thus the principles that guided Pevsner's entire work were present in his sculptures of the early twenties that were radical in abstraction, culminating his effort toward complete dematerialization. Transparent materials and wire, essentially weightless, were basic materials to this innovative expression, in which the shapes are pure and handled with mathematical precision.

Pevsner left Russia for Paris in 1923 and became a French citizen in 1930. In 1931 he became a member of the Abstraction-Création group and cofounder of the group Réalités Nouvelles in 1946. Pevsner received the French Légion d'Honneur in 1961 and died in Paris in 1962.

PEVSNER *Construction in the Egg* **1948**
Bronze dorée, 27 x 17¼ x 21 in. (68.5 x 44 x 53.5 cm.)
Gift of The Seymour H. Knox Foundation, Inc.   65:21

Giacomo Manzù

In Rome in January of 1934, Manzù saw the Pope enthroned between two cardinals in St. Peter's. At the time he made drawings of the figures, but it was two years later, in 1936, that he began his long series of sculpted Cardinals. The first large figures in this group date from 1949–50. By 1960, the series numbered over fifty, the subjects depicted in seated and standing positions, and in various sizes; only one of these is a portrait.

Manzù has said that the Cardinals do not interest him as a religious theme; he regards them as he would a still life, the subject for a study in simplified forms. The dominant motif of *Standing Cardinal*, 1957, is the tapered wedge-shape of the cope and miter, reiterated in the triangular neckline and front folds of the cope. A variation of this shape—a shield-like design with a decorative detail of cord and tassels—appears on the back of the figure and is repeated in the simply rendered face. The unpolished bronze of this unique cast retains surface details of the original wax sculpture. Although considerably less than life size and smaller than many of Manzù's sculptures on this theme, *Standing Cardinal* projects a sense of monumentality.

Giacomo Manzù, born in 1908 in Bergamo, Italy, received his primary education from local craftsmen—a carpenter, woodcarver, gilder, and a stucco worker to whom he was successively apprenticed from the age of eleven. Although isolated from modern sculpture, he studied illustrated books and became particularly interested in Maillol's work. His preoccupation with religious figures undoubtedly began in childhood through the influence of his devout mother and the location of a church (where he served as an acolyte) next door to his home.

After eighteen months of military service in Verona, in 1927–28, and a brief visit to Paris, he settled in Milan and began sculpting portraits, religious figures, and nudes. Manzù's interest in the long-neglected technique of shallow relief sculpture is characteristic of his independence from avant-garde trends and his affinity with the Italian classical tradition.

In addition to his many cardinals, portraits, dancers, and figure studies, he has received a number of important religious commissions, particularly for the bronze doors at the Cathedral at Salzburg, 1957–58, the Portal of Death at St. Peter's Basilica in Rome, 1962–64, and the portal at the St. Lawrence Church in Rotterdam, 1966–68. He presently lives and works in Ardea, near Rome, where a museum has been built for his work.

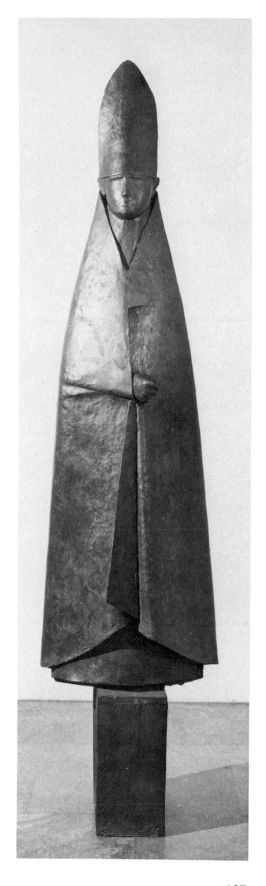

MANZÙ *Standing Cardinal* **1957**
Bronze, 88 x 21 x 13 in. (223.5 x 53.4 x 33 cm.)
George B. and Jenny R. Mathews Fund 69:13

187

Jean Dubuffet

Between September, 1966, and November, 1967, Dubuffet made eight sculptures in the "Borne au logos" series; of these, *VII*, 1967, is in the Gallery collection. The sculptures in this group, which retain the characteristics of his "l'Hourloupe" series, are painted off-white and patterned with heavy black lines, red and blue areas, and striations. Monolithic and essentially four-sided sculptures, each has designs that continue around the entire surface, presenting different aspects as the viewer moves.

The "Borne au logos" sculptures are of cast polyurethane, a durable plastic material which Dubuffet began to use after an earlier work of painted polystyrene (Styrofoam), *Le Domino* of 1966, proved exceedingly fragile. As is the case with a number of Dubuffet's titles, *Borne au logos* cannot be translated easily, and the artist prefers that the title remain in French.

Also in the Gallery collection are two paintings by Dubuffet—*M. Plume, Portrait of Henri Michaux*, 1947 (p. 223), and *Path Bordered by Grass*, 1956.

Biography of the artist, p. 222.

DUBUFFET *Borne au logos VII* **1967**
Cast polyurethane
39¾ x 18½ x 20 in. (101 x 47 x 50.8 cm.)
Gift of The Seymour H. Knox Foundation, Inc. 68:5

Fritz Wotruba

The rectangular, block-like forms in the limestone sculpture create stepped horizontal and vertical planes; the massive concave form suggests both a figure and an architectural structure. The artist has written of it: "This stone figure arose after the large relief for the Brussels World's Fair, 1958, and is the forerunner of the large kneeling figure in the Dortmund Museum. At that time, I was interested in the compact resolution of a sculpture—no cleavage, no holes—which in all architecture still governs the organization of a figure. A problem which always recurs with me, since it is a persistent one. From there, it is naturally not far to absolute architecture." *

Born in Vienna of a Czech father and a Hungarian mother in 1907, Fritz Wotruba was apprenticed as an engraver at the age of fourteen. He pursued this profession for several years but spent his free time copying reproductions of famous sculptors' drawings and sketching from the model at the Vienna Academy of Fine Arts. In 1926, he studied with the sculptor Anton Hanak, and in the following year, working independently, he began carving in stone. He became a prominent sculptor in Europe during the thirties, participating in several international exhibitions in Zurich and Venice. Wotruba spent the war years, 1938–45, in exile in Switzerland and returned to Vienna in 1946, when he was made a member of the Academy and Director of the Academy School.

Striving for the ideal form in sculpture, which encompasses and unites landscape, architecture, and the city, Wotruba's carved and bronze figures evolved from his early kouros-types to the monumental and simple architectonic forms of the fifties and sixties, composed of cylindrical and rectangular blocks and flat planes. In the late 1960's, he actually began working as an architect and has recently designed a church and cloister.

* Letter from the artist, October 29, 1968.

WOTRUBA *Seated Figure* **1959**
Limestone, 39⅜ x 27¾ x 19½ in. (100 x 70.5 x 49.5 cm.)
Charles Clifton, Edmund Hayes, and Sherman S. Jewett Funds 67:1

Marino Marini

Marini's *Dancer,* 1952, is far removed from the lithe and graceful tradition of Degas's ballerinas. This figure stands tense and rigid, with only her right leg curved into a point position. One of Marini's last in a long series of dancers, the sculpture retains the sense of substantial volume and weight of earlier figures while becoming somewhat more abstract. No attempt has been made to render exact details of musculature or physiognomy; the forms have become generalized into simple planes reminiscent of archaic sculpture, particularly Etruscan figures. To underscore the unfinished impression, Marini deliberately avoids the traditional polished bronze surface, and instead corrodes the sculpture with acid so that the scars and irregularities resemble archaeological treasures buried for years beneath the earth's surface.

An additional bronze cast is in the artist's collection, and another is in a private collection in Switzerland; a lead cast is in a collection in Milan.

Also in the Gallery collection is Marini's *Acrobats and Horse,* a 1951 gouache and ink drawing on canvas.

Marino Marini was born in 1901 in Pistoia in Northern Italy. He studied sculpture in Florence at the Accademia di Belli Arti, though until about 1928 he considered himself primarily a painter and etcher. From 1929 to 1940, he taught at the Villa Reale Art School in Monza. He was then named Professor of Sculpture at the Brera Academy in Milan, where he has continued to live and work, except for the World War II years when he was in Switzerland.

Influences as various as Etruscan and Roman statuary, the work of Medardo Rosso, and the classicism of Maillol have been proposed as sources for Marini's characteristic sober archaism. He is perhaps best known for his Horses and Riders, an extended series of equestrian statues dating from 1936, which explore dynamic, often contorted poses. In these works and in his numerous other stylized portraits, dancers, and figures, rounded volumes whose surfaces are textured by scratches, incisions, and occasional polychrome recall the interest and activity in painting which he has maintained throughout his career.

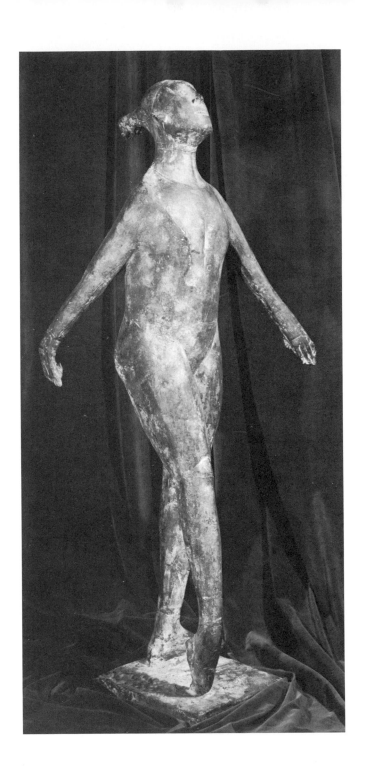

MARINI *Dancer* **1952**
Bronze, 60 x 24 x 17 in. (152.4 x 61 x 43.2 cm.)
base: 2⅜ x 12¾ x 14 3/16 in. (6.4 x 32.4 x 36.2 cm.)
Evelyn Rumsey Cary Fund   55:1

192

European Painting

Lawrence Alloway

European painting since the end of World War II is a complex of individuals and groups, some with international ambitions, others with a sharper sense of local identity. Some of these developments are clearly represented in the collection of the Albright-Knox Art Gallery, others are partially seen, and some are not seen at all. There is, in addition, the fact that the dominance of American art in the period under discussion has had the effect of reducing American interest in European art. The dispute between American and European sensibility persists in stereotyped forms that make the task of evaluation difficult. What I propose to do here is to describe aspects of European art, cued by the collection, with the hope of increasing the amount of information rather than of closing out arguments.

Characteristic of the general postwar relaxation of Cubism is a group of paintings by Italians of the fifties, in which Cubist structure is penetrated and loosened by color and painterly texture. Three of the artists (Birolli, Cassinari, and Santomaso) were members of the Fronte Nuova delle Arti, 1946–48, a group that signaled Italy's rediscovery of modern art after the war. In retrospect, it is clear that their discovery was mediated by a conciliating not an innovative spirit. The arabesques in Afro's *Concertino*, 1948, are quickly resolved into a pair of frivolously abstracted figures. Werner Haftmann has noted that Afro's pictures are based on experiences or memory: "The statement may turn out to be quite precise, though not actually visible—*Fear of the Dark* or *Repression*." * *Fear of the Dark*, 1952, in this collection, has a mild phantasmagoric character, evoking mood as well as making a visual display. Birolli's touch is sharper than Afro's ingratiating one, but his imagery exists at a similar level of legibility: *Rural Scene* combines Cubist surface pattern with spiky agricultural machinery. Cassinari's *Black Fish*, 1951, is a Cubist still-life format done with painterly dexterity, a decorative footnote to Braque. Santomaso's *Castilian Earth 1*, 1959, is not Cubist at all, but once again one style is modified by another, the way Cubism was modified by humor, mood, or facile handling. In this case an abstract painting is made to resemble, as the title indicates, landscape, not only in terms of horizontal space but also in terms of texture. All these artists were born before World War I, but a similar interest in modifying extremes, proposing reconciliations, shows in Cremonini, born in the 1920's. His *Boat on the Beach* plays with Cubist structure, struts from the picture edge leading across the painting, where they turn out to be the masts of a boat.

The dominant and unanticipated new factor in postwar painting was a florescence of painterly criteria. Modern art, understood in terms of Cubism and abstract art or in terms of Picasso's basically linear style, had been equated with line and with composition. The tradition of Monet, Bonnard,

* *Painting in the Twentieth Century* (New York, 1965), vol. 1, p. 370.

and Matisse had been relegated to a lower position than the constructive, supposedly classical, main line of modern art. In the late forties and fifties, all this was changed by a reordering of the way in which paintings were produced and in what they looked like when done. The emergence of painterly as opposed to linear criteria occurred in many ways, one of which was unobtrusive. The grid, by means of which the Cubists established a holding pattern on the canvas, took on another meaning, as in Ubac's *Still Life*, 1951, and Winter's *Composition in Red and Blue*, 1953. The armature is dilated until it becomes not the support but the subject of the picture, and as it spreads an abstract governing structure is turned into surface rather than line. The thickened bands are wide and definite enough to have existence as surfaces and hence are themselves painterly qualities.

In any discussion of painterliness in postwar European art, Nicolas de Staël is central, both for his thickly impasted and for his thinly liquid paintings. In the collection is *Landscape in Vaucluse No. 2*, 1953, one of the dense pictures in which the forms are less a depiction of landscapes than paint being carried toward signification. The loaded paint with ridged knife marks never blunts De Staël's sense of natural light, which confirms the impression of a landscape in process of being declared. The picture surface, so familiar a structural feature of painting since the 1890's, is defined by juicy and adhesive slabs of paint, the sensuality of which are part of a major reorientation of taste. De Staël's prominence was the result of his manual gifts coinciding exactly with the moment of a revision in aesthetics.

Various realignments and revivals were made on the basis of the new estimation of painterly quality, one example of which is a revival of Orphic Cubism. On the one hand, its principles were continued by Sonia Delaunay, the wife of the founder of this type of Cubism which depended on discs of pure color and on a higher level of abstraction than any other aspect of Cubism. On the other hand, Nay, in the mid-fifties, adopted the disc form that he has used ever since: the collection includes an early example, *Ovestone*, 1955, in which the discs are racked on an oblique axis, but in *Rhythms in Gray and Yellow*, 1959, the discs are less formally placed and more freely painted. (Sonia Delaunay's *Colored Rhythm*, 1958, was painted between these two canvases by a follower of another generation incidentally.) In paintings like this by Nay, or by Sam Francis, composition is not a matter of balancing and contrasting precise forms; it has more to do with judgment of color and its fusion with other hues. Max Kozloff has written of the difficulties of what he called "Venetian Painting and Florentine Criticism," * in which he points out that we have a vocabulary of fair scope for referring to the functions of line and form in paintings, but very few coherent terms for the illusive realm of color. As painterliness developed, it followed that color, and the experiences of color without linear boundaries or chiaroscuro, became of prime importance. Other painterly abstractions in the collection include a shimmering Damian, two impasted semi-organic images by Hosiasson, and two calligraphically based paintings by Georges Noel. Painterly criteria released line from its regularizing and boundary-giving functions, so that loose, open, flowing tracks, running across monochrome or colored fields, are the equivalent of paint surface and not directional divisions.

* *Renderings* (New York, 1968), pp. 321–35.

In 1952 Michel Tapié published *Un Art Autre*,* which was an argument for the *really* new in art. The title was derived from a conviction that from 1944 something *other* had emerged in art which dismissed early modern art to the past. Tapié chose that year because it was then that Fautrier painted his series Otages; in the following year, Dubuffet painted his first *hautes pâtes*, the series entitled Microbolus, Macadam & Cie. Wols's work of the forties also contributed to the shaping of Tapié's aesthetic. Although it is not what he stressed when he wrote it, it can now be seen that his choice of artists involves essentially the radical wing of the general expansion of painterly criteria. The 1947 Dubuffet in the collection, *M. Plume, Portrait of Henri Michaux*, not only represents the artist at his magnificent best, it also typifies what Tapié meant by *art autre*: art of high physicality and of primal iconography, the combination of which makes the skills of earlier twentieth-century artists look frail and overelaborated. It is not my intention to try to revive the term here, but it is a convenient way of drawing attention to one area in the spectrum of painterliness. The softening of Cubism and the thickening of matter are both aspects of painterliness. Tapié failed to develop his early instinct for something happening, but subsequently had considerable influence on European art as the adviser of an art gallery in Paris.

Antonio Tàpies was among the artists Tapié sponsored, though Tàpies was slightly too late a starter to be in the book, as can be seen in the collection from his early painting *Construction of Shah Abbas*, 1950, a symbolist dream-image. (He met and became friendly with Tapié in 1955 however.) Two excellent mature Tàpies are in the collection, *Painting*, 1956, and *Relief over Black Space*, 1958, in which the high pastes and scarred drawing of Dubuffet are translated into images of archaic sites. Tàpies is among the most lyrical of all those artists who have opposed the "sterilized" picture plane of Cubism and geometric abstract art, preferring to define the surface of the picture as a natural carrier of marks and materials.

The simple material basis of art was affirmed in opposition to the refinements and complexity represented by, say, Italian late Cubism. The literalization of the substance of painting was a kind of prolongation of collage into the materials of painting. Burri's use of burlap, as in *Composition in White*, 1955, moves painting in the direction of relief sculpture. The substantiality of the different materials is retained despite their pictorial unification. The evocation of space is blocked by the materiality of the means. This translation of sculptural mass onto the flat plane, which has been called Matter painting, is an area that European artists have explored more than Americans, many of whom are bound by a more acute sense of pictorial values. Bram Bogart in *The Fall* builds outward from his canvas by piling up his dense materials, without any attempt at the reconciliation of two- and three-dimensional space that would occupy an American.

* *Un Art Autre, où il s'agit de Nouveaux Dévidages du Réel* (Paris, 1952). Among the European artists in the Albright-Knox Art Gallery, the following are illustrated in Tapié: Appel, Dubuffet, Hartung, Mathieu, Matta, Riopelle, Serpan, Sironi, Soulages, Ubac. The American painters reproduced are Francis, Ruth Francken, Joseph Glasco, Hofmann, Ossorio, Pollock, and Tobey. What action painting was to the United States, *art autre* was to Europe, a slogan indicating, however vaguely, a shift in sensibility. It may be worth noting that an American critic, Gene Swenson, used Tapié's term, without acknowledgment, in a pamphlet entitled "The Other Tradition" and, like Tapié, meant by *other* an antiformalist aesthetic.

Another aspect of the renewal of painterliness can be touched on by reference to Riopelle, who was influenced both by Monet and by André Breton's *Le Surréalisme et la peinture*. The combination is not as odd as it sounds, inasmuch as Breton recommended automatic working methods, but it is a fact that automatism worked better in linear than painted forms in the Surrealists' hands. However, given an interest in automatism on Riopelle's part, Monet would have suggested to him how to work impulsively without being distracted by drawing or composition. Riopelle's *Eskimo Mask*, c. 1955, is the result of improvisation at speed with paint used in such a way that its physical characteristic of liquidity is stressed. Subsequently he evolved paintings which have a bearing to nature pretty much like De Staël's; Riopelle's *bocage*, like De Staël's horizon, is a possibility toward which the paint is moving rather than a given denotation.

Among the abstract painters in Paris was a group that checked the gestural and material freedom of *art autre* with the virtues of *belle peinture*. It is clear that Soulages is not like Franz Kline. His paintings are constructed with a solidity and a finish that Kline was at pains to avoid the look of, whereas it is part of Soulages's intention to assert traditional mastery at the core of large abstract paintings. Similarly with Hartung, whose graphic signs used to be compared with those of Mathieu; but where Mathieu works at speed, with an all-at-once aesthetic, Hartung works slowly and this characterizes the paintings quite differently. To compare the single curve of *T55-28* by Hartung with, say, a slash by Fontana is to see the resemblance collapse. The Hartung line is more like a single reed in a Chinese painting designed for meditation, whereas Fontana's cut, like Mathieu's calligraphy, is designed to be instantaneous in effect. Schneider's hard and scuffled paint tracks, too, for all their abruptness, preserve an internal standard of cultivated handling. Theirs is an adaptive style of real complexity; within the terms of prevailing painterliness they check topicality against technical learning and animate custom with surprise.

One of the shared themes of European art of the period was the function of signs. A reason for this interest is that signs, inasmuch as they are flat, conform to the two-dimensional imperative of much twentieth-century art; on the other hand, a sign assumes the existence of a language system, so that a painting with signs is not a purely formal or merely decorative construct. Mathieu's work is interesting here. In one way it was an art purified of everything but the physical gesture of its making. The 1957 painting in the collection is one of a group made in New York that year, which contrasts the movement of the wrist, recorded in the soft wriggle to the right or in the lower hook, with the instantaneous splatter and spray of thrown paint. Once performed, however, the picture, as a sign, acquires its meaning subsequently. Thus meaning, instead of being a property that inspires the artist to the act of production, becomes an experience in the act of consumption, the property of the spectator's.

The Cobra group is very significant in postwar Europe. Its name is formed by the first letters of Copenhagen, Brussels, and Amsterdam and the word is appropriate to the fact that the artists of the group developed a bestiary in which man and creature mingled. Appel in a letter to the Albright-Knox Art Gallery commented on his gouache *Man and Beast* that it means "the desire to live of man and animal." * Such a subject is typical

* In a letter dated November 28, 1968.

of the Cobra artists in their search for a basic subject matter which would provide a counterculture to the Mediterranean-derived aesthetics of Parisian formality and learning. Although they used Paris as a center, they were strongly opposed to its reconciling, synthetic spirit in the late forties and early fifties. They sought an iconography in which Danish folklore or Dutch Expressionism could be embodied. (Holland became the country of van Gogh rather than of Mondrian.) Appel's *Man and Beast*, 1950, is the earliest example of the group in the collection, but the group has an earlier history. In 1948–49 a Dutch group published two numbers of a magazine *Reflex* which led, in 1949–51, to a larger magazine *Cobra*. This sequence suggests Dutch priority, but this is not so: the Danish contribution was earlier and decisive, with the Dutch artists responding to the more Northern model. The Dutch artists Appel, Constant, and Corneille visited Denmark in the late forties and saw the more developed work of Jorn, Pedersen, and Ejler Bille. Jorn criticized Breton's definition of Surrealism as "pure psychic automatism" on the grounds that it must be "organically bound to physical automatism." * Here, as with Riopelle, is an assertion of the materiality of means linked to improvisation. Jorn's own work, and that of the rest of the group, is characterized by turbulent paint handling and, at the same time, the emergence of evocative figures, in and, as it were, through the paint. The work is both gestural and figurative. The earlier work, in which Cubist compartmentalization is pulverized—but not past recognition —resembles Pollock's contemporaneous mythological Cubism, but in the fifties the imagery becomes expressionistic and continuous. (Corneille's *Beginning of Summer*, 1962, alone retains some of this relaxed lyrical play with Cubist structure.)

The untitled painting of 1961 by Jorn shows what he meant by the notion of psychic-physical automatism. It is clearly improvised on the basis of hand and arm movement which make either knots of color or flowing curves and double curves. The forms that transpire from this improvisatory attack are organically enmeshed though not specifically identifiable; there seems no doubt, however, by reference to more readable cases of Cobra iconography, that this is an image of encounter, a pair meeting, as in Appel's *Flight*. (This theme has its origin in Munch, Nolde, and, perhaps, Gauguin's *La Perte du pucelage*, with its conjunction of girl and fox.) Man is treated at a biological and survival level, not in terms of individual identity. Alechinsky's *Greet the North, Greet the South*, 1962, is a more linear version of the painterly cellular structure of Jorn, but with another Cobra theme, that of the swarm, the crowd, the proliferation of beings, whether an Ensor-like carnival rabble or a Dantesque river of sinners. In Lataster, a second-generation Cobra painter, the imagery is less specific, but the turmoil of paint acts as a symbol of human anxiety, so that the material itself has an iconographic level of meaning.

Pedersen's *Flying Bird*, 1951, is one of a series in which folkloric birds occupy the picture, sometimes sharing the sky with symbolic suns, sometimes dominating childlike schemata for boats. The imagery certainly derives from Danish folklore, which does nothing to lessen the sexual implication of the imagery of heavy bird and small boat. It should be stressed that the Primitivism that in one form or another informs Cobra art should be construed as neither tourism nor withdrawal. The myths used are those

* Asger Jorn, "Discours aux Pingoins," *Cobra*, no. 1 (Brussels, 1948), p. 8.

linked with the artists' country and childhood. Their primitivism is not idyllic; on the contrary, it assumes a basic level of life, a primal scene, fraught with conflict. It is more Freudian than Rousseauistic. Thus the figuration of Cobra is an attempt to hold in pictorial form the themes that are shared in common and which can be nominated as fundamentally human.

The spread of painterly criteria was not unopposed. One alternative to it was centered in Concrete art, defined by Max Bill in these terms: "We call Concrete art those works of art which originate on the basis of means and laws of their own, without external reliance on natural phenomena or any transformation of them." * This was written in 1936, but the point of view it represents, of an art closed to external references, continued to support artists through the painterly fifties. Bill's 1965 painting in the collection, *Field of 32 Parts in 4 Colors*, declares its systematic structure. The colors are pink, orange, green, and blue, distributed logically on a crystal pattern. The uninflected layout, however, is optically activated by the close value of the pink and orange, so that the pattern is not perceived with equal clarity throughout. Bill's point is that nuance is only possible within a learnable system, because he considers that an unstructured painting dissolves into a mass of probabilities. The logical relationship of the parts, so that one bit of a work of art enables one to predict other bits of it, is indispensable in the creation of order.

In Paris, Concrete art was centered at the gallery of Denise René, who is certainly to be counted as one of the makers of taste in postwar Europe. Among the artists she showed, first in implicit, then in overt, resistance to *art autre*, the Informal, and Tachisme, were Herbin, Vasarely, Baertling, and Mortensen. Herbin's *Vie No. 1*, 1950, is a good example of deliberate geometric structure which stays within formal limits but without being subject to a total system, such as Bill's. The layout is a grid, the compartments of various sizes and colors, containing circles, triangles, and rectangles, none of them overlapping, all of them frontal. Herbin supposed his inventory of Euclidean forms to constitute a universal language, but it is impossible, without knowledge of his theoretical writing, to read it. However, he is not to be blamed for the idea that geometry is a universal; it is a notion with a lengthy and slightly absurd history. What is clearly stated by the painting is that the multiplicity of elements confers a spatial animation on the games board–like pattern of the picture surface. Thus syntactic order seems to be the subject of the picture, learnable from the regularity of the pieces, but not at all the semantic level Herbin desired. As the process provides the subject matter of much *art autre*, so order, embodied in the end-state of a clearly conceived work, is the subject of Concrete art. The differences between art as process and art as end-state are irreducible, and the two positions were polar opposites among the options facing European artists.

The work of Baertling and of Mortensen depend on being seen as imperturbable surfaces: the two large planes of Baertling's *Blanar*, 1953, though they reveal some irregularities in the application of paint, have to be largely undifferentiated if the surface of the picture is to stay still. The artist is basing his picture on the interlocking of the two colors, and the

* Margit Staber, *Max Bill* (New York, 1964), p. 23.

198

sharpness of their junction would be weakened by secondary elaborations within either color. Similarly, in Mortensen's *Broglie*, 1955, spatial kinks and ruptures would be introduced if the traces of hand and brush were not subdued. Pure color, free of Mondrian's armature and theoretical restrictions, characterizes postwar Concrete painting, but with a minimum of autographic traces. Such painting cannot be considered finished until the material deposit of paint reaches an agreed-on point of neutrality and inconspicuousness.

Vasarely is represented by three substantial paintings in the collection. The first, *Mindanao*, 1952–55, combines two motifs: the flat discs at the top, extrapolated from the pebbles of Belle-Île, where Vasarely worked in 1947, and the central zone of parallel and colliding lines, a systematization of his earlier Zebras. The forms are contrasted and brought together to form a traditional, diversified composition. *Bora III*, 1964, on the other hand, is an entirely united image, consisting of a series of six concentric squares, diminishing toward the innermost one.* In a text of 1959, Vasarely makes the point that "every plastic form-color represents a measurable and objective physical constant, but its interpretation will be subjective." † To achieve the quantification of the formal elements of painting, it is necessary to develop systematic and predictable composition and to exclude the physical variable of touch; both criteria are met admirably in *Bora III*. The later work of Vasarely has expanded chromatically, as in *Vega-Nor*, 1969, but the multiplicity of color and the increase in illusionistic volume are not necessarily improvements. Optical art, in which effects of visual movement are induced by close-valued color or by contrasting pattern, is a largely European movement, partly perhaps because of its pro-technological basis (quantification of means is linked to mass production by Vasarely), whereas American abstract artists have been either expressionistic or formalistic. Abstract illusionism, Op art's belated American equivalent, is color-oriented and decorative compared to the European original.

This is not the place for an account of the emergence of Argentine Concrete art, beyond remarking that it is one of the most arresting cases of international communication in postwar art. On the one hand, there is a connection between the Argentine Tomás Maldonado, who worked with Max Bill at the Hochschule für Gestaltung, Ulm, and later replaced him. Another link between Buenos Aires and Europe is through Vasarely to the Groupe de Recherche d'Art Visuel (GRAV). This group, founded in 1960, included Garcia Rossi and Julio Le Parc, the former Argentine, the latter French but born in Argentina, and Yvaral (Vasarely's son). The group picked up Vasarely's polemic against Bohemia and the related idea of the solitary genius and worked in various collaborative forms, often assembling separately executed works in unified environmental displays. Although the works were conceived separately, there was substantial agreement among the artists on the kind of standard inexpressive parts to be used and on the degree of spectator participation to be induced by changing forms (optical and physical movement) and reflections. The visual instability of Vasarely was studied as a form of involvement of the spectator's attention. Both Garcia Rossi and Yvaral, in their different media, animate the whole area

* Another version of this theme is *Bora*, 1959, reproduced in *Vasarely*, Introduction by Marcel Joray (Switzerland, 1965), p. 125, in which four squares with fewer stripes are contained within one another.
† *Ibid.*, p. 117.

by repetitive forms, and Sobrino, a Spanish member of the group, achieves this effect three-dimensionally in *Permutational Structure*, 1963–66, in which the standard parts are changed in their relationship by each movement of the spectator. Thus logical structure and a continually shifting visual stimulus are coordinated. Among Argentines not affiliated with GRAV but parallel to its interest in systematic form are Tomasello, Ary Brizzi, and Aizenberg. MacEntyre and Vidal share the common taste for repetitive form, but in their works it takes the form of linear rather than relief or painted displays.

The Zero group, which consisted of Otto Piene and Heinz Mack, was formed in 1957–58; the third member, Uecker, joined in 1961. Piene and Mack arranged a series of one-night exhibitions in Düsseldorf and for the last two they edited publications based on the themes of the shows. The first was *The Red Painting* and the second *Vibration*, both topics of importance in postwar art which were here identified promptly and clearly. *The Red Painting* was the first of a chain of exhibitions, first in Europe, later in the United States, of monochrome painting. The definition of art in terms of a uniform surface, without the contrast and interplay of different colors, was not only in opposition to early modern art, it was also a rejection of *art autre*. As Mack stated, "In place of 'interesting' detail we substitute a completely insipid structural element that is only meaningful when it is related to the whole." * The undisciplined complexities of *art autre* were dismissed as aberrant. Yves Klein, whom Piene and Mack met after the founding of Zero, is of course a key figure in this area. The collection includes two of his *International Klein Blue Sponges*, and one in red, 1960, like fossilized chrysanthemums on their slender metal stems.

The subject of vibration is defined by Mack as follows: "Lines, surfaces, and space must continually merge with one another, 'cancel out' one another (in the dialectical sense). If this integration is perceivable, a work vibrates, and our eyes meet with the resting restlessness." † This is not the place to trace the development of these terms since the first performance of Piene's light ballet in Düsseldorf in 1959, but we can see in the collection a strong group of Mack's work of the mid-sixties. In *White Light Dynamo*, 1964, a disc turns slowly behind fluted glass to create a rippling movement, or vibration.

The Zero group was the first artists' collaborative devoted to light and movement, preceding by two years GRAV and later groups within what was called the New Tendency. This term indicates a community of interests including pro-technology attitudes and a bias against subjectivity in art. Piene and Mack were predisposed toward technology in their art, both by the theory of the Bauhaus, with its stress on industrial design, and by the war, one effect of which was to familiarize their generation with a wide range of machines. In 1959 the Zero group showed at the Hessenhuis, Antwerp and, to quote Piene, "the theme of the catalogue was the Moholy-Nagy 'Vision-in-Motion–Motion-in-Vision.' " ‡ This point is relevant when we consider the three standing pieces by Mack in the collection. They are tall, slender, and repetitive and constructed of plexiglass and aluminum,

* Heinz Mack, "The New Dynamic Structure," *Zero*, no. 1 (Düsseldorf, 1958).
† Heinz Mack, "Resting Restlessness," *Zero*, no. 2 (Düsseldorf, 1958).
‡ Otto Piene, "The Development of the Group Zero," *The Times Literary Supplement* (London), September 3, 1964, pp. 812–13. Reprinted as *Astronauts of Inner Space* (San Francisco, 1966), pp. 24–26.

plexiglass and plastic lenses, and plexiglass and mirrors. There is an inescapable association with skyscrapers, and it is one that the artist himself has acknowledged by inserting night photographs of high buildings among photographs of his construction.* The regular storied progression of glittering forms changes in our attention and, also, reflects segments of the environment within the work itself.

Fontana's work has a significance that has not been recognized in the United States. In the late forties and early fifties, he investigated ways of opening up the picture plane, by both perforations and scattering ceramic chips across the surface to indicate a tangible layered space. One of his later works, *Spatial Concept #2*, 1969, is in the collection, in which the early random punctures have turned into a regular sequence of clean slashes. The economy and directness of Fontana's work, for all its occasional quirks, put him alongside the Zero artists, who admired him, as an important anti-Informalist. He is presumably an influence on Uecker's construction *Overgrowth*, 1962, in which nails hammered into the picture swirl like magnetized particles in literal space.

So far, I have treated European art in terms of groups and tendencies, but there are a number of pieces in the collection which, because of their isolation or the independence of the artists, cannot be covered in that way.† One of these is a late Max Beckmann, 1950, of which the artist had this to say: "*Hotel Lobby* is one of the first paintings I did here in New York after having moved from St. Louis, I was quite fond of, and often much engaged studying, people in Cafés and Hotel Lobb[ie]s. . . . After my work I often take a 'recovery cocktail' at the Plaza Hotel. Many people from New York and out-of-town as well [as] strangers pass along there, so that of these and other impressions my ideas took shape in the painting. I think also it isn't a bad picture, as it contains a certain part of my work in a relative close form." ‡ The lobby, with its diverse typology, is a kind of ship of fools, an area for the chance meetings of contrasted figures, the whole made slightly ominous by the screen like a ladder (as for a crucifixion), enframing and intersecting the heads on the right.

Important European artists went to England as refugees, Mondrian in 1938, Kurt Schwitters in 1940. Neither artist had the least influence in England though both worked there, Schwitters for eight years. Mondrian's *Composition London*, 1940–42, received its present title from J. J. Sweeney in 1945 according to Robert Welsh, "because Mondrian had said that the painting was begun during the blitz in London." § The grouping of vertical and horizontal lines is heavier to the right than to the left, but the over-all effect is that the grid is more uniformly distributed than in the pungent asymmetries of earlier pictures. The evenness of the grid prepares the way for the continuous surface activity of Mondrian's last paintings done in New York. This important painting is the last in which the grid is black; in

* Heinz Mack, *Mackazin*, 1957–1967 (n.d., unpaged).

† Although the collection is strong in American Pop art, there is comparatively little European art of this kind so that, for instance, Pistoletto, represented by an excellent work, is somewhat apart from the collection.

‡ In a letter dated December 8, 1950.

§ Robert P. Welsh, *Mondrian 1872–1944* (Art Gallery of Toronto, 1966). Welsh points out that the open squares of color on the left edge were added in New York.

the four pictures done in New York before his death, the grids are either varied in color or broken into rows of colored tesserae.

A group of artists younger than Mondrian, among them a strong contingent of Surrealists, were in New York in the early 1940's, including Salvador Dali, Max Ernst, André Masson, Matta, and Yves Tanguy. Tanguy is exceptionally well represented in the collection, and William Rubin defined the picture accurately when he wrote: "The stately sculptural presences in the foreground space of *Slowly Towards the North* (1942) and *Indefinite Divisibility* (1942) evoke a world more static and stable than the melting metamorphoses of *The Armoire of Proteus* or the primordial germinations of *The Storm*." * Our picture is a good example of the style Tanguy developed in the United States, in which the landscape dissolved progressively as the foreground forms hardened and clarified.

Schwitters's *Difficult*, 1942–43, is one of the most complex and substantially organized of his collages of the period. It might be located between Bauhaus construction, in the way the small image of the wheel is slotted into the radiating composition, for example, and Pop art's sense of the literal object, suggested by the large unmodified image of the Firestone tire. It is a collage full of references to things English, including a fat sample of chocolate wrappers: Pascall's, Rowntree's, Greville Assortment Soft Centres, Nestle's Smokers Semi-Sweet. Aside from these oral pleasures, there are references to monarchy ("By Appointmnt to the Prince of Wales") and its institutions (a letter from the Royal Academy of Arts). Numbers spin around the pictures: "300 Women," "Vat 69," "Four tempting ways to give your child More milk," and a crowd of trim, functional bus tickets. These evocations seem as much a part of the meaning of the work as its stringent interlocking of planes and the shifting nuances of tonal color.

Another late work by a master of earlier twentieth-century art is Willi Baumeister's *Growing*, 1952; it is a powerful summary of his later concerns, with texture—as a pliant generative part of the picture and with evocative imagery, sometimes archaic, sometimes, as here, connoting a botanical cycle of life. Fernand Léger's *Walking Flower*, 1951, one of his tough and incisive ceramic sculptures of the fifties, probably influenced Appel's sculpture, such as *Person and Flower*, 1967, in the collection (and may have led to Roy Lichtenstein's ceramics of the sixties). In 1955 Dubuffet moved from his dense and loaded *hautes pâtes* to *tableaux d'assemblage*, from which William Seitz derived the title for his exhibition *The Art of Assemblage*, at The Museum of Modern Art in 1961. He cut up paintings and assembled the parts in crystalline forms redolent of the landscape of Vence: "The grasses and tiny plants growing alongside the roadside, the roads themselves, and the feet of walls." † *Path Bordered by Grass*, 1956, shows exactly the closeup of nature and the pictorial distinctness of this phase of Dubuffet's art.

In Picasso's *The Artist and His Model*, 1964, the model appears to be Jacqueline Roque; the picture is, in any case, one of the artist's ongoing meditations on the connections of art and life and on sexuality as a metaphor of the creative act. The model's pose is slumped and impacted, a

* William S. Rubin, *Dada and Surrealist Art* (New York: The Museum of Modern Art, undated), p. 374.

† Jean Dubuffet, in *Jean Dubuffet Paintings* (Arts Council of Great Britain, 1966), p. 44.

pile up of anatomy, while the artist, with a diminished body is nonetheless frontal and compact. It is a theme Picasso has referred to continually since the twenties and our picture can, perhaps, be connected with one of the initiating works, *The Studio*, 1927–28 (The Museum of Modern Art, New York). The earlier picture is larger and wider but there are similarities of placing which characterize Picasso's way of handling recurrent motifs; there is plenty of surface change, but beneath is an infrastructure of great stability. In both pictures, the artist occupies the left third of the painting and the model's head is in profile in the upper right. Further than that, the main directional links are the model's raised hand, the triangular form of which corresponds to a compotier in the earlier picture, and the model's near leg, which runs across the picture at an angle close to that of the tablecloth in the earlier piece. In style, however, it belongs fully to Picasso's late, *brut* manner, in which a lifetime's painting takes the form less of mastery than of imperial impatience. Since Picasso knows all the things he can do with his late Cubist vocabulary, he takes the forms only part way, leaving them at indeterminate points between pictorial logic and summary encoding.

Piet Mondrian

"Gradually I became aware that Cubism did not accept the logical consequences of its own discoveries; it was not developing abstraction toward its
ultimate goal, the expression of pure reality. I felt that this reality can only
be established through *pure plastics*. In its essential expression, pure plastics
is unconditioned by subjective feeling and conception. It took me a long
time to discover that particularities of form and natural color evoke subjective states of feeling, which obscure *pure reality*. The appearance of natural forms changes but reality remains constant. To create pure reality plastic-
ally, it is necessary to reduce natural forms to the *constant elements* of form
and natural color to *primary color*. The aim is not to create other particular
forms and colors with all their limitations, but to work toward abolishing
them in the interest of a larger unity." *

From the moment of his encounter with Cubism in 1911, Mondrian dedicated himself to a systematic purification of all particular and nonessential
elements from his art. By 1913, he had arrived at the balance of horizontal
and vertical elements that characterized his entire later production. By 1918,
he had devised a format of colored rectangles bounded by black lines from
which he deviated only in his last few paintings, completed in New York.

Composition London, 1940–42, is a transitional work between the Paris
paintings of the late 1930's and those done in New York. Though begun in
London, the small red square at the middle of the left edge, unbounded by
black, undoubtedly was added in New York, since it predicts his last paintings, in which black was eliminated. The division of space in the composition is related to several drawings made in London, and the concentration of
vertical lines at the right reappeared in several canvases left unfinished at his
death. A second small area of red, bordered by black lines, appears at the
left directly beneath the first; the large square at the right is blue, and the
one beneath it is yellow.

*Pieter Cornelis Mondriaan was born in 1872, in Amersfort, The Netherlands.
He received some early instruction from his father, an amateur draftsman,
and his uncle, Frits Mondriaan, a painter. After becoming qualified, by state
examination, to teach primary and secondary school drawing, he moved to
Amsterdam in 1892, where he studied painting and drawing at the Academy
of Fine Arts until 1896. Mondrian remained in Amsterdam (except for brief
stays in various Dutch provincial regions), painting and occasionally exhibiting in group shows, until 1908, when he settled in Zeeland. In 1909, he
joined a Theosophic organization whose philosophy acknowledged a dualism between physical matter and its supersensible essence. The development of Mondrian's desire to push abstraction toward its ultimate goal, "the
expression of pure reality," was significantly influenced by this group.*

*In 1910, he was one of the founders of the Moderne Kunstkring, which
in 1911 organized an exhibition of French avant-garde painting, especially
Cubist work by Braque and Picasso, which so impressed Mondrian that, in
1912, he established his studio in Paris. Visiting in Holland when World
War I began, he was prevented from leaving and lived in the artist's colony*

---

* "Toward the True Vision of Reality" (1942), in *Piet Mondrian: The Documents of
Modern Art* (New York Wittenborn, 1945).

MONDRIAN *Composition London* **1940–42**
Oil on canvas, 32½ x 28 in. (82.5 x 71.1 cm.)
Room of Contemporary Art Fund   RCA11:10

at Laren. In 1915, he met Theo van Doesburg, with whom he organized the
De Stijl group in 1916–17. For the next ten years (until Van Doesburg reintroduced diagonal elements into his own painting), they worked and exhibited together and wrote in defense of an art (Neo-Plasticism) based on
straight lines, right angles, and primary colors that would integrate the fine
arts, architecture, and design.

In 1919, Mondrian returned to Paris, where he exhibited with the Cercle
et Carré group (1930) and joined the Abstraction-Création group founded
in 1931 by Georges Vantongerloo and Auguste Herbin. In 1938, he settled
in London, but he was soon forced by wartime conditions to emigrate to the
United States. Arriving in New York in October, 1940, he lost no time in
setting up a studio and, two years later, received his first one-man show. He
wrote several important essays during this period summing up his views on
Neo-Plasticism. In 1944, Mondrian died in New York.

Joan Miró

Woman and Bird in the Night, 1945, contains particularly poetic and romantic themes that recur frequently in Miró's work of the 1940's. Painted after he had completed the exacting, structurally intricate series of gouaches known as the Constellations (1941), it appears, in contrast, particularly free and spontaneous, containing rough brush marks, splashes, and drips. The bright colors are subordinated to the linear character of the work, which is emphasized by Miró's use of a white ground. At the time, he frequently used the device of capitalizing on an accidental, unconscious mark or splash, carefully calculating and directing in the second stage the development of his images. The resulting balance between spontaneity and control is central to Woman and Bird in the Night, where the graceful arabesque of the central form contrasts with the "brutal" brush marks and the precisely delineated rhythmic signs. Miró's imagery—stylized eyes, stars, sexual symbols, etc.—has evolved into a form of personal shorthand with which he is able to express human content in vivid plastic terms, for it is not in his nature to be satisfied with the purely abstract exploration of formal values.

Also in the Gallery collection is Carnival of Harlequin, a painting of 1924–25.

Joan Miró was born in 1893 in Montroig, near Barcelona, son of a goldsmith and watchmaker. He studied at the School of Fine Arts in Barcelona, 1907, where his teachers, Modesto Urgell and José Pasco, encouraged in him a romantic approach to nature and an interest in primitive Catalan art, which had a lifelong influence on his work. In 1912, he enrolled at the art academy of Francisco Gali in Barcelona, where he met as a fellow student José Llorens Artigas, the master potter with whom he was to collaborate in later years. Barcelona at the turn of the century had a lively artistic community, and, through the Dalmau Gallery, Miró became acquainted with Cubist works, as well as those of the Post-Impressionists and Fauves. In 1919, Miró made his first visit to Paris, where he met Picasso, and, from 1920 on, he was to spend his winters in Paris and his summers at his family's farm in Montroig.

Miró's earliest paintings in Paris were precisely rendered, primitive-inspired Catalan landscapes and farm scenes, but his friendship with the Surrealist poets and painters in 1924 led him to experiment with hallucinatory and dream-inspired art. He exhibited with the Surrealists in 1925, and, though he disdained the political activities of the group, was regarded by André Breton as "the most 'surrealist' of us all." The outbreak of the Spanish Civil War prevented Miro from returning to Spain until 1940, when he had to flee to Barcelona from the German invasion of Paris.

In 1947 Miró visited the United States for the first time, where he received much recognition that, in the following decade, was to turn into international acclaim. Following his penchant for sensual manipulation of materials, Miró devoted the years 1955–59 entirely to creating ceramics with the help of his friend Artigas. Since 1956 he has lived and worked in Palma de Mallorca.

MIRÓ *Woman and Bird in the Night* **1945**
Oil on canvas, 51 x 64 in. (129.5 x 162.5 cm.)
Gift of Seymour H. Knox   K58:10

Kurt Schwitters

Difficult, 1942–43, is a late collage, created at a time when Schwitters's life was touched with hardship and tragedy. Living in exile in London, he supported himself by painting portraits; in 1943, his life's work, the *Merzbau* in Hanover, was destroyed by bombs. It is probable that the images of the airplane, the pistol, and the generally explosive composition of this collage make reference to the devastation of war. Characteristically, however, Schwitters combined humble materials of every sort in *Difficult*: chocolate wrappers, a whiskey label, bus tickets, newsprint, advertisements, bits of lace, scraps of transparent and textured papers—all metamorphosed into a work of art. Through a process of overlapping and superimposing opaque and transparent materials, a complex spatial mesh was developed—essentially the shallow relief space of Cubism but lacking Cubism's central object. Schwitters was a skilled typesetter, and also a poet with a special Dada interest in fragmented words and sounds. Both of these talents enriched his manipulation of printed matter, even in his later pieces, when he was no longer working with his native language.

Kurt Schwitters was born in 1887, in Hanover, which was to remain his home until he was forced to flee Nazi Germany in 1937. He studied at the School of Arts and Crafts, Hanover, 1908, and at the academies in Dresden and Berlin, 1909–14. His early painting was influenced by Expressionism and Cubism; but, by 1918, he was painting abstractly. In 1919, he created his first Merz picture, an assemblage of paper, rags, parts of machinery, lace, and other elements, held together by nails and glue. Merz, a nonsense word originally derived from the German word "Kommerz" (commerce), came to be used by Schwitters for all his artistic activity. Throughout the 1920's and early 1930's, this activity encompassed poetry (written and recited), theater, children's books, and lecturing, as well as the publishing of his own magazine, Merz, and the creation of the Merzbau, a fantastic assemblage that assumed architectural proportions and eventually took over two floors of Schwitters's house. Among his friends were many members of Dada and De Stijl, but Schwitters's Dada activities were somewhat tempered by his lack of interest in the political role of art. Politics caught up with him, however, when, in 1937, some of his work was confiscated and burned by the Nazi government, and four paintings were included in the exhibition Degenerate Art in Munich. Schwitters had spent summers in Norway, and it was there that he first went in 1937, only to escape again to England when the Germans occupied Norway in 1940. After a seventeen-month internment in British camps, Schwitters settled in his son's home in London. When his health started to fail in 1944, he moved to Ambleside, Westmoreland, where he died in 1948.

SCHWITTERS *Difficult* **1942–43**
Collage, 31¼ x 24 in. (79.4 x 61 cm.)
Gift of The Seymour H. Knox Foundation, Inc.   65:14

Yves Tanguy

Indefinite Divisibility, 1942, is one of several similar works that Tanguy painted after his arrival in the United States in which his characteristic forms have increased in size and dominate the foreground. These bizarre constructions, neither animal nor machine, seem to tower over a vast plain, the depth of which is indicated by a series of flat bowls shown in perspective. Tanguy's palette, previously cool and restrained, has become more abrasive, with metallic blue, red, green, and deep yellow highlighting the over-all gray. Paint has been applied with a painstaking meticulousness reminiscent of the early Flemish painters whom Tanguy admired. In his craftsmanship, he differed from those Surrealists who advocated uncontrolled and spontaneous processes directed by the subconscious. Nevertheless, except for a brief period when he made preparatory drawings on the canvas, he followed them in working intuitively, allowing one form to dictate another as the painting progressed. "I found that if I planned a picture beforehand, it never surprised me, and surprises are my pleasure in painting." * The strong shadows cast by the forms, indicating a source of light from the upper right, are carefully and realistically rendered.

Raymond Georges Yves Tanguy was born in Paris in 1900, the son of a retired sea captain. According to the artist, he was born in a bed that had belonged to Gustave Courbet, the nineteenth-century painter whose dedication to realism is in complete contrast to Tanguy's unreal objects in an equally unreal space. As a boy, he was a schoolmate of Pierre Matisse, son of the painter, who became his lifelong friend and dealer. He spent his childhood vacations at Locronan, in Brittany, where the landscape and prehistoric stone monuments undoubtedly influenced the images in his later paintings.

From 1918 to 1920, Tanguy followed the family tradition and became an apprentice officer on cargo boats traveling to Africa and South America. He was drafted into the Army in 1920, serving for two years, where he met Jacques Prévert, later a poet and film-maker, who remained a close friend during the next years in Paris. Undecided on a career, Tanguy concluded that he would become a painter one day in 1923 when he saw an early metaphysical painting by De Chirico in a gallery window. In 1925, he met André Breton, the leader and chief theoretician of the Surrealist group, which he soon joined. In 1927, Tanguy, self-taught as an artist, began to develop his particular version of a limitless space where strange objects rest or float in a stark light, and this remained, with many variations, his subject matter throughout his lifetime.

Tanguy emigrated to the United States in 1939, married the American Surrealist painter Kay Sage, and lived in Woodbury, Connecticut, until his death in 1955.

* Soby, *Yves Tanguy* (New York: The Museum of Modern Art, 1955), p. 17.

TANGUY *Indefinite Divisibility* **1942**
Oil on canvas, 40 x 35 in. (101.6 x 88.9 cm.)
Room of Contemporary Art Fund RCA45:2

Matta

Poly-joueurs des cartes (Card Players), c. 1957, was painted after the period in the 1940's when Matta depicted recognizable, though fantastic, figures in his work. In later paintings, these are reduced to purely mechanical gestures, essences of the anthropomorphized cosmic forces that have constituted his subject matter. Painting in muted tones of blue, gray, and green, Matta created an ambiguous, etherlike space, mysteriously illuminated from within and structured by angled planes. A circular field of motion is activated by the images revolving around a central, gemlike constellation, and the energetic, swirling lines that intensify in the upper portion of the canvas. Although his symbolism eludes interpretation, the title itself reflects the common Surrealist fascination with the concepts of chance and accident, and is probably a pun on Descartes, whose rationalistic philosophy was the antithesis of the Surrealists.

Roberto Sebastián Antonio Matta Echaurren was born in 1912, in Santiago, Chile, of French and Spanish descent. At his family's insistence, he studied architecture instead of painting and received his degree from the National University in 1931. In 1933–35, he went to Paris as an apprentice to Le Corbusier. Matta had begun drawing in 1936, and the following year the Spanish poet García Lorca introduced him to Salvador Dali, through whom he met André Breton. He soon joined the Surrealists, whose guiding principle of automatism influenced him to begin painting "inscapes," fantastic landscapes of the inner self, in which psychological states are rendered in brilliant colors. In 1939, he went to New York, and there joined the other Surrealist artists in exile from Europe. Matta was one of several in this group whose influence on the Abstract Expressionists was considerable: in intellectual daring, in technique—automatism and the exploitation of painterly "accidents"—and in the development of shapes derived from the subconscious. During the war years, he became increasingly aware of the physical sciences and expressed the opinion that a new school of painting would evolve from contemporary physics, just as Surrealism had evolved from modern psychology. The artist's role, he believes, is to aid in integrating the discoveries of science within a cosmic framework. As he explored these ideas in paintings, he created a new demonology of technological creatures.

In 1949, Matta returned to Europe. He makes his home in Paris and Rome.

MATTA *Poly-joueurs des cartes* c. 1957. Oil on canvas, 55¼ x 89 in. (140.3 x 226 cm.)
Charles Clifton Fund 62:6

213

Nicolas De Staël

In 1953, De Staël moved to a château in Vaucluse, in the south of France. *Landscape in Vaucluse No. 2* dates from that year. Shortly before, he had begun to heighten his palette, rejecting his earlier muted colors. The forms also had become more simplified than those of the late 1940's, although he continued to render his view of the natural world by means of abstract compositional elements. He employed several kinds of knives to apply paint, including a spatula and putty knife as well as the conventional painting knife—a technique that resulted in a highly tactile surface. In this *Landscape*, the central portion of the painting, which suggests buildings and trees, is more thickly painted than the upper and lower portions, which probably represent sky and sand, respectively.

Nicolas de Staël was born in St. Petersburg, in 1914, son of a prominent family that was forced to go into exile in Poland during the Russian Revolution, where his father died in 1920 and his mother in 1922. He and his two sisters were then reared by friends of the family in Brussels, where De Staël studied at the Académie Royale des Beaux-Arts, 1932–33. For the next several years, he traveled in Holland, France, Spain, Italy, and Morocco. He served in the Foreign Legion at the beginning of World War II, settling in France after he was demobilized in 1940. During his travels, he visited the museums and galleries of Europe, in the meantime constantly drawing and painting, though he destroyed most of his early work. After the war, he experimented with complete abstraction but soon determined to combine the freedom of abstract compositional elements with visual experiences of the natural world. He worked with black and muted colors until 1950, when he began to brighten his palette, which became rich and luminous in the few years remaining before he committed suicide in 1955.

DE STAËL *Landscape in Vaucluse No. 2* 1953
Oil on canvas, 25 x 32 in. (63.5 x 81.3 cm.)
Gift of The Seymour H. Knox Foundation, Inc. 69:11

Afro

In *Fear of the Night*, 1952, two symbolic figures, male and female, and un-indentifiable demonic shapes are depicted. The predominant colors in the painting are pink, blue, and black, and the images are delineated by sensitive black lines.

Afro attempts to convey emotion as remembered. He has said, "Often I think of myself as a storytelling painter. If my most hidden feelings, my memories, my opinions, my intolerances, my faults and terrors, can be condensed into the course of a line, into the luminous quality of a tone, then the mysterious flow of my entire being into painting might be willfully reversed so that all my images could go back to the very origins of my life. . . . I want the sensation of things, the symbols of reality to regain the warmth of a forgotten sentiment within the certainty of pure form." *

Also in the collection is a 1948 painting, *Concertino*.

Afro Balsadella was born in Udine, Italy, in 1912. His father and uncle were decorators, specializing in the ceilings of Venetian mansions, and his brothers Mirko and Dino became sculptors. At the age of eight, Afro joined the family business and, after studying in Florence and Venice, continued to work as a decorator until 1937, when he turned to easel painting. His early paintings were traditional in both subject and composition. By the early forties, he had simplified the forms and altered the traditional concept of space in his work, and, in 1946–47, actual objects began to be replaced by symbols. In 1950 he visited the United States, where he was particularly impressed by the paintings of Gorky and Miró. In his subsequent work, he developed an interest in colors and rhythms derived from the subconscious. His paintings became further simplified in line and color during the 1960's.

* Andrew C. Ritchie, *The New Decade* (New York: The Museum of Modern Art, 1955) p. 79.

AFRO *Fear of the Night* **1952**
Oil on canvas, 69 x 57 in. (175.2 x 144.8 cm.)
Gift of Seymour H. Knox   K56:1

Sonia Delaunay

"Robert Delaunay and I continue the tradition of *real* visual paintings, which is neither literary nor sophisticated. We disengaged color from all its foreign elements and it became a means of expression, pure like notes in music and words in poetry.

"Taking this ABC of color, there are infinite possibilities of new creation. A poetry expressed by the means of color. It is the logical development from Impressionism, Neo-Impressionism, Fauvism, leading to Orphism—simultaneous colors—to the abstract—pure poetry." *

Colored Rhythm No. 698, 1958, is one of a series of paintings that Sonia Delaunay produced in the 1950's in which squares, triangles, and bisected circles of color create a rhythmic movement along diagonal axes. Continuing her lifelong interest in color, the artist has here used the brilliant shades of red, green, and blue—combined with white, in sharp contrast to the black background—that she frequently employs. A quasi-geometrical composition, the forms are soft-edged, and, though basic shapes are repeated, the repetitions are approximate rather than precise; the proportions of each triangle, circle, or square vary throughout the composition.

Sonia Terk Delaunay was born in the Russian Ukraine, in 1885, and was reared in St. Petersburg by her maternal uncle. She was particularly interested in mathematics but was encouraged in art by her drawing teacher and studied design in Karlsruhe, Germany, 1903–5, and at the Académie de la Palette in Paris, 1905. In 1910, she married Robert Delaunay. Their marriage was an unusual artistic collaboration, marked by a free exchange of ideas that shaped the work of both artists. Together, they explored the expressive qualities of color, their interaction, and the effect of light on color. "Color alone is both form and subject," Robert Delaunay stated, and his lyrical paintings led Guillaume Apollinaire to name the new movement "Orphism." Delaunay was the founder, joined by his wife, Frank Kupka, Patrick Henry Bruce, Maurice Raynal, Morgan Russell, and Stanton Mac-Donald-Wright.

In addition to paintings and graphics, Sonia Delaunay has worked in numerous allied fields—interior decoration, ceramics, book design, tapestry, stage costume, and dress design. Sonia Delaunay lives and works in Paris. Her husband died in 1941.

* Letter from the artist, August 27, 1970.

DELAUNAY *Colored Rhythm No. 698* **1958**
Oil on canvas, 45 x 34 in. (114.3 x 86.4 cm.)
Gift of Seymour H. Knox K64:23

Pierre Soulages

In *4 July 1956*, Soulages has developed a patterning of broad, angular black strokes against a more thinly painted background, to which blue and warm gray were added. In his spontaneous method of working, he approaches his canvas with no preconceived idea of the finished painting, but starts from a single brushstroke that evokes another and another, until the final form emerges. He has said, "I work guided by an inner impulse, a longing for certain forms, colors, materials, and it is not until they are on the canvas that they tell me what I want. It is what I do that teaches me what I am seeking." * Although this approach would seem similar to that of the action painters, the resemblance is superficial. When compared with the brash and impetuous canvases of the Abstract Expressionists, Soulage's paintings appear highly disciplined, austere, and meticulously balanced.

In *4 July 1956*, movement exists on two levels—a surface motion is generated by the black, slashing strokes, which, in turn, compose a dark form that appears to emerge from the background toward the spectator, creating a third dimension.

A second painting by Soulages, *3 April 1954*, is also in the collection.

Pierre Soulages was born in 1919, in Rodez, southwest France. As a boy, he became interested in prehistoric, Celt, and Romanesque art—all well represented in that area. After finishing high school, he went to Paris in 1938, where he studied briefly at the École des Beaux-Arts. Though impressed by his introduction to contemporary art, particularly exhibitions of work by Cézanne and Picasso, he was discouraged by the academic teaching at the Beaux-Arts and returned to Rodez. He served in the French Army, 1939–40, and spent the Occupation years working as a farmer near Montpellier. During this time, he did no painting but read extensively in French poetry. Joseph Déteil introduced him to Sonia Delaunay, and, through her, he first became acquainted with theories of abstract painting. In 1946, he moved to Courbevoie, near Paris, and, within two years, he had developed his individual abstract style of painting massive black forms, rendered in bold, sweeping strokes against a light ground. He has continued this basic theme, gradually employing more complex forms, increased luminosity and monumentality, and a wider range of color.

* Andrew C. Ritchie, *The New Decade* (New York: The Museum of Modern Art, 1955), p. 39.

SOULAGES *4 July 1956* **1956**
Oil on canvas, 51 x 38 in. (129.5 x 96.5 cm.)
Gift of Seymour H. Knox K56:13

221

Jean Dubuffet

M. Plume, Portrait of Henri Michaux, 1947, is one of a series of portraits by Dubuffet of leading poets and writers of his generation. Although many of his paintings of the human figure can be interpreted as portrayals of man as a genus rather than an individual, the paintings of his friends bear a strong resemblance to the sitters. Henri Michaux is depicted with a serious expression, wrinkles indicated at the eyes, forehead, and mouth. The shape of his head suggests a heavy growth of hair at the sides. The figure, dressed in shirt, tie, and jacket and rendered with a strict frontality, is dominated by an oversize head. The background of the painting, to which pebbles were added, is of a rougher texture than the figure.

Also in the collection are a painting-collage of 1956, *Path Bordered by Grass*, and a sculpture, *Borne au logos VII*, 1967 (p. 188).

Jean Dubuffet, born in Le Havre, in 1901, began painting at the age of seventeen and studied briefly at the Académie Julian, Paris. He lived in Montparnasse, where, in addition to painting, he read widely in ethnology, paleography, and ancient and modern literature. After seven years, he abandoned painting and became a wine merchant. During the thirties, he painted again for a short time, but it was not until 1942 that he began the work which has distinguished him as an outstanding innovator in postwar European painting.

Dubuffet's interest in art brut, the art of the insane, and that of the untrained person, whether a caveman or the originator of contemporary graffiti, led him to emulate this directly expressive and untutored style in his own work. His paintings from the early forties in brightly colored oils were soon followed by works in which he employed such unorthodox materials as cement, plaster, tar, and asphalt—scraped, carved, and cut and drawn upon with a rudimentary, spontaneous line. Variations of this method of working preoccupied him until 1962, when he wrote and illustrated a book, L'Hourloupe, in which he evolved a new stylistic and ideological concept for his later work, both paintings and plastic sculpture.

In addition to his paintings and sculptures, Dubuffet has been a prolific writer, the author of several volumes of essays and letters that are poetic and whimsical in spirit, comparable to his work as a painter.

DUBUFFET *M. Plume, Portrait of Henri Michaux* 1947
Mixed media on wood, 43 x 34¾ in. (109.2 x 88.3 cm.)
Gift of the Charles E. Merrill Trust and Elisabeth H. Gates Fund RCA67:2

223

Jean-Paul Riopelle

In Riopelle's paintings of the 1950's, he employed a technique of working with a knife by which he spread a number of colors on the canvas with a single stroke, creating a prismatic effect. By the time he painted *Preo* in 1964, the paint was more loosely handled, the individual patches of color had become larger, and the areas in which a single color predominated had increased in size. In addition to black and white, red, green, blue, and ocher were used in *Preo*. The paint was applied impulsively, and a richly textured surface was retained.

Composition in White, a 1955 painting by the artist, is also in the Gallery collection.

Jean-Paul Riopelle was born in Montreal, Canada, in 1923. He was self-educated as an artist, and his paintings before 1944 were traditional landscapes, figure studies, and still lifes. In 1940, when he was seventeen, he became cofounder with Paul-Emile Borduas of the Automatists, a Surrealist-inspired group of young Canadian painters searching for a free and unconventional approach to painting. Riopelle's experiments with abstraction were encouraged by the contemporary paintings he saw in 1946 during trips to France, Germany, and the United States. In 1947, he settled permanently in Paris, where he began to paint in a Tachiste style. From sweeping, gestural brushstrokes, he turned to applying paint in a colorful pattern of daubs. By 1953, he had begun to use a knife to spread these bits of pigment into a mosaic-like surface. This method of working became less rigidly controlled in subsequent years, although the shimmering paint surface was retained.

Even Riopelle's most abstract works are said to be derived from nature: a pool of water, an Alpine glacier, a sandy beach, or a segment of marine life is translated into an abstract harmony of light and color.

In addition to his paintings in oil, gouache, and watercolor, he has made a series of abstract bronze sculptures, begun in 1960.

RIOPELLE *Preo* 1964
Oil on canvas, 84 x 84 in. (113.4 x 113.4 cm.)
Gift of The Seymour H. Knox Foundation, Inc.   66:7

225

Karel Appel

Karel Appel has written that his painting *Flight*, 1954, depicts "the desire to fly away from this planet into space." * Based on the human figure, which began to appear in Appel's work around 1952, two "persons" are shown. The one indicated in the right background appears to be flying, and is painted as though seen through a blurred lens. The figure at the left is static and has a disproportionately large head and a typically Appelesque face with twisted mouth, hair standing on end, and enlarged, penetrating eyes. The bright colors, applied in uneven, heavy strokes, accentuate the dramatic content of the painting.

Also in the Gallery collection are an additional oil, *Fire World*, 1957, and a sculpture, *Personage and Flower*, 1967.

Karel Appel was born in 1921 in Amsterdam, where he studied at the State Academy of Fine Arts, 1940–43. His early work was influenced by Picasso, Braque, and, more importantly, Dubuffet. In the summer of 1948, Appel was cofounder, with Constant Nieuwenhuys and Corneille, of the Experimental Group in Amsterdam and, in November of the same year, participated in the founding of the Cobra group in Paris. In 1950, Appel moved to Paris and has continued to live in France.

During the Cobra years, his subjects were often animals, expressive of both symbolic and mythological content. In the 1950's, he turned more frequently to landscape and human figures, and he developed his free and unrestrained application of paint, using a knife as well as a brush, and sometimes applying pigment directly from the tube.

In addition to his paintings, in recent years Appel has been working in polychrome sculpture and reliefs, ceramics, and stained glass.

* Letter from the artist, November 28, 1968.

226

APPEL *Flight* **1954**
Oil on burlap, 43⅜ x 55⅛ in. (110.2 x 140 cm.)
Gift of Seymour H. Knox K55:1

Pierre Alechinsky

In *Greet the North, Greet the South*, 1962, Alechinsky has continued to follow the Cobra principles of spontaneous paint application and the depiction of unpremeditated images. His primary interest is in line, and the surface of the canvas—portions of which remain unpainted—is a twisting, frenzied mass of strokes made with broad and narrow brushes. In some areas, another variation appears as the blunt end of the brush or a similar object has been drawn across the paint. Although natural forms are not recognizably rendered, a variety of human and animal faces and figures are indicated.

Pierre Alechinsky was born in 1927 in Brussels, where he studied book illustration at the École National Superiéure d'Architecture et des Arts Décoratifs in Brussels, 1944-47. He joined the Cobra group in 1949, and, although the members of the group went their separate ways three years later, Alechinsky has continued to follow their expressionistic approach to painting.

Alechinsky moved to Paris in 1951, studying etching with Stanley Hayter at Atelier 17. He has also studied calligraphy and, in 1955, made a film in Japan of the Japanese masters of this art. In addition to painting and drawing, in which he is particularly interested, he has written extensively on art and poetry. In his more recent work, Alechinsky has combined oil or acrylic painting with a border of drawings surrounding the major portion of the canvas.

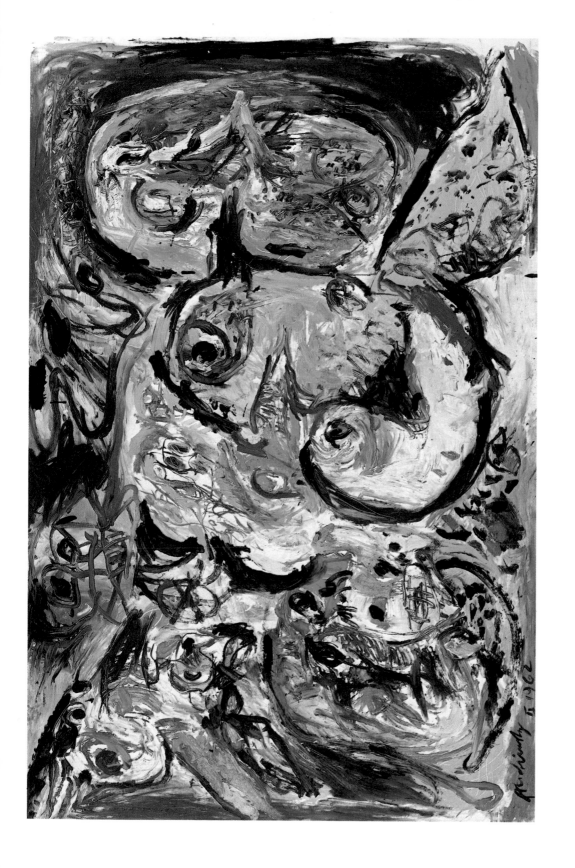

ALECHINSKY *Greet the North, Greet the South* 1962. Oil on canvas, 53 x 81 in. (134.6 x 102.9 cm.)
Gift of Seymour H. Knox K62:10

Asger Jorn

Untitled, 1961, is one of a large group of Jorn's works in which the movement of color, line, and areas of light dominates the artist's concerns. Inspired by the images of Nordic myths and legends, magic, and strange cults, Jorn has attempted to portray his visionary world in a direct and expressive manner, using primary colors and spontaneous, uneven application of paint. As in much of his work from this period, the painting is abstract, differing in this respect from the frequently figurative canvases of his Cobra colleagues.

Asger Jorn was born in Vejrun, Denmark, in 1914, and spent his early years in Tilkeborg and Copenhagen, where he studied painting and taught briefly. In 1936, he went to Paris, where he studied with Fernand Léger, but the School of Paris had little influence on him. Jorn's work is more closely related to the Scandinavian tradition and the work of Ensor and Klee that he saw during the war years when he lived in Denmark.

By the mid-1940's, Jorn had developed a basic iconography that includes images of phantasmogorical heads and bodies, and animals and flowers transformed into archetypal symbols—images inspired by Nordic legends and myths. In 1948, he became a cofounder of the Cobra group; his work is less figurative than that of other Cobra artists, but he shared with them the emphasis on free expression, energetic brushstrokes, and brilliant color. In 1953, he began working in ceramics, and his later paintings have incorporated the bright, shiny quality of ceramic glazes.

JORN *Untitled* **1961**
Oil on canvas, 38¾ x 51½ in. (98.5 x 130.8 cm.)
Gift of Seymour H. Knox   K62:12

Corneille

Beginning of Summer, 1962, as the title indicates, may be interpreted as a stylized landscape with the colors and shapes of plants and garden paths suggested, possibly as seen from an aerial view. The amoebalike shapes are thinly painted, except in the central and upper right areas, where the pigment has been rather thickly applied. *Beginning of Summer* is a colorful painting, although the artist used relatively little pure color, achieving his effects by placing one color on top of another and making extensive use of black and gray to intensify the quality of the more brilliant hues. As is true of *Beginning of Summer*, Corneille's paintings are usually less gestural and more formally organized than those of the other Cobra painters, though he shared their interest in brilliant color and simple shapes.

Corneille (Cornelis van Beverloo) was born in Luik, Belgium, in 1922, the son of Dutch parents. Except for brief periods of study at the State Academy of Fine Arts in Amsterdam, between 1940 and 1953, and at Stanley Hayter's Atelier 17 in Paris, 1953, Corneille is self-taught. In 1948, he was a cofounder (with Appel, Alechinsky, Jorn, and the poet Christian Dotremont) of Cobra, and exhibited with that group the following year at the Stedelijk Museum, Amsterdam, before moving to Paris in 1950, where he has continued to live. His earlier work was spontaneous; as his mature style developed, he retained a free and lyrical approach, but with the addition of a more patterned and controlled design. He usually begins his paintings from a subject in nature; during the early 1960's the subjects were transformed into basically abstract forms, while works from later years were more directly figurative.

CORNEILLE *Beginning of Summer* **1962**
Oil on canvas, 31¾ x 39¼ in. (80.6 x 99.7 cm.)
Gift of Seymour H. Knox K62:11

Carl-Henning Pedersen

Pedersen's paintings are the expression of an imaginary and poetic dream-world, filled with mysterious images drawn from his personal and unique mythology. He frequently depicts a bird that, he has said, represents freedom, and it is a symbol that has appeared in his work from his earliest paintings. In *Flying Bird*, 1951, the creature is shown with a disproportionately large head and body, presumably supported by one tiny wing, and hovering over a strange landscape that could be interpreted as waves or hills, with the three pointed structures at the right possibly representing buildings, or, perhaps, a castle. Although the black background implies a night scene, a stylized sun is shown with rays that echo the pointed, triangular motifs that reappear throughout the design.

Born in Copenhagen, in 1913, Carl-Henning Pedersen is a self-taught painter of fantasies. His work changed abruptly in 1939 from Cubist-influenced compositions in low-keyed color to expressionistic, lyrical paintings of imaginary landscapes, unreal figures, and fanciful animals. During the 1940's, he made extensive use of line, with color as a secondary element—roles that were reversed in the 1950's, when color began to dominate his canvases. He became a member of the Cobra group in 1948 and exhibited with those artists; however, his work evolves from a highly personal and mystical vision, mixed with elements of Nordic symbolism that preclude any significant influence by other artists or movements.

In recent years, he has made numerous spontaneous drawings and watercolors and begun and finished even large paintings in a single day, in accordance with his belief that the images should be transferred as quickly as possible from his imagination to the finished work of art.

PEDERSEN *Flying Bird* **1951**
Oil on canvas, 48 x 40½ in. (121.9 x 102.9 cm.)
Gift of Seymour H. Knox   K64:12

Max Bill

Max Bill's paintings are based on geometric abstraction, often involving the use of mathematical formulas. Having borrowed the concept of Concrete art from Van Doesburg, Bill has sought to create an art that arises out of its own internal laws and necessities with regard to structure and the ordering of color, space, and light. The resulting work has been highly cerebral and spiritual in its quest for proportion and harmony.

Field of 32 Parts in 4 Colors, 1965, is a square painting—the format favored by Bill for its unequivocal, objective nature. It is divided into four equal quadrants, each, in turn, bisected along the horizontal axis and on the diagonal. The resulting rectangles are again divided diagonally, and the remaining right triangles are divided finally in half. In a veritable color exercise in trigonometry, Bill has alternated the colors in such a way that no two symmetrically opposed triangles bear the same color, each of the four colors—green, blue, orange, and pink—being used once in each shape. The hard-edged triangles with evenly painted surfaces are arranged to form a central diamond shape and create a visual spaciousness and sense of depth within the otherwise tight surface arrangement.

Also in the collection are two sculptures by Bill, *Construction from a Ring,* 1942–63 (p. 101), and *Continuous Surface in Form of a Column,* 1953–58, and an additional painting, *Nine Fields Divided by Means of Two Colors,* 1968.

Max Bill was born in Winterthur, Switzerland, in 1908, and was trained as a silversmith in the School of Applied Arts, Zurich, 1924–27. He studied architecture at the Bauhaus, 1927–29, where he also attended painting classes taught by Kandinsky, Klee, and Albers. Bill's interest in the combination of architecture, painting, sculpture, and crafts into a harmonious environment began during this period and has continued to the present.

In 1930, he returned to Zurich, where he worked as an architect, sculptor, painter, and industrial designer as well as a writer and teacher. In 1932, he joined the Abstraction-Création group in Paris, and he organized the first international exhibition of Concrete art, in Basel, in 1944. He was one of the founders of the Hochschule für Gestaltung at Ulm, Germany, in 1951; he designed the school buildings and served as director, 1951–56, and then head of the Department of Architecture and Product Design. In 1957, Bill reopened his studio in Zurich, where he still works.

The formal harmony and order of his work and his appreciation of the inherent qualities of various materials place Bill among the outstanding followers and practitioners of the Bauhaus concepts.

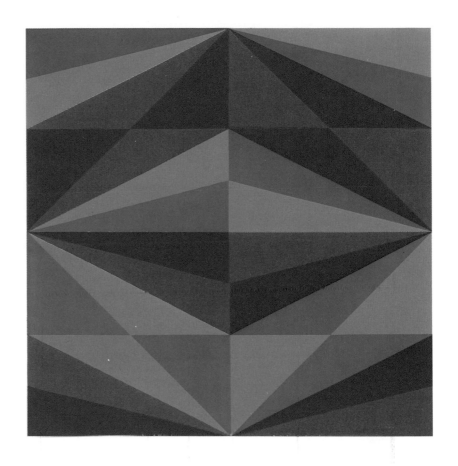

BILL *Field of 32 Parts in 4 Colors* **1965**
Oil on canvas, 52¼ x 52¼ in. (132.7 x 132.7 cm.)
Gift of Seymour H. Knox   K68:9

Gottfried Honegger

"I developed my pictorial structure of today from Cubism. The basic conception of my contemporary work was developed in the years 1958–60 . . . when I lived in New York City. This was also the time when my illusionistic Cubist space conception changed into the concrete space images. The year 1961—the year when your picture *Permanence* was executed—is significant, because at that time I built mathematics, i.e., numerical sequences, into my compositions for the first time. This method of work had developed so far until the present, that now I am trying to program my reliefs and sculpture also.

"Geometrical forms, logical conceptions and numbers are today the basic material of my working method. Furthermore, I am interested in overcoming standardized elements, repetitions and norms. These questions—as it seems to me—are also of significance in connection with our architecture and industrial production. All these legible and provable composition experiments serve the search for an adequate order appropriate for our time. These principles may, however, not be obvious, but may only be sensed as harmony. I do not even refrain from using the word 'beautiful.'

"The use of color and the monochromy of my pictures should put the process of thinking into the background. The manual treatment of the relief makes it possible for the light to supplement, coincidentally, the strict order of my work. The form stands for the measurable, the color stands for the immeasurable.

"Minimal form and color hues shall activate the individual imagination of the spectator." *

Also in the Gallery collection are *Saugus*, 1960, and *Z-611*, 1970.

Gottfried Honegger was born in Zurich, in 1917, but grew up in Engadine, Switzerland. He attended art school in Zurich, 1931–32, and was trained as a decorator, 1932–35. Three years later, he opened a commercial design studio with his wife and also began producing graphics, reliefs, and paintings. He went to New York in 1958, where he worked as a designer, but returned to Europe in 1960 and set up studios in Paris and Zurich.

Intended by the artist as subjects for meditation with spiritual significance, Honegger's works are precise, abstract designs of circles, squares, arcs, and right-angles, often in a single color and incorporating repeated harmonic images. Receptive to new materials and techniques, Honegger has used polyester and other synthetic materials, and industrial processes of sandblasting, stenciling, and casting. Most recently, he has become interested in computer-programmed reliefs and linear designs.

* Letter from the artist, November, 1968.

HONEGGER *Permanence* **1961**
Oil and cardboard collage on canvas, 59 x 59 in. (150 x 150 cm.)
Gift of Seymour H. Knox   K63:3

Auguste Herbin

Vie No. 1 (Life No. 1), 1950, is one of Herbin's many series paintings in which his aim was to express the connotations of a particular word in terms of color and geometric shapes. The development of a "plastic alphabet," as he termed it, occupied the artist for almost twenty years, from the early 1940's until his death in 1960. His brilliantly colored forms, placed in sharp contrast to the background colors, are precisely painted, with no visible evidence of brushstrokes.

Auguste Herbin was born in Quiévy, near Cambrai, France, in 1882. After attending the École des Beaux-Arts in Lille, 1900–1901, he went to Paris, where his early paintings were in the Impressionist and Fauve styles. In 1909, he took a studio in the Bateau Lavoir, where, influenced by Picasso, Braque, and Gris, he began to work in a Cubist manner. As his style evolved, he ceased to use the object as inspiration and turned increasingly to the relationships of color and form. After a return to figurative painting, 1922–25, followed by another period of abstract painting, 1925–39, he devoted himself for the rest of his life to nonobjective abstract composition, developing a kind of pictorial language, a "plastic alphabet" of geometric forms and colors. He painted various series of works on such themes as Life, Evil, Bird, Christ, Christmas, Rose, and Wheat, in which his aim was to express the particular qualities of the word and idea through plastic means. In 1949, he published his theories in a book, L'Art non-figuratif, non-objectif. Herbin died in Paris in 1960.

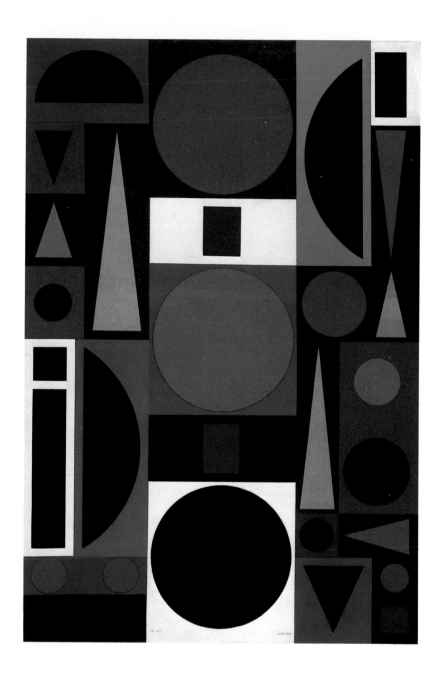

HERBIN *Vie No. 1* **1950**
Oil on canvas, 57 x 38 in. (144.8 x 96.5 cm.)
Gift of The Seymour H. Knox Foundation, Inc. 66:1

Otto Piene

"Any *Fire Flower* is related to a series of Black Suns which I painted with soot from bundles of candles directed at prepared canvases suspended horizontally over my head and with liquids (mainly fixatives) to fix the soot on the canvas in many layers or similar liquids—inflammable ones—that after ignition burnt on the canvas briefly while flowing on it.

"The first Black Suns originated in 1961, after I had already been working with smoke on canvas and paper for about two years. While the work with smoke provided something like negatives to my work with light itself as a medium, the Black Suns and many other paintings I did between 1959 and 1965 can be regarded as retina after-images or negative images of the sun; they can also be regarded as metaphors for any expanding, vibrating, pulsating volume or force. Current microphotography shows that they closely resemble pictures of human eggs in the state of fertilization.

"Looking now at *Any Fire Flower* and similar paintings and gouaches I did between 1959 and 1967, it occurs to me that they can also be understood as designs for what has been one of my chief concerns in recent years—flying sculptures, art in the sky." *

Otto Piene was born in Laasphe, Germany, in 1928. He attended several art schools in Munich and Düsseldorf, 1948–53, and then studied philosophy for three years at the University of Cologne. Concerned with utilizing natural elements such as fire and light to create moving and changing art forms, and with viewer participation in the art experience, he and fellow-artist Heinz Mack formed the Zero group and held a series of one-night exhibitions, analogous to happenings, in Piene's studio in Düsseldorf in 1957–58. During this time, he began making vibrating stencil paintings, light graphics, and smoke paintings and developed his Light Ballet of projected kaleidescopic light patterns, which throughout the 1960's was performed in avantgarde and kinetic exhibitions throughout Europe.

Working both with the Zero group and independently, Piene had published three Zero magazines, produced a film and two plays, The Fire Flower and The Light Auction, in Germany, and published a portfolio of his poetry. He came to the United States for the first time to serve as artist-in-residence at the University of Pennsylvania in 1964. The following year, he designed a permanent light theater at the Stedelijk Museum in Amsterdam and, returning to the United States, cofounded the first electromedia theater in New York, in 1967. Since then, he has experimented with television as an artistic medium and created sky art and outdoor-sculpture environments, notably one at the Massachusetts Institute of Technology in 1969.

* Letter from the artist, November 20, 1968.

PIENE *Any Fire Flower* **1964**
Oil and smoke on canvas, 30 x 40 in. (76.2 x 101.6 cm.)
Gift of Seymour H. Knox   K65:7

Max Beckmann

Hotel Lobby, 1950, is a straightforward depiction of a familiar and commonplace scene. During the last three years of Beckmann's life, when he lived in the United States, he frequently painted his immediate surroundings—in contrast to his numerous allegorical, monumental, and often violent canvases of the 1940's, filled with a highly personal and enigmatic symbolism. A perceptive observer, who had experienced two World Wars, he was particularly sensitive to suffering and tragedy, conveyed in this painting by the tense and somber facial expressions. Although the figures are crowded together in a constricted space, they appear indifferent to each other, isolated and lonely. The man at the center, the only figure shown full face, appears to be the principal observer of the scene, possibly identifiable with the artist. The ladderlike form at the right, a design device Beckmann used repeatedly, serves both as a unifying structural element in the painting and as a barrier that separates the viewer from the scene.

The emotional impact of the painting is amplified by the broad and expressionistic brushstrokes that create flat patterns of deep color, with heavy black outlines. The faces are garishly highlighted by artificial light. By using colors of equal value for the foreground and the background figures, and by repeating designs such as the stripes in various parts of the canvas, Beckmann has maintained an essentially flattened perspective—a dominant characteristic of his paintings.

Max Beckmann was born in Leipzig, Germany, in 1884. He studied at the Weimar Academy of Art, 1900–1903, moving to Berlin late in 1904, where he became a member of the Secession group, 1906–11. He was successful as a young painter, working in a style influenced by German Expressionism, French Impressionism, and Verism, as well as by his studies of the Old Masters in Paris and Florence. In 1914, he enlisted in the army as a medical corpsman, serving near the front line in Belgium and the Netherlands. Wounded in 1915, he was confined for a prolonged period in a hospital in Frankfurt-am-Main. After his release, he remained in Frankfurt, teaching at the art school. His war experiences had a profound effect on Beckmann, and his mature work became characterized by violent subject matter and distortion. Slashing, brutal paint strokes, hard contours defined by heavy black lines, highly personal symbols, and sharply contracted space replaced his earlier, more academic style, resulting in a new balance between emotional content and structural elements.

Beckmann was a prominent German painter when the Nazis came to power; he was then labeled a "degenerate artist." His work was removed from the national museums, and he was dismissed from his teaching post. By 1937, he had fled to Amsterdam, where he lived during the war years, coming to the United States, in 1947, to teach at Washington University, in St. Louis, for two years. In 1950, he moved to New York, where he taught briefly at the Brooklyn Museum School of Art before his death in December of that year.

BECKMANN *Hotel Lobby* **1950**
Oil on canvas, 56 x 35 in. (142.2 x 88.9 cm.)
Room of Contemporary Art Fund   RCA50:1

Willi Baumeister

"From time to time in my work, I have done very simple pictures in black and white only. I value these basic paintings (or studies) highly, since, in the absence of color, I can concentrate on form.

"The first studies [for this painting] were all in black lines. In the next ones the lines became thicker and appeared to be moving. Here, in a scattered arrangement, one has the impression that the forms are moving, drawing together, separating and changing. The edges of the forms were lighted with ocher and gray and a little blue was added to the black. The last step was to paint the light background more precisely.

"Growing [1952] gives the impression of a tree seen against a very light sky. It is an organism similar to vegetable growth, but which was indirectly created out of abstract forms which in themselves have different movements.

"To sum it all up, the finished picture suggests an upward striving caused by the dark mass below." *

Willi Baumeister was born in Stuttgart, Germany, in 1889, where he studied at the Academy of Fine Arts, 1905–12. As was the case with many artists of his generation, his early work was influenced by Cézanne and the Cubists. Unlike many of his contemporaries, however, he did not adopt pure abstraction; even his most completely nonobjective works have some relationship to the visible world, and, in this respect, he remained closer to the School of Paris than to the Bauhaus. An artist with a wide range of interests that included archaic art, myths, legends, fables, and history, these preoccupations can be discerned in various periods of his work: resemblances appear to African rock paintings, to rubbings of old inscriptions, to Chinese ideograms, and to metaphysical landscapes, as well as to symbolic and mythical references.

He was also an influential teacher at the Academy of Fine Arts, Frankfurt-am-Main, from 1928 until 1933, when he was forced to leave by the Nazis. He managed to continue his work in Stuttgart during the war years, to study materials at a paint factory in Wuppertal, and to complete his book The Unknown in Art, which was published in 1947. After the war, he was appointed professor at the academy in Stuttgart, where he remained until his death in 1955.

* Letter from the artist, April, 1953.

BAUMEISTER *Growing* **1952**
Oil on masonite, 39 x 51 in. (99 x 129.5 cm.)
Room of Contemporary Art Fund   RCA52:7

Picasso

In Synthetic Cubism, particularly the collages, Picasso had playfully explored the relationship of art and reality, nature and illusion, largely through the use of trompe-l'œil and visual puns. He continued his meditations on these fundamental issues in the theme of the artist's studio, beginning with the 1927 etching for Balzac's *Le Chef-d'œuvre inconnu* and the abstract painting *The Studio* of the same year. The fascination of the theme has held him throughout his entire career, and he has returned to it often, generally in an autobiographical way, the models reflecting the changing moods of Picasso's own amorous involvements. Thus in *The Artist and His Model*, 1964, one can recognize in the piercing gaze of the artist Picasso himself, and the profile of his wife Jacqueline in the languid reclining model. The model is gazing at a parakeet in her hand, thus at life; the artist is absorbed not in her, but in the very canvas we are looking at, the one he is painting of her. The comfortable eroticism of her pose is another aspect of Picasso's reflection on the creative process, the muse serving as both sensual and artistic inspiration. The painting is one of a series of the same title executed in 1963–64, and is reminiscent of the studio pictures painted at Picasso's villa La Californie in 1956. It is painted in the artist's late *brut* style and in its limited color range recalls canvases of the series of Interior Landscapes, also begun at La Californie.

In addition to the 1958 sculpture (p.177), other works by Picasso in the collection are *Woman's Head*, a 1909 sculpture, and the paintings *La Toilette*, 1906, *Nude Figure*, 1920, *Harlequin (Project for a Monument)*, 1935, and *Glass, Vase and Fruits*, 1937.

Pablo Ruiz Picasso was born at Malaga, Spain, in 1881. After attending the School of Fine Arts in Barcelona, 1896, and Royal Academy of San Fernando in Madrid, 1897, he came to Paris in 1900, where he resided permanently from 1904 until 1948, when he moved to the south of France. His first paintings were executed under the strong influence of the international turn-of-the-century style.

In 1901 he began his so-called Blue Period, consisting of melancholy subjects painted in somber tones of blue, which lasted till 1904. Also before 1903, the first small-scale bronze sculptures were executed. After 1905 Picasso changed the cold blue tonality for warm rose hues and thus his Rose Period was established and lasted approximately two years. Influences of Pre-Roman Iberian and Negro sculpture culminated in his painting and sculpture in 1907.

In 1909 Picasso and Braque clearly articulated a new style, Analytical Cubism, which was to be replaced by Synthetic Cubism after 1912. At the same time new materials, mostly found objects, were first included in Picasso's paintings establishing the principal of collage, which was later also applied to three-dimensional constructions. During the 1920's Picasso, who had almost completely abandoned sculpture for more than a decade, concentrated fully on painting. Two different streams were simultaneously carried on in his work—massive Neoclassic compositions—coexisting with works still painted in the style of Synthetic Cubism. His Surrealistic period started around the mid-1920's and lasted almost a decade. In 1928 Picasso became

PICASSO *The Artist and His Model* **1964**
Oil on canvas, 38⅛ x 51¼ in. (96.8 x 130.2 cm.)
Gift of The Seymour H. Knox Foundation, Inc. 65:19

interested in welding, and in the early 1930's, while continuing painting, he executed numerous constructions. Then followed a period of an almost monochromatic and diagrammatic style which culminated in Guernica, 1937. Since the 1940's Picasso has concentrated less on the formal structure of painting and more on the role of color.

Picasso's mastery in all mediums—painting, sculpture, graphic arts, and, after 1947, ceramics—established him in a central position among the inventors and creators of twentieth-century art.

Ernst Wilhelm Nay

"To paint," Nay said, "is to form the picture from color." By 1955, the date of *Ovestone*, Nay's color studies had led him to adopt the disc as a basic shape for his color areas, which he then placed in various patterns of movement over the canvases. In *Ovestone*, the motion of the white, ocher, and black ovals is between the upper-left and lower-right corners of the painting, reiterated in a series of blue discs flowing in the same direction. These dominant forms are counterpointed by the more loosely painted areas that serve in unifying the basic elements. The animated surface of the painting conveys a sense of endless harmonic rhythm, extending beyond the confines of the picture's actual edges.

Also in the Gallery collection is *Rhythms in Gray and Yellow*, 1959.

Ernst Wilhelm Nay was born in 1902, in Berlin, where he studied with Karl Hofer at the United States School for Fine and Applied Arts, 1925–28. He lived in Paris for several months in 1928 and Rome, 1931–32.

During the early 1930's, he became interested briefly in Surrealism, but he soon began his studies of color that continued throughout his life, and which resulted in his being named one of the leading colorists in modern painting. His first significant series of paintings was made during a stay in Lofoten, Norway, in 1937 and 1938, at the invitation of Edvard Munch. These were figurative and landscape paintings, yet the representational elements are secondary in importance to the intense coloration. Although he had been declared a "degenerate artist" by the Nazi government, he was required to serve in the German Army, 1940–45. While stationed in Le Mans, France, he continued to paint, further reducing the figurative element and concentrating on the relationships of color. Nay returned to Germany in 1945, and by 1951 all references to nature had disappeared from his works in favor of a luminous harmony—rhythmical and melodic—that has frequently been compared to musical compositions.

He lived in Cologne until his death in 1968.

NAY *Ovestone* **1955**
Oil on canvas, 39⅜ x 63 in. (100 x 160 cm.)
Gift of The Seymour H. Knox Foundation, Inc.   K59:24

Serge Poliakoff

As in *Composition*, 1953, Poliakoff's paintings tend to be dominated by one or more central images. He began his works at the edges of the canvas, adjusting the shapes and colors as he proceeded to the center. In his paintings, he maintains a careful balance of interwoven forms, colors, and textures. His work is said to have been influenced by the many icons he saw when visiting churches in Russia with his devout mother. Although the importance of the center areas and the opulent, glowing colors would seem to support this theory, he was also unquestionably influenced by the Russian Constructivists and worked in an abstract style—without reference to nature—for three decades.

In this *Composition*, the marks of the brush are clearly visible and the underpainting is readily seen, particularly beneath the lighter areas.

Serge Poliakoff was born in Moscow, in 1906. A talented musician, he became an expert guitarist at an early age. When he left Russia in 1919, following the Revolution, he traveled through Europe with an aunt who sang to his accompaniment. In 1923, he settled in Paris, where he earned his living as a musician. He began to paint in 1930 and studied at the Académie Frochot and the Académie de la Grande Chaumière. He went to London in 1935, and there studied at the Slade School. After his return to Paris, in 1937, Poliakoff became friends with Sonia and Robert Delaunay and with Kandinsky, who greatly influenced his work. His first abstract paintings were executed in 1938.

Poliakoff's paintings are distinguished by a harmonic balance of rich color and texture, derived originally from geometric shapes but transformed into a personal vocabulary of forms.

He died in Paris in 1969.

POLIAKOFF *Composition* **1953**
Oil on canvas, 35 x 45½ in. (88.9 x 115.5 cm.)
Gift of Seymour H. Knox   K60:16.1

Assemblage, Pop, and *Nouveau Réalisme*, 1957-67

Jan van der Marck

In 1957, the year of Robert Rauschenberg's *Painting with Red Letter S*, Abstract Expressionism had passed its apogee, but there were few to challenge its dominance of the art scene. The small oil and collage was hardly radical in its departure from common practice. The brushstroke has a familiar cant. The collage elements are discreet, considering the "combines" with which Rauschenberg had already established a reputation. The composition is rooted in Cubist principle and the "push and pull" between passages of an almost casual informality and others that are rigorously constructed shows a debt to Hans Hofmann. The picture plane not only shows us the end of a journey but the vagaries that went into its making as well. And yet, this relative adherence to Abstract Expressionist recipes did not produce a painting typical of that style. It was almost a disguise for picture-making intentions that went beyond the goals Pollock and de Kooning had set for themselves. To properly understand what makes *Painting with Red Letter S* differ from the reigning norm, we must consider it a subtle reinterpretation of, not a radical break with, Abstract Expressionism.

By integrating collage elements into a painted surface, Rauschenberg extended a tradition going back to 1912, when Picasso first glued scraps of paper to his canvases, and updated by some of his Abstract Expressionist predecessors, who used this device for specific formal or pictorial reasons. What set the younger artist's handling of collage apart, however, from that of the Cubists or the Abstract Expressionists was its a-literary, non-interpretative, and seemingly anticompositional insertion into the painted picture plane. Bits of fabric, newspaper transfers, and stenciled letters are randomized foreign elements introduced for no other apparent reason than to heighten the viewer's awareness of the abstract quality of the painted areas. They serve a dialectic purpose—they comment on the difference between art and life—and in this sense they constitute a dramatic innovation. That does not mean, however, that *Painting with Red Letter S* permits easy reading, formal, iconographic, or otherwise. We are mostly aware of the artist's investigation into the nature of picture-making as we follow the trajectories of his search. It is a sharp contrast with the easy self-confidence verging on sheer brinkmanship displayed by many of the so-called second generation Abstract Expressionists to which Rauschenberg technically belonged.

Painting with Red Letter S does not give us the full measure of Rauschenberg's departure from Abstract Expressionist practice, but even *Ace*, another and more ambitious painting in the Albright-Knox collection, does not begin to suggest the role assemblage played in the artist's works between 1954 and 1962 in particular. Ace was painted on the eve of an important shift in Rauschenberg's work from the assemblage of found objects to that of found images. On the one hand he started to experiment, like Warhol that summer, with silkscreens to take the place of the rather primitive method of transferring photographs from newspapers and magazines. On the other hand he drew a stricter line between the combine as painting, which had run its course, and the combine as sculpture, into which he introduced electronics of an increasingly sophisticated nature. Just before entering these new areas of endeavor Rauschenberg painted Ace, a major five-part canvas.

The late critic G. R. Swenson visited the artist in his studio on Broadway, south of 14th Street, shortly after the completion of Ace. He noticed drawings by artists Rauschenberg admired pinned to the wall and observed how apparently he took clues from Frank Stella on how to construct an unusually shaped canvas, from Jean Tinguely on how to connect one object to another, and from Jasper Johns on how to handle a composition made up of numbers. Rauschenberg told Swenson, "When an object you are using does not stand out but yields its presence to what you are doing, it collaborates, so to speak—it implies a kind of harmony." He must have had Ace in mind when he continued, "The objects blend indistinguishably into the pure colors and forms of the painting. It ceases to be a simple tonality, but is part of a harmony in which no note can really be heard because the over-all vibrations are so unified." Without conceit he tries to accommodate the viewer: "I would like my pictures to be able to be taken apart as easily as they're put together—so you can recognize an object when you're looking at it." * Clearly, Rauschenberg is as interested in our ascertaining as he is in his own operating in that much-cited gap between art and life.

Letters are a recurrent subject in Rauschenberg's paintings. Like anything else, they are treated neither logically nor sequentially. The title, again, can be deduced from looking at the picture, but an explanation is harder to come by. These three letters are just as likely to refer to the second, fifth, and tenth letters in the artist's name as to a man of great feats or the top card in a game. Quiet and majestic, Ace has only a few protruding components; rather than using a variety of assemblage elements, as he often did, Rauschenberg must have decided to emphasize painterly aspects in this work. Used besides paint are wood, crumpled metal, cardboard, part of an umbrella, a box top or poster fragment, a tin can, pieces of linen, and shreds from a pair of boxer shorts. One has to take pains to identify these items, for quite apparently they are chosen for their color, texture, and accidental lettering. Also, they do not impede, as larger encrustations might, a sense of speed, an almost breezy handling of paint, and the establishment of quick connections between all elements of the composition. A casual integration of materials and colors on a mural-size scale gives Ace that almost offhand authority.

Jasper Johns, no less than Rauschenberg, has challenged the principles of Abstract Expressionism, and he too has shown a remarkable respect for his elders. His argument with the then-dominant school was perhaps more intellectual and dialectic than material or stylistic. In part this can be explained in terms of Johns's being as methodical and static as Rauschenberg is sweeping and dynamic, but a generalization like that goes only so far toward explaining the artist's work. Numbers in Color is a superb painting introducing a flamboyant manner that was to culminate in the "map" pictures. The artist's brush appears to have caressed those figures and lavished the kind of painterly attention on them that Cézanne once reserved for apples. With its drips and smears and dabs of thick paint it is really not that dif-

* "Rauschenberg Paints a Picture," Art News 62, No. 2:44–47, 65–67, New York, April, 1963.

ferent from the average Abstract Expressionist impasto, while the edge-to-edge crowding of the picture plane is reminiscent of Pollock. The paint surface itself has become the structure obfuscating the underlying composition and almost negating whatever meaning the numbers possess. And here is where the difference with Abstract Expressionism comes in. Johns has set himself limitations that were new and atypical. Despite an effusive manner and an apparently spontaneous application of pigment, subject, structure, and color are all predetermined and tightly controlled.

Compared with the white, gray, and black encaustic of the earlier number paintings—going back to the 1955 small *Figure 5*—the colors in *Numbers in Color* are joyously extravagant. Yet, they are limited to the subtractive primaries—red, yellow, and blue. A voluntary limitation to the primaries by artists who admired Mondrian without in other ways accepting the rigors of Neo-Plasticism can be noted in the works of Jasper Johns but also in those of Ellsworth Kelly, Barnett Newman, and Dan Flavin. But the limitations of color do not appear as drastic as those of subject and structure. As in the targets and flags, easy recognition is meant to permit the eye to zoom in on matters worthier of attention than mere subject matter. The latter, indeed, can be disposed of quickly. Within a grid—what greater straitjacket for any composition?—and starting with a blank upper left corner, the numbers are aligned from 0 to 9, down and across, staggered progressively by the interval of one digit and covering a rectangle divided in eleven by eleven spaces. Johns recalled that he saw a chart in a book with that arrangement. And if proof were needed that composition prevails over meaning and visual effect over intellectual portent, in *Numbers in Color*, the artist explains, "I'm certainly not putting the numbers to any use, numbers are used all the time, and what's being done is making something to be looked at." *

Thus Johns negates the communicative function of numbers and whatever purpose a chart may have. It's to be seen and not to be read. But the "ready-made" structure a chart with numbers provides is pressed into service to convey painterly information. The numbers serve a painterly message instead of the painting's serving a numerical message. But there remains something ambiguous about a subject denying its own referential content, for it cannot escape a reading as icon. Numbers have an iconic intensity approaching hypnosis; but as soon as our attention flags they tend to become a blur. The ticker tape in a broker's office would be a good example. Johns operates on the premise that our mind's eye focuses only so long on content, then invariably turns to form. He reduces its "tellingness" until the structure speaks for itself and we stop wondering what the content might be. The use of stencils as a neutralizing and unifying device underscores this favoring of structure over content. Johns seems as infatuated with numerical notations and chance order as is his friend John Cage. He responds to the ambiguity latent in all sign systems and he attempts to heighten our awareness of it until that becomes the main subject of his work. Couched in the mature style of the 1950's is a treatise on perception that would endure well into the 1960's.

Abstract Expressionism did not produce much sculpture to compare favorably with painting, undisputedly the leading art form by far. Sculpture seemed to lack the critical attention and fundamental encouragement so

* Walter Hopps, "An Interview with Jasper Johns," *Artforum* 3, No. 7:33, San Francisco, March, 1965.

clearly bestowed upon painting. A time lag developed between the two modes. After Abstract Expressionism had peaked, having made its mark and delivered itself of its historic contribution, younger artists of the generation of Rauschenberg and Johns applied some of the movement's pictorial and compositional principles to sculpture. John Chamberlain and Mark di Suvero were most prominent among them.

Chamberlain's *Kroll* demonstrates its Abstract Expressionist derivation in the painterly treatment of the found forms and colors. It is taut with gestural energy and asserts, in an almost cocky way, its three-dimensionality. Form—roughed up, scraped, and partly rusted—and color—the pastel tones that went out of style and into the automobile graveyards by the end of the 1950's—are used to structure and articulate mass. The procedural rationale with its reliance on chance and its insouciance about covering the tracks of hand or tool is akin to that of Pollock, De Kooning, and Kline. The fragmentation of form, real and found in the material, is further enhanced by the play of light and shadow as well as by an effective manipulation of found colors.

Few sculptors have been able to suggest speed as effectively as Chamberlain. We are reminded of Futurist stylizations of speed in the sculpture of Boccioni, but equally compelling is the association with the motorized environment from which these forms are taken. A centripetal force seems to draw forms on the periphery of the sculpture toward the center, sheltering and concealing its core. In a clattering whirlwind of jagged shapes folding over crevices and hidden inner passages, the scrounged components attain a volumetric continuity which brilliantly disguises the efforts which must have gone into its making. Sensitive to the properties of his material—romantically brutalized junk metal—Chamberlain restages the drama adhering to its origins.

Temperamentally as well as in manner, John Chamberlain belongs to the Abstract Expressionist generation. There is nothing cool or meticulous about his approach to the sculpture at hand. In response to a question whether metaphorical reference was intended, the artist claimed that his works are self-portraits and that the force of the anger he felt at that time in his life has a great deal to do with it. Métier in the conventional sense is scorned to the point of flaunting a lack of it. Like Tinguely, Chamberlain publicly admits that he was never able to weld properly—welding being the least important part of the whole process of making a sculpture. "If I could have gone zap and pointed a finger and a big flash of lightning would strike across to fuse the parts into one piece, that would have been fine." When Chamberlain talks about the need for the parts of his compositions to fit, one is reminded of Franz Kline: "It's the idea of the squeeze and the compression and the fit." * Velocity, that is, the speed of the making, the "throwing together" of forms so they fit, is as important to Chamberlain as it was to many of the Abstract Expressionists. In Harold Rosenberg's terminology, he was an "action sculptor."

Chamberlain's fortunes have flagged with the winds of artistic change and a shift toward a cooler orientation in sculpture, despite the loyalty shown him by colleagues and critics of the Minimal persuasion. Deprived of even that lingering loyalty, times have been rougher for Richard Stankiewicz, who in the late 1950's made a unique contribution to sculpture.

* Phyllis Tuchman, "An Interview with John Chamberlain," *Artforum* 10, No. 6:38–43, New York, February, 1972.

A student of Hans Hofmann's and the brightest hope of the cooperative Hansa Gallery, Stankiewicz had all the proper credentials. He was trained on a course that lead from Julio Gonzalez via David Smith to what was thought to be a long and secure future for sculpture fashioned from junk metal. Instead of just being the beginning, *The Art of Assemblage* at The Museum of Modern Art in the fall of 1961, in which Stankiewicz was prominently featured, spelled the end of that fledgling mixed-media direction. Upon entering a decade that put such a premium on color as well as on formal organization, Stankiewicz was found to lack Chamberlain's casual but all-important embrace of color and David Smith's genius for bold, overriding, and almost geometric order. In addition, his exploitation of wear and tear (unlike Chamberlain's slash and bang) in the materials from which he built his sculptures appeared a little pathetic and sadly out of joint when Pop art came around with its preference for newness, gaudy colors, and slickness of form. This, however, does not diminish the fact that Richard Stankiewicz was unequaled in the flavor he lent to the art scene of the late 1950's and has an originality of vision that may yet come up for a well-deserved reevaluation.

Our Lady of All Protections is a junk metal assemblage carrying the literary overtones that seemed to have been inherited not only from Dada assemblages but also from that thin strain of Surrealist sculpture that had enjoyed a modest fame in the preceding decade. For the artist who had been educated in the Catholic faith, *Our Lady of All Protections* was "a light joke on Mariolatry, miracles, superstition and hypocritical power in churches." Behind it lies the fact that Stankiewicz, in his own words, "was influenced early and strongly by institutional religion and then later threw it over as a ridiculous anomaly made of comical and tragic nonsense." * Obviously, the arched and spheric elements, like umbrellas or halos perched atop head or body, are metaphors of protection. There is a suggestion of cradling and shelter adherent to the chosen shapes of the metal components. This junked hardware can be traced back to its likely source—a scrapped truck—but, as an ironic reversal, the stance created by these heavy parts is light and coquettish.

Junk sculpture equilibrates the affective qualities of the mutilated or abortive remains of moving vehicles and household appliances, weathered and rendered anonymous by nature and neglect, with the formal requirements of their reinterpretation as well as with the interpretative requirements of the subject to be portrayed. Heterogeneous objects, divorced from their original use or context, are taken out of context once more (that of the scrap heap) as the artist assigns them a third life, redeeming them from certain neglect and ultimate corrosion, and consecrating them as art. Stankiewicz, who understands these possibilities better than anybody, engineered a chance encounter, in *Our Lady of All Protections*, of a brake drum, rear-view mirror, chain, shaft, and stepping board to create an image in which former functions linger, new connotations replace old ones, and the topical is subjugated to a demand of formal discipline. There is something quixotic and almost tragic in this sculpture, bucking the tide and braving those winds of change ahead.

Sculpture around 1960 was affected by an almost romantic involvement with materials and textures and a love for that gentle pathos exuded by the old and no longer useful. An interest in abrasive and weathered surfaces

* Letter from the artist, August 15, 1968.

was clear from Robert Mallary's thickly impastoed paintings of the early 1950's. This interest carried over in his assemblages for the making of which he was the first sculptor in America to extensively employ polyester resins, methacrylate monomers, and epoxies. *Apothecary* has the aged and rickety look of an archaeological find, but we sense that it is the instant aging brought about by fire and acid. Mallary says he is intrigued by that bastard area where the painted or sculptured object is uncertain of its parentage. In Europe at the time Tapiès, Burri, and Schumacher showed a related interest in surfaces bearing the effects of age or willful destruction. For want of a precise definition, the French critic Michel Tapié called it an *art autre* —other, that is, than the gestural abstractions of artists who held a position in Europe equivalent to that of the Abstract Expressionists. Wresting effects that range from the macabre to the ornate from textures and materials proved to be a short-lived infatuation for artists on both sides of the Atlantic, although it ranks as a salient episode, like the art of assemblage, linking painterly abstraction and the new realism.

Robert Mallary has brooded over man's self-destructive impulses. In his work he presents us with the specter of future decay—walls that need no writing to serve an ominous warning. A few years hence, the wall as an anonymous record would develop into the life-size survivor of an imaginary holocaust, half scarecrow, half crucifix. An evolution from abstract allusion to iconic representation is typical for the polymaterial assemblage art of the late 1950's and early 1960's. Lee Bontecou is another case in point.

Untitled, 1960, by Lee Bontecou is more than an allusion and less than a representation. One could call it an abstract icon, indicative of the vanguard position on the threshold of a new decade. The artist's imagery was to become more explicit and descriptive, moving in the direction of three-dimensional renderings of hybrid creatures hovering between plant and insect. Recent changes in Bontecou's work reflect more gently on those fiercely opened, abysmal looking jaws of wire braces and tautly stretched canvas. Yet, in her works of the early 1960's, she heavily traded on the scare-provoking forms of quasi-natural phenomena, isolated and magnified beyond ordinary perception. With great effect she has used the hallucinatory image of an ambiguous orifice, many times enlarged, whose function, we feel, is to swallow and devour. Her works promise the ultimate embrace to the timid prey. They have the primitive cant of a deity to be placated by human or animal sacrifice. But there is another layer of threat—that of destruction through mechanical devices, such as cannon mouths, animal traps, and meat grinders.

Lee Bontecou was one of the first artists to whom Donald Judd's term "specific object" applied. Her three-dimensional forms which hang from the wall are neither sculpture nor painting, yet they share a number of ambitions with both. *Untitled*, 1960, is an early and relatively abstract construction made of laundry bag canvas, cut in radial sections and stretched over metal rod and wire armatures. An impression of forward thrust is deliberately reinforced by the advancing and narrowing circles that seem to emanate from the black-tunneled holes. They strike the viewer like dark whirlpools or the mouths of dead volcanoes. As an image, pure and simple, *Untitled*, 1960, resembles a "moderne" sunset gone haywire or perhaps a Piranesi prison scene. The latter may not be all that far-fetched, considering that Bontecou lived in Rome the year before she embarked on her startling constructions.

Between the works of Robert Mallary and James Wines one notices a superficial resemblance. Yet one is as interested in the tectonic qualities of form as the other is in surfaces and textures. Wines was predisposed to casting as a sculptural method, in contrast to Mallary's assemblage, by a prolonged stay in Rome. He was one of a group of young American sculptors who were attracted to that city's inexpensive facilities for bronze casting as well as to its classic spirit and tradition. Among colleagues whose works inevitably appeared a trifle *retardataire* when compared with what was done in the home country, James Wines stuck out through an original use of technique. His sculptures of the early 1960's, of which Metro, 1962, is a typical example, consist of solid slabs of cast cement transfixed by steel or bronze bolts, grills, and hinges. When more elaborate, they evoke the paraphernalia of torture, fastened to the wall of a dungeon, or the metal bars securing a prison window. The tectonic blends with the organic in what appears like a miniature version of fortifications nestled in a mountain flank. From a sculpture that looks architectural Wines has moved, in later years, to a more rigorous form of casting and construction that can be made to function within an architectural context.

Louise Nevelson and Chryssa both have sculptures to their credit, the "cathedrals" and the "gates" specifically, that are architectural in essence but in no way subject to the functional demands of architecture or relinquishing their autonomy within an architectural setting. Never, with the historic exception of Schwitters's Merzbau, has the designation "assemblage" been more fitting than when applied to the work of Louise Nevelson. With that same sense of building an environment from the trivia that wash up in everybody's life and yet discriminating between formless trash and modest objects rendered beautiful by association, Louise Nevelson has harnessed a pack-rat instinct and appetite and built monuments to acquisitiveness of an exquisite order. If sculpture operates through essential elimination, assemblage relies on selective addition. Like late Gothic altars crammed with the godly and the wicked, these wall-size assemblages pack a mad carpenter's arsenal of forms and fixtures, ornaments and moldings in which the odd and the sublime are precariously balanced.

From treasure chest to reliquary, the box format has always been a vehicle of mystery. Stacking boxes filled with dislocated and barely recognizable contents has the effect of raising the stakes. They become altars consecrated to more than one saint or crypts in which many people are buried. The artist is not averse to associations with altars, reliquaries, or iconostases. Her choice of over-all colors like black, gold, and white decidedly underscores it. Yet there is enough Yankee pragmatism in Louise Nevelson and a down-to-earth Shaker sensitivity to dispel any visions of worship in front of these sky cathedrals. The associations these elaborate assemblages have prompted are many; they range from altars to rain forests to moon caves to the coast of Maine. One more might be ventured: that with a giant typographer's composition table filled with nineteenth-century ornaments and vignettes.

Louise Nevelson has compared herself with the poet: "In back of all my work is the Image and the Symbol. I compose my work pretty much as a poet does, only instead of the word I use the plastic form of my images." * Starting with objects, as the poet uses words, Nevelson builds a fabric that is

* John Gordon, *Louise Nevelson* (New York: Praeger, 1967).

stronger and more meaningful than the individual objects. The spaces in between (the "dawns" and "dusks" as the artist calls them) are the yarn that hold the fabric together. The color dematerializes the components as it stresses their integration and subservience to an over-all vision.

Sky Cathedral is among the first of Nevelson's full-size wall constructions. It contains an agglomerate of newel posts, table legs, balusters, finials, acanthus scrolls, and moldings in various patterns. Boxes of varying size and depth are crammed to overflowing with furniture delights. Their architectural unity is determined by and large by the right angles of the containers and their stacked composition. The loving articulation of detail and the unfailing sense of juxtaposition, tempered and obscured by a subtle manipulation of light and shadow and the uncanny choice of an over-all black, conspire to create an aura of magic and mystery. The effect is quite different from that of a smaller Nevelson in the Albright-Knox collection, the 1961 *Royal Game*. Three-tiered and shallow, simpler of composition and resplendent in gold, it holds less mystery perhaps but makes up for it by living up to its regal title. Noticing a shift from the gothic to the baroque may be altogether subjective and brought on by the title of this work and its color, but there is curvilinear detail galore to support this stylistic inference.

If Nevelson found her materials in Victorian attics, Chryssa has said more than once that the city at night is the source of her inspiration. She admits to have found an equivalent for the glow and radiance of the Mediterranean skies under which she was born in the gaudy firmament of Times Square with its blinking, flashing, and racing signs. Letters, just barely lifted from their typographic context at first and then borrowed from the signmaker, were her staple. Freeing them from servility to word, legend and communicative function, she made them into vehicles for her own formalist ideas. *Letter T* is made up of a field of nine rows of eleven T-shaped cast aluminum elements, all horizontally arranged, on top of a vertical shaft of fourteen rows of three elements each. Their formation is far from straight and orderly, nor are they perpendicular to the background. This intentional irregularity of the white T-shaped elements on the flat white background creates a paradoxically informal and painterly effect, particularly when enhanced by shadows. The title no doubt refers both to the basic components and to their aggregate, designed as a T-shaped configuration.

Chryssa shared a love for letters most notably with Jasper Johns and Robert Indiana. Her approach is more formalist than the former and less emblematic than the latter. Their sculptural properties above all, from low relief to high relief and eventually freed from their background, are the substance of her investigations. But, as *Letter T* demonstrates, three-dimensionality is inseparable from, and can only be fully explored in the context of, light. This, above all, she would address herself to in the years to come. She was the first American artist to incorporate neon in her work as an integral part of its formal structure: a further step was the structural use of neon in Chryssa's sculpture and, ultimately, neon as a preferred and basic material.

Lucas Samaras and Mary Bauermeister have both been tangentially involved with intermedia experiments, the former with Happenings, the latter with Fluxus. A mixing of modes; assemblage turned environment; one-word, or one-action "events"; interaction between poets, composers, painters, and dancers were all part and parcel of a strong undercurrent that started in the late 1950's and ran well into the 1960's. Not market-oriented, its "fall-out" was largely overshadowed by mainstream art. What made insertion into that mainstream difficult was an avoidance, by those artists, of the conventional vehicles of painting and sculpture and the choice of a super-private language. The box became their favorite format and the diary their main preoccupation. This applies even to Bauermeister and Samaras, who had remained on the sidelines, had never taken an extreme position, and had always found a public anxious to buy their work. To call these works "specific objects" sounds almost bland; "obsessive" in the Surrealist sense would be a more appropriate description. Mixing the visual with the literary, they can be read as well as seen. The tectonic concerns most sculpture is preoccupied with are raised to the level of parody in an almost slapstick formal permutation. The mind is allowed to run rampant, but on a circulatory course. Colors, virtual as in the lenses and prisms, or real as in the yarn and tinsel, all seem to refer to the rainbow. Scale is relativized as though we had walked into a Swiftian world of Lilliputian proportions.

In *Transformation: Boxes* Lucas Samaras appears to be punning the "Primary Structures" of Judd, Morris, Smithson, and others, which in 1966–67 were very much in evidence. Their ill-fit or impossible fit parallel life's own frustrated logic and man's desire to make fit what cannot be properly combined or put together. The dotted, striated, and sweet Day-Glo colors are a far sight from the avoidance of color in those "Primary Structures." They add to the mockery of lids that won't shut and shapes that are wildly askew. Samaras uses transformation and the irrational to make us reflect on the hidden absurdities of form and reason that so often escape our awareness.

The twelve boxes in this three-tiered stack are kept in animated suspension as by a magic wand. They appear condemned to immobility at the moment when each one of them is opening up, their lids ajar like abstract renderings of predatory animals ready to swallow their prey. Samaras began making boxes of a secretive nature, heavily metaphoric and of an evil beauty, in 1960 when the art of assemblage was reaching its zenith. Six years later the emphasis had shifted from the box as container to the box as form. It may be empty of contents, in a literal sense, but it is not empty of content inasmuch as shape and color have become the content. In contrast to the earlier boxes, filled like reliquaries with autobiographical ex-votos, drawing our attention to the enclosed, they now have become entirely self-referential, drawing our attention to the enclosure.

Either way, Samaras powerfully suggests that the viewer is about to be caught with his fingers in the cookie jar. We fear that the lid might come down in retaliation for an indiscretion on our part. Mary Bauermeister, instead of grudgingly allowing us to look inward, enthusiastically invites us to look outward, as through a window, onto a world all her own. She may puzzle or mystify us, but she does not hold back or guard her secrets. *Four Quarters* is a mixed-media construction of objects and drawings crammed into a double box and visible from two sides. The crowded and encrusted container teems with the ambivalent and indeterminate emanations of an extraordinary mind that operates on several levels simultaneously. Objects, images of objects, images of images, and images of processes combine with nonlinear, nonsequential, straight, reversed, and mirrored writing in creating an infinity effect through accumulation, permutation, and repetition.

Mary Bauermeister abhors a vacuum and shuns the simple or single statement. She uses words with a vengeance, as though words came easier to her than images and images would have to be explained by words, or explained away or contradicted as mood would move her. "This is not my handwriting" we read somewhere on the inside, and "This is nothing." She cancels elements of the composition by crossing them out or marking them "destroyed." She warns the viewer that a mistake is included or writes "needless" on whatever should not have been there, or could have been eliminated by her but isn't.

The spheres and cut-sphere segments act as lenses, guiding our eye to what the artist wants us to concentrate on. They stand out because of their glitter and refraction of color. Usually they draw attention to an equivalence of form (lenses-balls-moons-pebbles) or multiplicity of meaning as they magnify scribbled words in sequences like "Dreck, Schmutz, Dirt, Dirt-schmutz, painted dirt, a job dirty." In wavering elongated handwriting which in places skirts or embellishes the painted wood hemispheres and, in others, is magnified or distorted by optical lenses glued to the glass cover of the box, Mary Bauermeister charts her mental voyages and records the process of creation in the act of creation, letting the chips fall where they may as she proceeds on course or feels the need to change direction, telling it all and baring it all, to finally wrap it up and let others call it a work of art. A one-time student of mathematics, astronomy, and electronic music, she has learned that formulas, charts, and scores are the keys to discovery and understanding: "To find out what I know or want," Mary Bauermeister once said, "is the actual reason why I paint."

John Willenbecher's *Change Game* is as cool and orderly as Mary Bauermeister's *Four Quarters* is hot and frantic. It does not draw from the sources that have informed Bauermeister and Samaras. Instead Willenbecher appears to have patterned his *Change Game*, possibly with a nod to Joseph Cornell, on the amusement arcade's containerized and automated chance game. He is a formalist, interested in the emblematic treatment of popular imagery. Like Robert Indiana, to whom he can be likened and whose influence he may have undergone, Willenbecher simplifies and organizes his subject in a tight, frontal way. His colors show as much restraint as his handling of form, pared down to essentials.

Since Cornell, artists have made "game boxes" that would take the viewer on a magic mystery tour full of nostalgia and simple delight. Not Willenbecher. There is no hidden catch or slow yield; his materials are new and shiny; everything is visible and out front. Yet there is a perverse twist the artist has given to the title as well as to the construction of his work. Obviously he refers to a game of chance. But he may have preferred the reference to *change*, because what superficially looks like a game that can be played has been changed by him into a static and deadlocked formal composition. Willenbecher is a purist who avoided easy gamesmanship when it was popular to make art spin or light up at the flick of a switch. His boxes tantalize but do not deliver anything but formal repose.

A Pop artist of the first generation, Robert Indiana did not turn to banal or tawdry subject matter, nor did he gloat over the visual clutter of our consumer-oriented environment. His inspiration came from the highways he had traveled and a unique part of Manhattan, Coenties Slip, where for years he lived and worked. Indiana never showed any interest in Abstract Expressionism. The nearest to a formal influence or alliance was with the work of Leon Polk Smith and Ellsworth Kelly. From brightly colored semi-abstract shapes for which, among others, the leaves of the ginkgo tree under his window had served as a model, he moved to fully abstract geometric shapes, enlivened by stenciled words or legends in straight or circular bands. *Year of Meteors*, a painting of great splendor and authority, is an early but already mature example of Indiana's emblematic style.

The source of the words in the painting is *Year of Meteors* by Walt Whitman, a poet much admired by Indiana and from whom he has quoted verbatim. The poem celebrates the transatlantic crossing of the ship the *Great Eastern*, which coincided with a meteor shower. The image chosen by the artist is a stylization of the mariner's compass—an eight-pointed star described between two circles—and the green and blue colors reinforce the marine associations. From the window of his studio Indiana could have seen the *Great Eastern* as it swam up the bay, a century before he decided on this commemorative painting. Everything around was reminiscent to the artist of the "wooden ship days of sail and mast," with its active piers, loaded warehouses, and colorful ship chandlers.

Indiana, in fact, collected waterfront debris—crudely spoked wheels, roof beams of demolished buildings, commercial brass stencils of numbers, sailing terms, and nineteenth-century companies—from which he fashioned marine totems. One such totem is *Star*, a stiffly formal assemblage of a weathered beam flanked by four rusty wheels on each side and emblazoned with stars and numbers. Just as *Year of Meteors* would have ranked as color-field painting without the circular legend, so *Star* would have largely gone unnoticed as a junk assemblage had not the artist adorned it with numbers and stars. It was the insistent and solemnly stylized use of stencil printing that propelled Indiana, for better or worse, into the Pop art arena. There is a subtle irony in the fact that the insignia of authority, officialdom, and mercantile prosperity—the rubber stamp, the brass stencil, and the trademark vignette—have been turned into the hallmarks and objects of Pop art. Indiana has contributed, through the lapidary use of the stencil, to our readings of target images as Pop images, and heraldic lettering as an invention of the 1960's.

If we understand Pop art to be a style uniquely derived from the American way of life and the spiritual and material environment it created, then Marisol Escobar is a Pop artist only by coincidence and through association. Her background betrays an interest in Surrealist imagery and expression. By seizing upon folk art she updated those concerns and arrived at a personal style which could be easily mistaken for Pop at a time when both the term and what it covered were only dimly perceived. To portray the Kennedy family or John Wayne on a horse may have zoomed in on Pop, but only as far as the subject. The two works by Marisol in the Albright-Knox collection skirt the issue, inasmuch as, with no pretense at Pop, they frankly concede their Latin inspiration.

The Generals, an elaborate jab at the power of the military south of our borders, is the artist's most ambitious work of the years since she came to prominence. It has the anti-authoritarian ring of Pop and trades heavily on the outrageous. The block-and-barrel forms, deliberately primitive as if they had sprung from a child's imagination, are Cubism-made-easy. The heads with their faces drawn or painted on the sides suggest a lazy woodcarver who has walked away after marking the areas he was going to attack with his chisel. Obviously, the method and its effect are intentional. The interplay between two- and three-dimensionality is a Marisol trademark but goes back to Picasso and primitive sculpture. Face masks, noses, and hands, for which the sculptor invariably chooses herself as a model, are simply stuck on the flat and chunky blocks and alternate with illusionistic drawings of faces, hair, and clothing. Ironically, the only part of this assemblage deemed worthy of being sculpted is the horse's head. A tape of march music specifically composed by David Amram is hidden inside the barrel as an audio accompaniment—a device made popular at the time by Rauschenberg and Tinguely, which may or may not have influenced the artist.

Baby Girl is an updated Brobdingnagian version of one of Velázquez's dwarfs and a close kin to the fatsos of the Colombian painter Botero. There is something frightening and almost vicious about this portrayal of infancy. As a girl herself, Marisol refused to talk for several years as the result of a traumatic experience. It may have heightened her perception of a world from which she separated herself behind a barrier of silence. That *Baby Girl* may be autobiographical is suggested by the portrait doll of the artist standing on the baby's knee.

The contemporary Surrealist flavor of Marisol's sculpture can best be understood when compared with George Segal's deadpan cast of a man changing the lettering on a movie marquee. Stark and abstract, Segal's work is generic and almost archetypal. The artist reduces every aspect of the composition to its bare essentials, but he applies that same reductive attitude to gesture and action portrayed, just short of our ability to "read" the subject. In that respect it is interesting to note that basic to the rendering of the subject in this form is an inaccurate reading of its real-life model.

George Segal recalls that the idea for this sculpture came to him one night when he was driving home from New York and in a flash saw a man, high up and alone, changing the title of a movie on a suburban drive-in theater marquee. The impression was strong and the image stayed with him—not the way it was, however, but the way he had imagined it to be. He decided to recreate this midnight vision, and *Cinema* was the outcome. When he returned to refresh his memory regarding a detail, Segal discovered that the marquee was lit not from within but by spotlights across the road. He considered it a fortuitous circumstance for what makes his solution preferable to the original is that the sculpture is self-contained, carrying its own light and suitable for indoor exhibition at eye level without loosing any of its impact and magic.

Cinema is a key moment in Segal's œuvre, because it is the first work in which light is functionally integrated, eliminating the need for an exterior source of illumination. This wall of fluorescent light, strong enough to make the white plaster figure appear dark by contrast, is not a "prop" or merely a component. It ranks, in the artist's estimation, as the cast subject's essential counterpart, no less a sculpture, no less endowed with aesthetic value. As it uses fluorescent light for its sculptural potential, *Cinema* antedates the more systematic use to which Flavin put it. It can be argued that Segal's strictly formal attitude to the environmental definition of his sculptures places him in the context of Minimal rather than Pop art.

In Pop art it is possible to distinguish between a "hard core" to which, in particular, Warhol and Lichtenstein are judged to belong and an affiliated contingent that is subject to opinion. Brydon Smith saw an Expressionist derivation in the works of Jim Dine, Claes Oldenburg, and George Segal when, in 1966, he combined them in an exhibition seen both at the Art

each can is clearly labeled *Beef Noodle*. An identical version exists in the collection of Karl Stroeher at the Hessisches Landesmuseum in Darmstadt. Warhol used stencils for his *Dollar Bills, S & H Green Stamps, Glass, Airmail Stamps, Coke* and *Soup Can* pictures. Then, in August, 1962, he began using silkscreens, as did Rauschenberg around the same time. Not only did silkscreening permit faster execution and the instant printing of whole banks of images when desired, but it allowed Warhol more control and modulation of a painting's over-all surface. One way to tell that *100 Cans* was printed by means of a stencil is that the colors are realistic and not arbitrary, as they would be in the later works, and that there are no signs of "slippage," the deliberate unevenness in color registration. *Troy Donahue* is the first Warhol image printed from a silkscreen.

Andy Warhol forces us to redefine the painting medium and make allowance for the stencils and silkscreens he was the first to introduce as painting and then used to the exclusion of all other methods. Silkscreens from found images are the ultimate joke on "everybody can paint." But it was Warhol who proposed it, and he has been unrivaled ever since. Marcel Duchamp has said: "If a man takes Campbell's soup cans and puts them on canvas, it is not the retinal image that concerns us. What interests us is the concept that wants to put Campbell's soup cans on a canvas." * The concept, of course, is that of deliberate impersonality, of draining the image of subjective communication and of creating a sledgehammer impact through the serial repetition of identical images. Warhol aims at the hypnotizing effect of assembly-line manufacturing or at the blatant redundancy of commercial promotion.

Next to Warhol, Lichtenstein has adopted, in his work, the most commercial orientation. If one borrowed popular products, from Coca-Cola to Marilyn Monroe, the other borrowed a popular style, that of the comics, and a popular process, that of cheap illustration. The key difference, however, is that while Warhol *used*, Lichtenstein merely *simulated*. He preserves the analogy with the source—comic strip, box top, tabloid advertising, or mail order catalogue—and eradicates whatever idiosyncratic qualities still adhere to it. Masking his formal concerns behind the novelty of the image used, he subjects generally sub-aesthetic material to a transformation, at once subtle, lucid, and systematic. The device that has gained Lichtenstein notoriety is the so-called Ben Day dot, which he borrowed from the mass-circulation printing process, turning a mark of coarseness into a mark of distinction.

Head—Red and Yellow, simple of color and composition, is characteristic of early Lichtenstein. The subject, taken from a vacation ad in a newspaper, is a girl, healthy, radiant, and cheering. As a picture nobody will have trouble identifying it. And yet this pictorial abbreviation is extremely unreal when compared with an actual girl, seen or photographed. It is taken for real by so many because of the authority wielded by the mass-printed image, graphically stunted to make it economically feasible and more recognizable to a broad public. This leads those people to accept as normal what in reality is a distortion. Lichtenstein has achieved, as no other artist, the rendering of what is very compelling, literally, in the area of commerce and mass communication, similarly compelling, aesthetically, in the area of art.

* Rainer Crone, *Andy Warhol* (New York: Praeger, 1970), p. 22.

About *Head—Red and Yellow* Lichtenstein has remarked, "One of my interests at the time was in configurations generated by economic consideration as used in some commercial illustration. For instance, the use of red instead of black in this painting to give both a line and a hue without additional expense." * The artist put himself in the position of the tabloid color printer who had to scrimp on extra inking and press runs; departing from this self-imposed limitation, he relished finding a solution that was coloristically acceptable without giving away the secret of his cutting corners. Organized perception and an intrinsic economy of means are among Lichtenstein's ground rules. While doting on the vitality of commercial imagery, he has always intensified and stylized it and, above all, submitted it to ruthless simplification.

In setting out to paint a picture, Lichtenstein first stencils in the dots. Starting with the lightest hues, he works his way down to the black or colored line. A pristine application of dots is essential as the artist has said that he wanted his paintings to look as if they had been programmed. But despite that impersonality of touch he wished to attain, the formal treatment soon became more personal than hand or brush could ever be. At this point Lichtenstein could free himself, with equal ease, from confinement to cartoon-related subject matter and move into other areas of visual concern, unafraid of losing his bearings.

Although he draws from commerce and communications, like Warhol and Lichtenstein, James Rosenquist differs greatly in focus and treatment. A stint as a billboard painter high above Times Square may have helped him to develop an eye that relies on piecemeal visual input to arrive at a mental calculation of how a picture will look once completed and seen as a totality. But it is just as likely that this journeyman painter's experience was merely the topping, or a practical application, of insights won from the study of Cubism, to which Rosenquist's style is clearly indebted. The artist employs a form of visual gigantism as a headlong assault on normality, cramming the space of his pictures with cropped images of inflated proportions. He deliberately misfits parts so his paintings look like a scrambled jigsaw puzzle. The images used are so common and public that the non-fit becomes a metaphor for noncommunication. Since his work relies so heavily on relationships, its reading can become an exercise in frustration.

On *Nomad*, Rosenquist has given us a nonreading which may contain clues to the picture's meaning: "An announcer on service 6 radio in Connecticut said: 'Today's gardening tips. When separating your fall annuals don't be afraid to throw away left over tops because, as you know, many parts of automobiles are replaceable.' In *Nomad* I'm concerned with the scale and speed of recognition of ordinary things. It has to do with what I have to bring with me into the future. Generally I'm trying to prove to myself what I remember." † The same fracturing of image sequences occurs here in thought sequences. We glean meaning from them as we glimpse related images in the painting.

Most prominent in *Nomad* is a partially obscured upside-down light bulb that looks like a space capsule. Behind it we notice an open wallet and, with a shift in scale, a picnic table and bench. A grassy landscape with barbed wire and an upright microphone is treated like a painting within

* Letter from the artist, October 4, 1968.
† Letter from the artist, June 1, 1969.

a painting, although the microphone sticks over the edge of one into the other. On the left are the overlapping images of what looks like a detergent boxtop and the legs of ballerinas; on the right the background consists of the culinary delights of spaghetti with sliced olives and meatballs in sauce. A comb fills the right corner and a paint-spattered plastic bag hangs suspended in the left corner. The paint spilling out of it falls on a palette on a small sawhorse in front of the painting.

A description of *Nomad* may allude to the subject—a summer picnic?—but falls short of defining it. Images tumble over one another no less than the forms that contain them. There seem to be close-up and medium and long shots, but they alternate without apparent logic. None of the images presented attests to firsthand observation of the items they portray; instead they seem faithful copies of commercial renderings of these original items. Thus *Nomad* is not once but twice removed from reality. The painter's tools in the lower left corner underscore that we are not in the realm of things observed but rather in that of things imagined. This real-life addition in the Johns-Rauschenberg-Dine manner makes the painting look even farther removed and synthetic. Besides, we wonder whether this is a cryptic comment, perhaps, on painting's progress from the drips and spatters, administered from above, in the 1950's, to the sleeky painted diorama, to be seen from afar, in the 1960's. Rosenquist's is by all odds the most hermetic painting Pop art has produced.

Tom Wesselmann shares with Warhol, Lichtenstein, and Rosenquist an interest in secondhand reality. Most of the pictorial burden in his earlier work is borne by ready-made imagery. It varies widely from painted clichés (the *Great American Nude*) to cliché paintings (posters of works of Mondrian and Matisse) and from make-believe edibles in color reproduction cutouts to a real sink, light, or television set. The artist could not formulate his intentions more succinctly than when he said, "I am interested in assembling a situation resembling painting, rather than painting." He has carried the art of assemblage into the land of Pop, and no painter or sculptor has done it better.

Still Life # 20 ranks as early among the still lifes, all dated between 1962 and 1964, but already it shows the balanced composition and the sureness of detail that are typical for the later work. As our eyes move from a real object to the reproduction of a real object, to the poster of a painting to the painting of a star (the illusionistic rendering of the kitchen counter is the only instance where the artist resorted to "hand-painting") they are constantly forced to adjust to different types of reality, all set within one pictorial framework. Wesselmann likes to "trade off" different types of reality against one another. He does not attempt to obscure or question their difference, as have Johns and Rauschenberg. Nor does he shift their scale or proportion, as have Oldenburg and Rosenquist. Their integration is ruled by logic and perspective but above all by purely visual demands. In this respect Wesselmann arranges his priorities in the manner of Matisse, in whose style and example he would more and more steep himself in the years to follow.

The relation between Assemblage and Pop art in America and *Nouveau Réalisme* in France is tenuous and so far ill-researched. In Paris, artists who had come from the south of France, Switzerland, and Italy rallied around the art critic Pierre Restany and, in the late 1950's, started to exhibit works that seemed to strike a balance between the conceptual and the material.

Pure ideas, on the one hand, and a welter of trash and trivia, on the other, were converted into an art of gesture. Yves Klein *presented* (a gallery with bare walls), Arman *accumulated* (any object he found in good supply), Spoerri *tilted* (the meals his friends had eaten), Tinguely *moved* (junk to which he attached motors), and Christo *wrapped* (what did not need a cover). *Nouveau Réalisme* was the spirited reply of a younger generation of artists to the tired abstractions of a School of Paris already nudged aside by a triumphant entry into Europe of the New American Painting. These artists appropriated from their everyday environment objects and ideas not generally deemed worthy of attention and presented them in new, idiosyncratic fashions. Though clearly informed by a different spirit, their works prompted comparison with those of Rauschenberg, Rivers, Chryssa, and Stankiewicz, in whose company they were shown in Paris, Amsterdam, and Stockholm. The issue of "who did what first" has never been properly reviewed. Most writers have already decided it in favor of the Americans. Yet motorized junk metal, the elemental monochrome, and serial repetition were inventions of Tinguely, Klein, and Arman, clearly in anticipation of similar or related approaches in the work of American artists.

Lecteurs IKB 1 and 2 and IKP, three painted sponges on stands by the late Yves Klein, are a typical example of the artist's attempt at appropriating and combining the material as well as the immaterial elements of a Mediterranean world which had deeply and lastingly impregnated his imagination. As later he would tell an American audience at the Chelsea Hotel, one day, when lounging on the beach in Nice, feeling possessive about the azure above (he dreamed about signing his name to the underside) and angered by birds flawing the purity of "his most beautiful creation," he decided to "remake" the sky. And this he did, in a deep, sensuous, resonant, and electrifying cobalt to which he proudly attached his name. I(nternational) K(lein) B(lue) was later to be followed by IKP(ink) and IKG(old).

Blue, red, and gold were to Klein (whose parentage was Dutch) what red, yellow, and blue had been to Mondrian. But if the older artist strove toward universal harmony, balancing those colors, the younger artist aimed at universal synthesis in which each color aspired to a cosmic absolute. Mondrian was a gradualist, Klein a radical. For Klein, fire and not the spectrum was the source. Blue, red, and gold were the colors of the alchemists; this appealed to his love of ritual and was consonant with his philosophical beliefs. Klein was a Rosicrucian (Mondrian had been a Theosophist). His search for pure color in the purifying blaze of fire was Yves Klein's quixotic search for the Grail. In the monochrome he found the tranquility of an absolute order; to him this meant "pure sensibility" in complete identification with space.

The sponge is a creature of the sea with which Klein was intimately familiar. A form of coral rock, skeletal, and a remnant of animal life, the sponge prompts cosmogonic speculation as its shape and appearance are a wasteland in miniature. But another association, more perturbing, is that with the human brain—a microcosmic prefiguration of human life on earth. Klein must have been as aware of one as he was of the other, for to him they were "portraits," not in a specific but in a universal way. He soaked these "portraits" in pure pigment until they were fully immersed in IKB or (infrequently) IKP. Klein first used sponges in mural reliefs for the opera house of Gelsenkirchen, 1957–59. Separately and individually they were presented at an exhibition in Paris in 1959. *Lecteurs IKB 1 and 2 and IKP* were made in October, 1960, for an exhibition at the Krefeld Museum in January, 1961.

Lucio Fontana, like Yves Klein whom he greatly admired, had philosophic aspirations that went beyond conventional expression through painting and sculpture. The common ground they shared was an experimental interest in transcending the limitations of the media they used and seeking, in acts of transgression (Klein dived out of a window, Fontana slashed through the canvas), personal liberation, and a spatial extension for their work. Fontana, whose life was cut short like Klein's, wanted to integrate pictorial and extrapictorial space by new methods and in a wide variety of nontraditional media. *Spazialismo*, the programatic application of Fontana's ambition to art, is reminiscent of the Baroque in its treatment of volume and space; in its evocation of motion and its romantic appeal to technology, Futurism comes to life again. Heir to his country's Baroque and Futurist traditions, Fontana seized on some of the principles of the Baroque style and some of the manifest intentions of the Futurist Movement to become a germinal force for the avant garde of the 1960's in Europe.

In Fontana's œuvre, what distinguishes one work from another is not so much the color, the imagery, or the medium, but the specific *spatialist gesture* employed. The perforations, incisions, or lacerations to which the artist subjected canvas (bare or monochrome), metal (cast or hammered), clay (fired with or without glaze), paper (with or without drawing), or whole environments (Walker Art Center, Minneapolis, 1966) act as a unifying device and obliterate the specificity of the medium. *C.S.* (*Concetto Spaziale*) is the term for all works in whatever medium. *C.S. "Natura" I 1961* is one of a series of roughly formed spheric shapes marked by brutal laceration. Made in fired clay in 1959, this series was cast in bronze to be publicly introduced in *Della Natura all'Arte*, a significant exhibition at the Palazzo Grassi in Venice in 1960. The images of birth and gestation merge with those of cosmic upheaval. "Terra Madre" is written on the wall of Fontana's sculpture studio in a photograph of the *Nature* in their original clay form. Pinned on the wall of his painting studio was a picture of a meteorite found in Siberia. The artist delighted in such a coincidental resemblance of his sculpture and a hunk of primeval matter separated from its celestial matrix with the kind of raw force he wanted to convey. *C.S. "Natura" I 1961* is a form unlike forms created by other artists before, at once sensuous and repulsive, mysterious and heroic, revealing an inner and outer space. It eludes categorization and almost belies the fact of its human manufacture.

In Paris, the Niceois Yves Klein and the Swiss Jean Tinguely were drawn to each other because they recognized, each in the other's work, a radical alternative to art's familiar uses. Iris Clert, godmother to the avant garde, offered them a joint show in 1958. Tinguely motorized Klein's monochrome propositions and they called it (or Pierre Restany called it for them) "pure speed versus monochrome stability." To this programatic polarity Tinguely brought the idea that the only durable element is motion (updating Heraclitus's *panta rhei*) and Klein his immovable belief in the supremacy of pure color derived from fire, the underlying substance of the universe, and beyond change or motion. It may have been Klein's influence inspiring the down-to-earth Swiss to a metaphysical interpretation of his machine art. But with equal historic likelihood we can relate Tinguely's machines to the wondrous inventions of Paul Klee, that other animator of the inert from the land of clocks.

Peut-être No. 11 is a tribute to Swiss genius. In this work Tinguely combined Jean Arp's historic invention of the chance arrangement of arbitrarily cut pieces of paper, with (a spoof of) the native skill for precision engineering. The title would indicate that the arrangement may or may not be satisfactory to the viewer or that, owing to a mechanical breakdown, the elements will or will not move. Since motion is slow, a deliberate challenge to our senses ("Does it or doesn't it move?") is the most likely of the artist's intentions. After all, reliefs had never moved until Tinguely decided to change that, and one could not expect the viewer to take it for granted! One precedent in the realm of mobile art, whether auto-mobile or motorized, was the American, then living in France, Alexander Calder. Tinguely was undoubtedly familiar with his work or, at least, conscious of Calder's specific morphology and experiments in kinetics. The forms in *Peut-être No. 11* are those that can be found in Arp, Miró, and Calder, but they look a little ragged, as though cut out with a less than steady hand. Suggestive of a rickety constellation or an attempt at non-Euclidian geometry, they move slowly and erratically, constantly rearranging themselves and escaping a fixed design. As he did in his "writing machines," with which he parodied the works of Mathieu and Hartung, Tinguely makes fun, in this mobile relief, of every artist's trial to arrive at an optimal arrangement of components in a formal composition.

Even more whimsical, often outright humorous, and sometimes wryly absurd are the "metamatics" or machines that go beyond what machines can, or are supposed to, do in a society so reliant on them. *Homage to New York*, a super metamatic that intentionally destroyed itself in the garden of The Museum of Modern Art on March 17, 1960, firmly established Tinguely's reputation. Calder began with mechanical movement, then gravitated toward aerodynamism, and ended up with stabiles. Tinguely took up the challenge of movement where Calder had left it. The encounter with Yves Klein may have enabled him to break out of a momentary geometric impasse. The use of heavy scrap by sculptors such as Richard Stankiewicz, Ettore Colla, Robert Jacobsen, and, eventually, César in his compressions, may also have been contributing factors that jolted him out of a predilection for light and spidery constructions. It was only after his New York "debut" that Tinguely began to take full advantage of the limitless potential of that fortuitous marriage between metal scrap and mechanical propulsion, with or without the assistance of combustibles and explosives. From orderly movement, with overtones of the absurd, he changed to disorderly movement, with overtones of the burlesque.

Cocktail au cheval is a motorized assemblage in the classic Tinguely style, no longer as clanky and frenetic as those he used to make in the early 1960's. Arabesque and curl, as well as horse and leaf, give it a gracious appearance. It would seem that the title refers to the mixing of elements in motion, most prominently the horse. But why not read it as referring to a drink for friends at the former Auberge du Cheval Blanc, the artist's home and studio in Soisy-sur-Ecole? Tinguely, like Arman, sometimes attaches more than one meaning to a title.

It would not detract from others if we were to claim for Arman the distinction of having been the purest as well as the most typical of the Nouveaux Réalistes. Between 1957 and 1960 his creative personality crystallized in close proximity to that of his fellow Niceois Yves Klein. In quick succession he invented the gestures that were to become his trademark and the solid basis of a steady production of great internal logic and thematic width. Arman started with multicolored impressions of rubber stamps (*cachets*), then followed with the *allures* or impressions of inked objects on paper or canvas. What propelled him to the forefront of the avant garde, first in Nice and then in Paris, were the *accumulations*. In a historic reply to Yves Klein's *Le Vide*, an exhibition at the Iris Clert Gallery of empty walls, Arman proposed *Le Plein* by filling the same space to the brim with trash. The idea of *accumulation* evolved from random stashes to homogeneous collections of odd subjects, neatly contained in boxes. The *allure*, when infused with aggressiveness and speed, became the *colère*, i.e., an actual act of destruction suspended at the height of its drama, in a material rendering visualizing the result. The *sections* or slicing of objects can be considered a synthesis between controlled destruction and serial accumulation. *Toccata and Fugue*, a harmonious assemblage of vertically sliced violins, is a perfect example.

The object, in Arman's work, is important for its form as well as for its actual and/or former associations. Its presentation—repeated, smashed, or dissected—enhances the formal aspects and multiplies the associations. Sliced violins (the unusual angle is one of Arman's surprise offerings) turn into a rhythmic pattern of abstract graphic signs. Yet we continue reading them in the context of music—no longer as instruments, perhaps, but as musical notations. The rich red background of the box and the natural wood color of the violins are a clearly experienced visual surrogate for corresponding harmonies in sound. The cocked necks and finger boards of the dissected violins are a formal translation of the toccata preluding the fugue's interweaving of melodic themes in contrapuntal fashion. This continuous interweaving of voice parts into a well-defined single structure involves repetition and imitation, the very principles Arman has used in arranging the violins' elongated bodies. *Toccata and Fugue* demonstrates the artist's uncanny sense of form, matched by a poetic gift for association.

Arman carries the gestural aesthetic of Mathieu and Hartung to its Cartesian conclusion. In theme and style, as well as in mood and rationale, he relates to the Cubists who attempted, in reaction to expressionist abandon in their time, to represent the world according to a predetermined order. But if the Cubists gave a humanistic interpretation to their sense of order, Arman, half a century later, gave a mechanistic interpretation to his sense of order. Analytical Cubism, to Arman, is the gestures of smashing and slicing; Synthetic Cubism has an equivalent in Arman's accumulation. Combined with an extreme sense of order, accumulation is bound to lead to serial repetition, distinct from what can be construed to be a Cubist principle. Among his contemporaries, however, serial repetition became, some time after Arman had started using it in the form of evenly stacked identical objects, of paramount importance to Warhol. But if Warhol aimed at a hypnotizing visual bombardment and laid great stress on flatness and regularity (after a while his images "wear out" and become an abstract vibration), Arman drives home a message of quantitative expressiveness and demonstrates the unity that can be found in multiplicity. Setting them apart even further are the facts that Warhol works with clichés while Arman works with common objects, and that Warhol accumulates images not bound by any particular scale while Arman accumulates things having their own scale.

The episode in French avant-garde art known as Nouveau Réalisme lasted only from 1957 to 1963, but it had a liberating effect on artists all over Europe. Not only were direct presentation, common subject matter, and mechanical processes no longer taboo, but a wave of younger artists became "Pop" with a vengeance. They saw no obstacle to combining Paris and New York sources and, in point of fact, they were almost naturally led to do so because the Nouveaux Réalistes had become the "New Yorkers" of Europe. There is no general agreement on this matter, but artists like Alain Jacquet and Michelangelo Pistoletto, who, technically, were never affiliated with or accepted by the Nouveaux Réalistes, nonetheless show enough common traits and attitudes to qualify as that movement's second generation.

Michelangelo Pistoletto affixes the life-size effigies of contemporary men and women to mirror-polish stainless steel backgrounds. His cutout images, sometimes also including a dog, plant, or light fixture, are drawn and painted on tissue paper with the aid of photographic projection and pasted face down onto the reflective surface. The quasi-absorption of Pistoletto's mundane subjects in their own world, their conversing with one another and their casual turning away from the viewer, either physically or mentally (none of them ever stares us in the eye), is in ironic contrast to the fact that the imaginary space they occupy reflects us and the environment in which we happen to find ourselves. Being placed in a position of confrontation with perfect strangers and looking in, against our will, on a party to which we are not invited, powerfully suggests and dramatically demonstrates alienation as a pervasive condition of life in our time.

Perceiving, simultaneously, the unfamiliar painted and the familiar reflected image, we feel a moment's hesitation as we are caught in a field of conflicting exclusive and inclusive forces. Our own image begs us, but we are embarrassed; the strange image works forbiddingly, but we are intrigued. *Sacra Conversazione* is a group of four people standing in a room, two facing each other, the others distracted and staring away. The title, in mock fashion, refers to a traditional subject, *Madonna Surrounded by Saints*, for which Domenico Veneziano's *Sacra Conversazione* (1445) may have served as the prototype. Pistoletto deals with several ironies simultaneously. The group portrayed would surely not qualify as sacred, nor is any conversation likely, for we are mostly aware of a puzzled pause or gap in the conversation, heightened by the girl's bored expression. Pistoletto places the banality of a cocktail party within the venerable framework of art-historic precedent, thus commenting that new art continues to feed on the art of the past.

CHAMBERLAIN   *Kroll*   **1961**
Steel, 26½ x 27 x 21½ in. (67.3 x 68.6 x 54.6 cm.)
Gift of Seymour H. Knox   K61:9

John Chamberlain

In *Kroll*, 1961, the relationship of Chamberlain's early style to that of the Abstract Expressionist painters has been frequently noted. In an analagous romantic vein, Chamberlain chose as his materials the crumpled and rusted metal parts of cars which in *Kroll* were originally painted blue, green, yellow, and gray; to these he added a yellow toy truck. Despite the superficial appearance of random organization, Chamberlain has constructed a rugged assemblage of related thrusts and counterthrusts in a vertical and near-horizontal design.

John Chamberlain was born in 1927 in Rochester, Indiana. He studied at the Art Institute of Chicago, 1950–55, and taught at Black Mountain College in North Carolina, 1955–56, where he encountered the work of Franz Kline and other New York School painters. Shortly afterward, he moved to New York; he now lives and works in Stony Point, New York.

By 1953, Chamberlain had discarded the traditional sculptural techniques of carving and modeling in favor of welding. About 1958, he began to work with scrap metal in open, silhouetted constructions reminiscent of some of David Smith's sculptures. He began to use remnants of automobiles in 1959 and continued with this material until the mid-sixties. After a short period of adding further color to these sculptures and of making square, geometric paintings with automobile lacquers, he returned to sculpture using a new material—soft polyurethane, rolled, tied, and cut. These were followed in 1966–67 by a series of unpainted, crushed metal boxes, and in 1970 by large works of heat-crumpled, iridescent plexiglass. In addition, he has worked with photography, films, and videotapes.

Richard Stankiewicz

Our Lady of All Protections, 1958, is constructed of scrap metal parts which not only retain the rough texture of their origin but are transformed to provide subtle allusions to familiar animal or human forms. Although Stankiewicz acknowledges a connection between the sculpture and religious statues, he adds, "It is whimsical and I shouldn't try to read it too closely or solemnly." *

Our Lady is one of Stankiewicz's last sculptures to allude to specific human situations. In the early sixties, he began to simplify shapes and eliminate metaphorical references from his work.

Born in 1922 in Philadelphia, Stankiewicz studied painting at the Hans Hofmann School in New York, 1948–49, and later at the studio of Fernand Léger in Paris. Gradually renouncing painting in favor of sculpture, he studied with Ossip Zadkine, 1950–51. Finding modeling and carving to be rigid and time-consuming, he experimented briefly with terra-cotta and subsequently with wire and plastic. After his return from Paris, he accidentally stumbled upon the material he would adopt for his work while digging out a courtyard to make a garden.

"I sat down to catch my breath and my glance happened to fall on the rusty iron things lying where I had thrown them in the slanting sunlight at the base of the wall. I felt with a real shock—not of fear but of recognition—that they were staring at me. Their sense of presence, of life, was almost overpowering." †

* Letter from the artist, August, 1968.
† Jan van der Marck, *Stankiewicz and Indiana* (Minneapolis: Walker Art Center, 1963), p. 5.

STANKIEWICZ *Our Lady of All Protections* **1958**
Iron and steel, 51 x 31 x 32 in. (129.5 x 78.7 x 81.3 cm.)
Gift of Seymour H. Knox   K59:5

Lee Bontecou

Untitled, 1960, is one of the first of the more complicated relief structures which Lee Bontecou made in the early sixties. The central black void, created by an oval-shaped opening, projects from a black board on which the entire relief is mounted. From this cavity, the variously shaped strips of canvas are arranged on a rectangular welded steel frame, attached by pieces of copper wire which were twisted in place and remain visible on the front of the work. She used as her material discarded laundry bags which she obtained from a steam laundry located on the street floor below her studio.

The construction exists on two visual as well as physical planes: one organized simply around the central void from which ray-shaped strips connect it with the frame, and the other consisting of smaller, irregular elements, each designed in a complex pattern.

Lee Bontecou was born in Providence, Rhode Island, in 1931 and lived as a child in Westchester County, New York, and Nova Scotia. She studied at the Art Students League, New York, 1952–55, and in Rome on a Fulbright Fellowship, 1957–58. At that time, she produced birds and imaginary animals of terra-cotta and plaster, later cast in bronze. In 1958, she made her first drawings for reliefs, which she later constructed from canvas, steel, and wire. In 1967, she began to use vacuum-formed transparent plastic to create fish to be suspended from the ceiling and free-standing flowers.

BONTECOU *Untitled* **1960**
Metal and canvas, 43¼ x 51½ x 12 in. (109.9 x 130.9 x 30.5 cm.)
Gift of Seymour H. Knox   K61:8

Claes Oldenburg

Oldenburg has said, "I notice that every time Manhattan is represented it is represented differently, like ancient maps."

Although the muted color and the imprecise linear demarcations of *Soft Manhattan #1 (Postal Zones)* suggest an old map, the three-dimensionality, the materials the artist used, and the subject matter—postal zones were introduced in 1943—are contemporary and innovative. This construction from 1966 is one of a group of soft sculptures in which Oldenburg continued to employ printed canvas filled with kapok, which he had introduced the previous year in his Chrysler Airflow series of car parts.

The artist's interest in maps is one of the numerous preoccupations of his childhood and has continued to occupy him as an adult, supplying the major portion of his subject matter. Despite the soft quality, the map is legible (zones are indicated in pencil) and the total outline as well as the divisions are rendered in accurate scale. Color—predominately gray and terra-cotta—has been applied to the surface by spraying and by pressing corrugated cardboard, previously sprayed with paint, to the canvas in a technique similar to blockprinting. The artist also made a "hard" version of the same subject.

Also in the Gallery collection is the artist's *Glace en dégustation*, 1964.

Claes Oldenburg, son of a diplomat, was born in Stockholm in 1929 and reared in Chicago, where his father was the Swedish Consul. He graduated from Yale University, B.A., 1950, attending art classes only during his final year. Returning to Chicago, he worked at a variety of odd jobs, including that of a newspaper reporter, and studied sporadically at the Art Institute.

In 1956 he went to New York, where he continued to paint in a figurative style and became involved with theater, Happenings, and Environments. During the early sixties, he developed his well-known soft and hard sculptures, frequently producing the same subject in both versions, and sometimes increasing the scale to giant proportions.

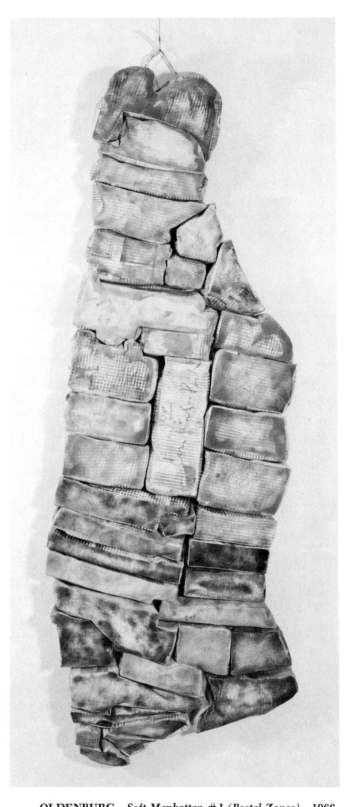

OLDENBURG *Soft Manhattan #1 (Postal Zones)* **1966**
Canvas filled with kapok
76½ x 28 x 8 in. (194.3 x 71.1 x 20.3 cm.)
Gift of Seymour H. Knox   K66:7

Mary Bauermeister

Drawing on Dada's all-inclusive attitude, Mary Bauermeister combines both a variety of materials and a number of processes: drawing, painting, relief sculpture, and assemblage. Accretions of pebbles, straws, shells, fabric, and driftwood, spheres and lenses are often drawn together by her mysterious spidery script.

Despite the appearance of random confusion, a very deliberate logic underlies the 1965 piece *Four Quarters* (or ¼, *Four Quarts*, FOUR QUARTerS, "what-for," "What-4," as the artist has also titled it). The original background layer is divided into four equal squares which are then subdivided into four unequal rectangular segments, according to a regular system which then significantly determines the distribution of the collaged elements. To contradict these logical underpinnings, Bauermeister deliberately chose "more illogic, absurd, chance elements and less geometric": numbers, words, patches, tacks, and photographic details of some of her earlier drawings and linen pieces. "I also tried to use different working methods: (like writing, drawing, ink design, watercolor, collage) and different speeds of the process." The background layer was covered with a sheet of glass embedded with her characteristic optical lenses. "The lenses reverse, double, distort the images. . . . I somehow wanted to unfix what I did in the background, or make it more ambiguous." A final layer of glass, with wooden spheres on which copies of some of the configurations are seen through the lenses, further removes and distorts the background. "I tried to reach a state where one cannot discern any more what is a real drawing or a distortion, or a drawing of that distortion, what is illusion (color) (momentary or stable) or what is really there. Maybe the color is really there? Maybe it's the only thing, which is real? Or?" *

Mary Bauermeister was born in 1934 in Frankfurt, Germany, the daughter of a distinguished scientist, and began painting at the age of nineteen. Although she had no formal art training, her study of composition with the eminent and revolutionary German composer Karlheinz Stockhausen significantly influenced her work. Since 1962, she has made several visits to this country, where she has exhibited her constructions frequently. Retaining her interest in music, she has introduced many American avant-garde compositions to Germany through concerts in her studio.

* Letter from the artist, July 31, 1971.

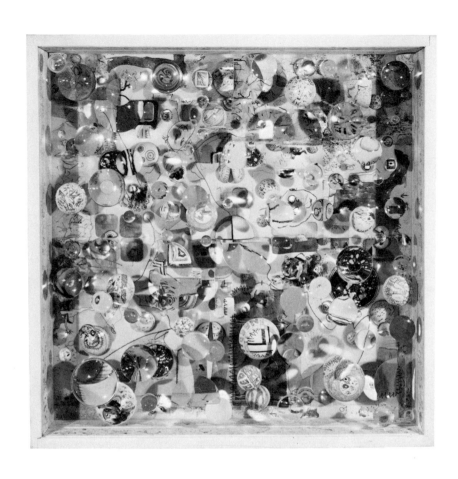

BAUERMEISTER *Four Quarters* **1964–65**
Mixed media, 30 x 30 x 6¾ in. (76.2 x 76.2 x 17.1 cm.)
Gift of Seymour H. Knox   K68:15

Michelangelo Pistoletto

"In the first tableaux, which he executed in 1961–62, Pistoletto was concerned with individual figures, seen face on or in profile. Around 1963, he began expanding his imagery to groups of figures, thereby filling the space and limiting the number of points where the spectator's reflection could fall. In *Sacra Conversazione* [1963] . . . the only empty space is in the center of the conversation group. The artist has emphasized the impassive faces and allowed the figures and garments to remain completely flat, devoid of texture and folds. In color, the picture is made up of silvery grays, the lighter ones close in value to the stainless steel. It is perhaps this type of composition that inspired the analogies with Antonioni films, for the sense of detachment and isolation is strong here, and the languid attitudes of the characters suggest a continuum, more than a moment, of time. . . . The general mood of his tableaux and the grouping of figures in them seem more related to the work of certain Italian Renaissance painters, such as Andrea Mantegna and Piero della Francesca than to modern [figurative painters]." *

The title *Sacra Conversazione* is an allusion to religious paintings of the Italian Renaissance in which figures were depicted conversing. The man in the light gray suit in this work is a self-portrait of the artist.

A second tableau by Pistoletto, *Philodendron*, 1965, is in the Gallery collection.

Michelangelo Pistoletto was born in Biella, Italy, in 1933; the following year his family moved to Turin, where he has continued to live. Until 1956, when he began painting, Pistoletto worked with his father as a restorer of old paintings. His early works were figurative and among them was a series of large compositions with gold, silver, and bronze backgrounds, which stimulated his interest in the use of reflection as an integral aspect of his work. In 1961–62, he began to make his "tableaux," in which photographs of approximately life-size figures and objects are reproduced, usually in shades of gray, on tissue paper, which is then applied to sheets of stainless steel. Some areas remain uncovered, and in these the viewer, the surroundings, or other tableaux are reflected.

* Robert M. Murdock, *Ceroli/Pistoletto* (Albright-Knox Art Gallery, 1969), pp. [5-6].

PISTOLETTO *Sacra Conversazione* 1963
Painted tissue paper on stainless steel
67 x 39½ in. (170.2 x 100.3 cm.)
Gift of Seymour H. Knox   K64:26

George Segal

The multidimensional kind of art which could "incorporate the pressure and presence of . . . immediate surroundings, plus memory, myth, psychology," * finds expression in Segal's characteristic composite tableaux. With a minimal number of straightforward and ordinary props, *Cinema* manages to evoke a poignant mood of late-night loneliness. Against the cold fluorescent light and ominously mute marquee, the frozen figure performs his banal operation with a paradoxical grace which recalls classical sculpture, itself familiar largely through plaster casts. Segal's "models" are his friends and neighbors. The models are wrapped in plaster-soaked gauze strips which, when hardened, are cut away in sections. The interior surfaces of these molds scrupulously duplicate every physiological detail of the person, whose life-cast, however, remains invisible, since Segal reconstructs the figure and alters the exterior to achieve a deliberate anonymity.

Born in 1924, George Segal lived in New York until 1940, then moved to New Brunswick, New Jersey, where he currently lives. He studied painting at Cooper Union, New York University, where he received a B.A. in Art Education in 1949, and Rutgers University, M.F.A., 1963. While teaching at Rutgers in the late fifties, he met Allan Kaprow, several of whose early Happenings took place on Segal's chicken farm. Like Kaprow, Segal became aware of the incompatibility between painting and his own concerns for plasticity and a totality of experience. By 1958 he had begun to experiment with life-size sculptured figures of plaster and burlap over chicken-wire armatures, making a complete break with painting in 1961.

* The artist, in Albright-Knox Art Gallery, *Gallery Notes*, Autumn, 1966, p. 23.

SEGAL *Cinema* **1963**
Plaster, illuminated plexiglass, metal
118 x 96 x 30 in. (299.7 x 243.8 x 99 cm.)
Gift of Seymour H. Knox   K64:3

Robert Indiana

Indiana's Lower East Side neighborhood supplied not only his ideas and motifs but also the actual material for his work. In former chandler's shops, he found old wood, iron wheels, and various insignia as well as brass stencils. This material was first used in the late fifties on wooden assemblages and later appeared in paintings.

In *Star*, 1960–62, the discarded wooden beam, removed from its previous and structural situation, has been placed in an upright position. Impersonal stenciled letters and numbers spell out the decoration of the piece, counting off the five superimposed deep relief slots, labeling the work and dating the piece at the base on one side. Four pairs of iron wheels suggest the possibility of independent movement. The symbolic star appears four times on the side shown in the illustration. On the reverse, the same motif is repeated with the addition of thinly painted circles in which each star is placed.

Also in the collection is *Year of Meteors*, 1961 (p. 383).

Robert Clark adopted Indiana as his surname in tribute to his home state, where he was born in New Castle in 1928. He studied at the John Herron Art Institute in Indianapolis, 1945–46; Munson-Williams-Proctor Institute, Utica, New York, 1947–48; Art Institute of Chicago, 1949–53; and in Great Britain at Edinburgh College of Art, 1953–54, and London University, 1954. In 1956, he moved to New York, where he rented a loft on Coenties Slip on the Lower East Side, a locale that was to play a major role in his work. Dating from the time when New York was Nieuw Amsterdam, Coenties is the oldest, largest, and busiest of the slips and is constructed in the form of a Y, a shape that also appears in the leaves of nearby ginkgo trees and which Indiana frequently employed as a design motif. He has stated that his use of lettering derives from several sources: the thickly lettered wall of a neighboring building; letters and numbers on passing boats, ships, and trucks in the area; and his discovery of old commercial stencils that he put to new use in his work.

He developed a hard-edge style during 1957–59 and made considerable use of the circle and variations on the circle after 1960. During 1960 he created a number of three-dimensional constructions, returning to painting the following year. Although related to Pop art, Indiana's work is more literary, poetic, and nonobjective than that of most artists associated with the movement.

INDIANA *Star* **1962**
Oil and gesso on wood, iron wheels
76 x 18 x 13 in. (193 x 45.7 x 33 cm.)
Gift of Seymour H. Knox   K63:9

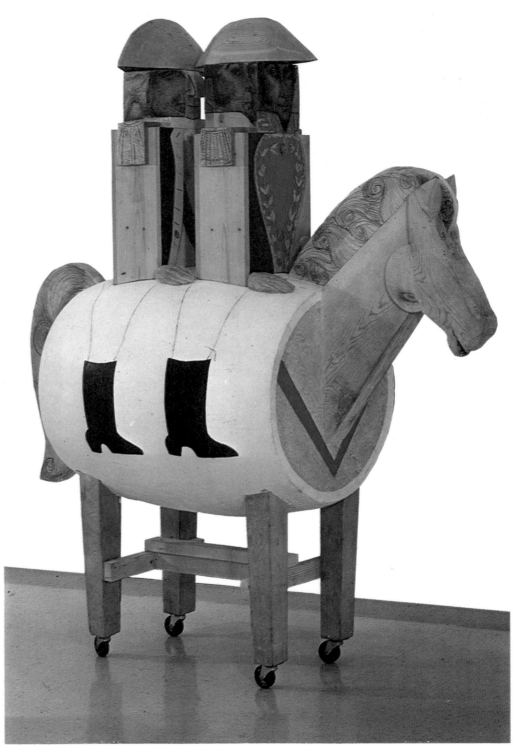

MARISOL *The Generals* **1961–62**
Wood and mixed media, 87 x 28½ x 76 in. (221 x 72.4 x 193 cm.)
Gift of Seymour H. Knox   K62:7

KLEIN   *Lecteur I.K.B. 1960 (No. 1)*   1960
40½ x 12 x 5½ in. (102.9 x 30.5 x 14 cm.)
Lecteur I.K.P. 1960   1960
38½ x 11¼ x 4½ in. (97.8 x 28.5 x 11.5 cm.)
Lecteur I.K.B. 1960 (No. 2)   1960
46½ x 11 x 5½ in. (118.1 x 27.9 x 14 cm.)
Painted sponges on brass bases
Gifts of Seymour H. Knox   K61:11.1,2,3

Marisol

In *The Generals*, 1961–62, nearly life-size caricatures of George Washington and Simon Bolívar are seated on a large toy horse. The block-like figures appear to be unfinished, as does much of the painting and drawing, although other areas, such as Bolívar's face, are rendered with detailed precision. Bolívar's cubical head is painted on three sides, but on the back side the reflection of Washington's face is sketched so that he is looking at himself. The hands of both generals are plaster casts of the artist's hands. A naturalistic feature is the teeth, both real and gold, in the horse's mouth. The barrel forming the body of the horse contains a tape recording of a march by David Amram, *Koronal Kreplach*, composed for the sculpture.

Also in the Gallery collection is the artist's sculpture *Baby Girl*, 1963.

Marisol (in Spanish Mar y Sol, "sea and sun") Escobar was born of Venezuelan parents in Paris in 1930. Her family moved frequently—from Paris to Caracas, then back to Europe, to Venezuela, and finally to the United States. She has said the experience of living in different environments as a child was more important to her development as an artist than her later attendance at art schools. However, she was trained as a painter at l'École des Beaux-Arts, Paris, 1949, the Art Students League after her arrival in New York in 1950, and with Hans Hofmann in Provincetown, 1951–54. In 1953, she turned to sculpture and studied with William King, who was an importance influence on her work. Her first sculptures were small clay figures which she later enclosed in boxes. As she employed additional materials, her works became assemblages, gradually increasing in size, in which she combined carving, modeling, painting, drawing, and found objects. Although she is interested in pre-Columbian and folk art and her work is often intentionally childlike and superficially naïve, Marisol's sculptures are sophisticated and reflect her completely original approach to caricature.

Yves Klein

In 1958, Klein began to use "living brushes," nude models covered with paint who pressed themselves against his canvases at Klein's direction. The sponges used to apply the paint to the models were then hardened with fixative and mounted on wire bases. *Lecteur IKB 1960 (No. 1)* and *Lecteur IKB 1960 (No. 2)* are sponges soaked with International Klein Blue (IKB), a color which symbolized infinite space and pure sensitivity for Klein. "My monochrome attempt has conducted me to the blue, the blue showed me the immaterial." * IKB was used in Klein's works frequently after the mid-fifties. The red color of the third sponge *Lecteur IKP 1960* began to appear in his work in 1960.

Yves Klein was born in Nice, France, in 1928, the son of two painters, Marie (née Raymond) and Frits Klein, a Dutch Malaysian. In 1946 Klein began to paint, encouraged by his friends, Claude Pascal and Arman.

The artist has written, "It was in 1947 that I had the idea, the conscious vision of 'monochrome.' I painted and drew during this period [1946–47] but not much: the fact that my mother and father were painters annoyed me. . . . Thanks to them, however, I was aware of the extremely avant-garde theories in painting. It was in these circumstances that . . . my research led me to the gaudy painting, in gouache, of surfaces of monochrome color in a sort of pointillism, but with only one color; then . . . I decided to discard all this and cover the surfaces with one, uniform scrupulously monochome color." † He chose the color blue for his monochrome experiment. In London, where Klein lived in 1949, he used the name Yves le Monochrome for the first time. After studying in Japan, 1952–53, he returned to Europe, spent a year in Spain, and lived and worked in Paris from 1955 until his death in 1962 at the age of 34.

* *Yves Klein le Monochrome* (New York: Leo Castelli Gallery, 1961), p. [2].
† *Yves Klein* (New York: Jewish Museum, 1969), p. 32.

Donald Judd

"I don't like sculpture with a handled look, just as I don't like the evidence of brushwork in painting. All of that implies expressionism, implies that the artist is involved with the work as he goes along. It's a particular attitude that comes out of the European tradition. I want the material to be material when you look at it." *

Judd's 1969 *Untitled* consists of ten boxes cantilevered at regular vertical intervals from a wall. The identical units (each 27 inches wide and 24 inches deep) are separated by intervals exactly equal to their height of six inches in a predetermined and totally symmetrical scheme. This "stack" configuration has recurred frequently in Judd's work since the mid-sixties, in a variety of different materials, colors, and dimensions.

Judd has consistently sought to avoid a traditional European hierarchical composition of balanced individual parts in favor of a structure apprehended as a single integrated experience. Since 1964, his pieces have been manufactured industrially according to his specifications, giving them the meticulous anonymity he favors.

The absence of any visible means of attachment, the exaggerated extent of projection, and the use of translucent orange plexiglass within the galvanized iron bands create a dramatic impact far greater than the simple materials would imply.

Donald Judd was born in Excelsior Springs, Missouri in 1928 and spent his childhood in the Midwest, Philadelphia, and New Jersey. After a year in the Army in Korea, he attended the Art Students League in New York, 1947–53, the College of William and Mary, 1948–49, and Columbia University, from which he received a B.S. degree in philosophy, 1953, and an M.A. in art history, 1957–62. From 1959 to 1965, his writings in several major art periodicals exercised considerable influence on the direction of both criticism and avant-garde painting and sculpture.

Judd was originally a painter of dark, flat abstractions, but his desire to avoid even the slightest degree of illusionism in his work inevitably led him to sculpture. His first reliefs were exhibited in New York in 1963. His subsequent free-standing boxes and objects constituted a rejection of the additive and assembled approach to sculpture—as practiced by Picasso, Gonzalez, and David Smith—which has characterized much modern sculpture of the twentieth century.

* The artist, in *The National Observer*, February 20, 1967.

JUDD *Untitled* **1969**
Galvanized iron and plexiglass
10 ft. x 27⅛ in. x 24 in.
(304.8 x 68.9 x 61 cm.)
Edmund Hayes Fund   72:4

Joseph Cornell

Like much of Cornell's work, *Soap Bubble Set (Ostend Hotel)*, c. 1958, cannot be precisely dated. The blistered paint and deep blue sand relate it closely to the Hotel series, which he began in the early fifties, while the horizontal bars, planetary chart and blue cork sphere recur frequently in the Space Object Boxes of the fifties and early sixties.

Metamorphosis and enigma are the core of Cornell's work. Within a closed and shallow space, he manages to suggest the vastness of the universe. Exploiting the process of decay through broken glass, chipped plaster, and cracked paint, the artist still communicates a sense of order and permanence. The glass at the front not only enhances the remoteness of the objects within but also emphasizes the sense of the contents having been deliberately lifted out of time. Along one side and the front edges, yellowed pages from foreign encyclopedias continue the enumeration of disparate objects abstracted from life.

Born in 1903 in Nyack, New York, Cornell in 1929 moved to Flushing, New York, where he has continued to live. Although he attended Phillips Andover Academy, he is largely self-taught as an artist, having absorbed important if informal schooling from the expatriate European Surrealists dominating the New York art world in the 1930's. His earliest works were collages and subtle groupings of found objects. By the time of his first one-man show in 1933, the objects had been combined with two-dimensional collage and the resulting constructions were enclosed in the theatrical framework of a shallow box. His boxes, although frequently exhibited with the Surrealists and undoubtedly influenced by their methods and ideas, never adopted the acerbic irony of Surrealist assemblage. Instead, Cornell continues to evoke a quiet and intense nostalgia.

CORNELL *Soap Bubble Set (Ostend Hotel)* **c. 1958**
Construction and collage, 8 x 16½ x 3⅜ in. (20.3 x 42 x 8.5 cm.)
Edmund Hayes Fund   71:3

Movement, Optical Phenomena, and Light

George Rickey

A group of some sixty works in the Albright-Knox Art Gallery collection demonstrates the recent use of certain visual devices that have hitherto been ignored, deprecated as minor art, dismissed as curiosities, or only served up as a side dish. I speak of the artist's substitution of movement, light apparatus, and optical phenomena for painting, carving, and modeling; of physical and psychical stimuli for subject matter, static order, and cultivated satisfaction. The sample in this collection shows how some twentieth-century artists have brought a startling new set of unsanctified practices into the long and holy succession of artistic modes.

This invasion is a consequence of Constructivist ideas of nonobjective art that have emerged during the last half-century. The idea of an art without reference to the observed environment, and often using geometric figures as motif, followed the invention of Cubism in France in the first decade of this century. The Constructivist style crystalized in Russia and Holland between 1913 and 1920. Partly through the influence of the Bauhaus in Germany, partly through the displacement and dispersal of artists during World War II, the style became international. At first it won only a few dedicated adherents, but after 1950 both recruitment and recognition increased. Ten years later, it began to displace Abstract Expressionism as the dominant international style. By 1970 the Constructivist movement, after fifty years of continuous development, had shown itself to be one of the strongest and most persistent of the twentieth century. Whether in painting or sculpture, Constructivism can be described as a nonmimetic art, without association or symbolism, without handwriting or any other assertive "process" that could express the artist, often rectilinear, often sharing materials and technology with industry; in short, premeditated, self-effacing, deliberate; therefore unartistic.

This kind of "cold" art tapped a different kind of talent, developed different ideas, exploited different resources. To the *sight* of nature, which had been an inspiration for thousands of years, these artists seemed blind, but they quickly came to examine nature, not for its appearance but for its hidden forces, for its physical energies, for its performance. Thus did movement become a sculptor's material; thus did the space in which movement occurred become as important as mass; thus did the immediate effects of sound, light, and color on the senses offer a more direct road to the spectator than did recollections of previous experience, allusions to myths and legends, or symbolic constructs. The spectator exposed to such forces need not be either educated or tasteful; he is a sensitive organism to be stimulated by the phenomena that nature, with some stage setting by the artist, has provided.

KINETIC ART. The term dates from 1920, when Naum Gabo used it for a motor-driven vibrating spring he had made in Moscow and exhibited two years later in Berlin. But the great exponent and popularizer of sculpture that moves has been Alexander Calder, who first exhibited such works in 1932 in Paris. There are two works by him in the Gallery collection, dated 1950 and 1960. These are classical Calder "mobiles," an invention that has come to be understood, respected, and loved the world over. They consist essentially of wires with a loop at one end, a loop near the middle, and a free end to which a vane is attached. The end loop of one wire is linked to the mid-loop of the next, making a zig-zag chain from top to bottom. The chained vanes respond to breezes in a graceful, lyrical, rhythmic, ever self-renewing dance. They are drawings in space, sometimes with witty visual surprises, such as the long, slender, curving branch of *Conger*, with its three vertical leaves among all the other horizontal ones, which hang in clusters or catenaries from the ceiling. *The Cone* contains only vertical vanes, all circular; this mobile hangs from a rigid lever arm, itself mounted on a pivot-cup turning on the point of a conical "stabile." Such stabiles, without any mobile adjunct, have, in the last decade, been Calder's principal preoccupation.

By the time Calder had made the earlier of these two mobiles, other artists had begun to explore much wider possibilities of kinetic art. Some of these were presented at an historically important exhibition, *Le Mouvement*, in Paris in 1955. By 1961 the interest in kinetic art had spread so widely that a huge exhibition was organized for the Stedelijk Museum, in Amsterdam, the Moderna Museet in Stockholm, and the Louisiana Museum near Copenhagen, in which virtually all the artists then working seriously with movement were shown. In the subsequent decade the activity in kinetic art increased enormously in Europe, in North and South America, and in Japan.

The Albright-Knox collection includes kinetic works by five artists who, besides Calder, had shown at the *Mouvement* exhibition: Jesús Raphael Soto, Jean Tinguely, Pol Bury, Yaacov Agam, and Victor Vasarely.

Soto hangs thread-supported wires and sticks in front of a pin-striped panel. When these move in response to the touch of the wind, they set off vivid optical effects, which are discussed later as "moiré." Tinguely often uses a sardonic combination of abandoned manmade objects, driven uselessly, endlessly, and noisily in a breathless tempo, by electric motors. His *Cocktail au cheval* is typical. An earlier work, *Peut-être No. 11*, is more a kinetic abstract painting, or relief; the black-and-white crescents rotate, also by motor, in a whirling, overlapping, kinetic collage.

Bury also uses motors but avoids the repetitiveness and risk of boredom that appear in those motor-driven sculptures doomed to a repeating cycle. If the cycle is simple enough and short enough to be remembered, the interest ends when the cycle is learned. Pol Bury's movement is so slow and so limited that at first glance the work seems stationary. Only as one contemplates it with close attention does one begin to see the changes and that the amount and direction of the movement are unpredictable. Bury has devised a simple but ingenious transmission of power from a motor to the moving parts. In the *Nine Balls on Five Planes*, there is infinite diversity of the tiny creepings, twitches, and jerks in ironic contrast with the simple, classic mass of the nine balls teetering on the edge of their precipices, from which they retreat just in time.

Yaacov Agam is a resourceful artist with several ways of introducing movement. He had earlier used motors to rotate abstract shapes on a panel. Later he invited stroking by hand for motive power, as in his *Loud Tactile Painting*, where the polished buttons, mounted on spring steel rods, when brushed by the hand, dance in patterns of their own, making a brief kinetic painting. He has also designed works for the observer to arrange. Agam's most serious statements, however, are the transformable paintings, of which *Free Standing Painting* is an outstanding example. Movement of the spectator is required in many kinetic works to bring about the relative displacement of the parts, but Agam, in this work, rotates the whole painting for the same result. The observer discovers successively ten distinct paintings, five on each side of the panel as follows:

Side A 1. Black bands separating the graded bands of single colors— white, purple, green, red—and merging colors—red to yellow to white to orange—blue to white to yellow. Then as the painting turns

2. The above elements combined with white and colors and mixed rectangles against white. Then, turning further

3. The whole panel becomes visible showing the combination of all facets

4. 1, 2, and 3 are subtracted, leaving the combination of 4 and 5. Then

5. As 4 disappears, a simple painting of circles and triangles against black survives.

There is then an equivalent series of five successive compositions on the other side, from the single motifs at each end to the combination of four in the mid position.

Victor Vasarely, who was the pioneer of "art cinétique" in Paris in the fifties, also made sculptures in which there was relative displacement of the parts as the spectator moved. He became more interested, however, in the sensations of *apparent* movement resulting from optical phenomena. His paintings will be discussed later, together with other optical works.

Len Lye's interest in movement dates from an even earlier time than Calder's. He did his first kinetic explorations in 1928, when he began drawing directly on celluloid film to make moving images on the screen. He became a documentary filmmaker, then began making kinetic constructions that he could photograph under controlled light conditions, and then concentrated on the kinetic constructions themselves. His *Grass*, which is an electrically driven, programed machine, produces mechanically a striking analogy with random, wind-caused movements in nature. He writes: "*Grass* came about without any preconceived ideas about its imagery. It came from watching a single rod swaying and then doubling up to emphasize the accelerating stroke of its oscillation. It was the 'lurch' part of the sway I liked. It should be timed to slow music, a suitable tempo is given by Miles Davis doing 'These Foolish Things,' but I would prefer something in similar tempo in the Satie style."

Julio Le Parc, a member of the Groupe de Recherche d'Art Visuel, together with Jean Pierre Yvaral and Francisco Sobrino, of whom more later, uses both light and movement in a simple device that yields a very rich result. In his *Unstable-continual Light*, small squares of highly polished metal are hung on nylon threads at regular intervals within a square format. The slightest disturbance of air causes a large degree of movement of the individual squares. These catch and lose their reflections with sudden and brilliant contrasts in a random play of light and shade.

Paul Talman's *K—121, Black/White* requires participation of the spectator. One hundred and twenty-one balls, each half white, half black, are set in sockets on a black panel so that they can be rotated by hand. The spectator may turn the black sides up, making an all-black relief, or the white sides up, making a series of white hemispheres against black, or any of the infinite permutations between, part black, part white. Since the work does not move of itself, it might perhaps be called a "movable." The artist's surrender of control to a spectator (an extension of Constructivist self-effacement) is a further step toward depersonalizing the artist, who thus engages in a dialogue.

Harry Kramer's *Cylinder with Three Paws* is only incidentally kinetic. His animal form, of wire mesh, is static, but it contains, as his other animals do, a group of moving parts, arranged by Kramer as a little comic theatrical performance. As an artist he began on the stage and he has never really left it.

Alfred Dunn's *Echoes* combines sight, sound, and chance. A hanging ball hits a rotating wheel and bounces off to strike against seven musical rods, tuned in a scale and with differing timbre and pitch.

Tsai combines movement and light in *Harmonic Sculpture #11*. The square plates, mounted on spring wires, as in Agam's above, are agitated by the motor. The wires dance, each according to its own individual nature. The intermittent strobe light appears to stop the movement so that the spectator perceives an infinite sequence of altered still images, which he may modify. Tsai writes, "In reality your activity does not alter the motion of the rods or plates. These are in a constant and unvarying rate of harmonic motion (most at the rate of 30 vibrations per second, some at 20 per second). But you are varying the rate of the strobe flashes (one flash lasts about one millionth of a second). The strobes flash at regular intervals. When the rate of the flashes is the same as the rate of the vibrations of the rods, i.e., 30 per second, the motion of the rods appears fixed, and they appear to be stationary. But they appear to be in the shape of a harmonic curve, and not a straight line as would normally be expected.

"When the rate of the strobe flashes is altered to slightly slower or greater than the rate of the rods' vibrations (30 per second) then the rods appear to be slowly undulating, like the tentacles of a sea anemone under water. The greater the rate of the strobe flashes deviates from the constant harmonic motion of the rods, the more rapidly the rods appear to be moving and the more excited they seem to become."

OPTICAL PHENOMENA. In the middle of the nineteenth century, the chemist Chevreul, while doing studies for the Gobelin tapestry factory, noted and described the phenomenon of "simultaneous contrast," wherein two colors of similar value on the light-dark scale but contrasting in hue, appear each to enhance the other and to shift the apparent hue of the one toward the complementary of the other. The mutual intensification is highest when the two colors are exact complementaries.

This discovery was understood and exploited by the Impressionists and their successors. It was understood earlier by Delacroix and, doubtless, by other painters. It has since become universal knowledge among painters who have never heard of Chevreul.

During the nineteenth century, color came to be used more and more for its own sake, rather than to describe the appearance of objects, so-called local color. This development culminated in the arbitrary selection by the Fauves in Paris in 1905 of intense colors that *contradicted* hues in nature. Among twentieth-century artists, color has ranged from the arbitrary transpositions and intensifications of the Fauves and the German Expressionists, through the monochromy of early Cubism, to polychromy in its later, decorative stages; then came the clear, hard-edged primaries of Mondrian, the Bauhaus, and early Kandinsky, the geometric containers for color of Josef Albers and Auguste Herbin (the former preoccupied with the nuances of relationship, the latter with richness of color sensation). These were followed by the romantic Abstract Expressionism of Mark Rothko and the flooding sensation of Yves Klein's saturated blue.

In the last twenty years, color has been a topic of increasing interest and dispute. It has been rejected by some as a personal indulgence (note the black-and-white exhibitions of the sixties) and exploited romantically by others at the risk of indictment for saccharine decoration (Frank Stella and Kenneth Noland). Victor Vasarely's paintings in the Gallery collection illustrate the range in a single artist.

Still others have reacted against romantic color by using it for its unpleasant qualities (Olle Baertling is an example) or, without feeling, simply to mark provinces as mapmakers do or to separate areas, like a yellow line in the road.

A further development has been the isolation of the phenomenon of "color vibration," and its use in a very intensified form, to penetrate the consciousness of the spectator. The optical disturbance set off by juxtaposing very intense contrasting colors of similar light-dark value arises out of Chevreul's simultaneous-contrast observations. The colors appear more vivid, they seem to flow over their edges, they advance from the plane on which they are painted and make the reading of distance uncertain. Anuszkiewicz, in both of his paintings in the collection, uses this effect. Each color enhances its neighbor and is itself enhanced by the juxtaposition. Larry Poons, in his *Orange Crush*, places electric green-blue dots against slightly darker orange (blue and orange are complementary colors; when mixed they make gray). For the observer, the dots jump forward and seem to stagger. With intent observation appear (as the eye is fatigued) residual images of the dots now displaced and floating on a lighter, more intense orange, the complementary of the original blue. Poons thus obtains a very considerable consequence from a composition so apparently simple that it could be thought inane. On the contrary, there is also a deeper order; these dots are not distributed at random but are organized on a complex and entirely methodical system, which distributes the basic motif (note, for example, the vertically twinned dots, the diagonal twins, not quite so close), over a calculated but hidden grid prepared on graph paper.

This kind of play of colors, one against another, for agitation and stimulus, rather than for harmony or pleasure, can be found in a somewhat more restrained way in the two works of Henry Pearson (in addition to other optical qualities caused by the undulation of the lines). Color enlivens the circles of Tadasky, Peter Sedgley, Julio Le Parc, the red and green structure of Getulio Alviani, and, together with other powerful visual forces, the *Polychromatic Diffraction* of Yvaral.

Since these stimuli are physical and immediate, like a pinprick, they lend themselves naturally to nonobjective art. Though retinal stimulation has been used, sometimes intuitively, by painters and decorators within a figurative context, attempts to combine emphatic optical stimuli with figuration have not been happy, as can be seen in early works (1932) by Vasarely.

In these situations it is the figuration that suffers, confirming the finding that the eye and the mind read *value* contrasts more readily than either meaning or color. Subject matter dilutes; without it the forces are more controlled and gain in force.

These optical assaults, in their pure form, without divertive association, recollection, or symbolism, sometimes bring violent physical reactions that are far from pleasurable. They can even cause dizziness and nausea. Such teasing of the retina, however, does not mean that these are mere calculated statements with no component of expressive feeling. Vasarely can be seen as lyrical; Albers as romantic; Soto even as fantasy.

OPTICAL PHENOMENA, ACHROMATIC. Color, whether in isolated, pure tones, such as the canvases of Yves Klein, or in relationships like those of Matisse, or in vibrant, contrived situations like those of Anuszkiewicz, may provide the richest direct experiences for the eye. But there are also many colorless (achromatic) optical phenomena that, in the last twenty years, have been exploited by artists.

The best known of these devices is probably moiré, which takes its name from an ancient treatment of ribbed silk, where the two surfaces were laid at a slight angle and pressed with an iron, each set of ribs then making an impression on the other. The intersections of the lines seen under a reflecting light made a secondary pattern on the silk. Soto, in his *Wood—Iron Rods*, hangs linear forms on threads in front of a pin-striped panel. One notices how the otherwise invisible threads combine energetically with the pin stripes and how depth perception is diminished. Similar circumstances are set up in Yvaral's *Acceleration #15, Series B* and Miguel Vidal's *Focus of Light*; the latter, though on dark blue, is functionally achromatic. Josef Levi's *Simurgh* employs an equivalent device of superimposed grids and spots resulting in "interference" patterns, somewhat similar in principle to those analyzed in crystallography.

Another device is the abrupt dislocation of patterns, as in Vasarely's *Bora III*, where black and white stripes are cut off by transverse lines supplied by the observer's eye, not by the artist's hand. The cuts give the illusion, in this painting, of a secondary image of concentric squares. In addition, there appear, for some, after-images of deeper black and even of color.

Optical illusions (one may write "allusions" also, as these images evoke recollections of previous visual space experiences) are employed to lead the observer into awareness of contradictions: a design, known to be flat, may compel a reading in three dimensions, as in Vasarely's *Mindanao*, where the related zig-zags of the linear pattern combine to be read as relief. Even more compelling is Bridget Riley's *Drift No. 2*, where the identically drawn (but shifted) light and dark lines, each uniformly shaded throughout its length, oblige the observer to see the rippled surface of a column. Illusionistic perspective may be forced by shading, by convergent lines, as in *Convex, Concave I Dimensional* of Anuszkiewicz, and by other devices that make spaces and volumes appear and disappear.

While such illusions are not confined to achromatic painting, it is the light-dark relationships, as noted above, that determine the illusion. This will be seen in such colored examples as Anuszkiewicz's *Water from the Rock*, Stanczak's *Unrest*, Pearson's *Relax, Relax* and *Gandabrod Ball II*, Yvaral's *Polychromatic Diffraction*, and possibly most assertive of all, Vasarely's *Vega-Nor*. All of these, including Anuszkiewicz's cube, are illusionist distortions of a flat surface.

A fourth means of penetrating directly to the observer's nervous system is the use of concentric rings. Noland and Jasper Johns seem to have been the first to use target rings to desanctify the image and to nullify the customary vertical and horizontal orientation given to a picture on a wall. Fangor and Peter Sedgley use the endlessness of the circle to set their color afloat and free it from landscape or vertical-horizontal norms. In all these the circle is a neutral container. But concentric circles of narrow, contrasting lines, whether colored or achromatic, can arouse a special response in the seeing apparatus; their close alternations make it difficult for the eye to ride around the curves. Agitation follows, as one sees in Tadasky, in Le Parc's *Series 14, No. 2* and, in an even more intensified way, because of the movement, in Celentano's *Kinetic Painting III*, which combines two phenomena.

LIGHT. Another medium for the painter or sculptor, as distinct as movement, is the use of light itself, with its properties of reflection, refraction, and diffraction, as a means of ordering form or arousing the spectator by its impact. Light is a form of energy, and it can arrive at the eye by many different roads, from the blinding blink of stroboscopic lamps, to the barely reflecting surfaces of Ad Reinhardt's black canvases. Light's function in art has been, for thousands of years, to reveal the work, whether by torchlight in a cave, by sunlight on the façade of a Mayan temple, or by concealed spotlight in a museum. But now, within half a generation, light itself has been adopted, just as color or mass or sound or space has come to be used by painters, sculptors, composers, or architects. In this collection one finds light radiating from incandescent lamps in Howard Jones, from neon tubes in Millonzi, reflected from faceted surfaces in Richter, Mack, and Agam, from mirrors in Samaras, transmitted and refracted through transparent colored plexiglass in Sobrino and Lamis, and off the white painted heads of nails in Uecker.

It is obvious that an enormous variety of means and manner is available to the artist who uses this kind of energy as his equivalent of paint or clay. To classify by source, such as neon, or by modulation, such as mirrors or colored glass, becomes academic and unilluminating. Here are a few unclassified examples:

Martha Boto in *Optical Interferences* works with a programmed light source that comes through slits into polished metal tubes. These slits are, she writes, "installed in the turning disc and the fixed facing panel. These connections constantly sent through the tubes in different places are multiplied by four mirrors installed on the four interior surfaces of the box. These luminous projections can fill a large space if the work is placed in shadow."

In his untitled double box, Larry Bell first encloses a large, sharply defined space within four clear, clean, glass walls—an irreducible minimum for the eye to recognize and accept as a container. The space could not be more positively enclosed, yet the eye passes unhindered past the frontiers and through the space. In the box above it, the skin is closed and the interior mostly hidden, except where a figure of two ellipses, one inside the other, makes a window on each face that is silvered on the inner surface. Through this window one is allowed only a confusing glimpse of a part of the interior plus a fraction of the other windows. Thus an enigmatic space and a fully disclosed one are brought together and kept in contrast.

Samaras also has made a box, but one into which one is permitted to enter. Once inside, the visitor finds that the walls of this cube disappear, or rather are replaced by endless, receding landscapes of reflection. Walls, ceiling, and floor are mirrors; each enclosing wall disappears into the reflection of its reflection. A mirror-covered table and chair are standing in the room, but they, too, disappear into the endless hazy distance above, below, and on all sides. This is a masterpiece of rational illusion.

With the plexiglass structures of Francisco Sobrino and Leroy Lamis, the light passes through the surfaces, with each overlap subtracting something, and with surprising concentrations of light and dark marking the emission and absorption at the edges. Reflections of the environment also occur, mixing the most disciplined control with accident.

Luis Tomasello uses light in the most restrained way one could imagine. All his compositions are compiled from white painted cubes or similar blocks of wood, mounted on white panel, so that some facets are concealed from the observer. These hidden facets are painted with brilliant red, blue, yellow, all unseen. However, the white light falling on the panel illuminates these colors, which, in turn, are reflected on the panel as a tinted halo around each cube. This is an art of extreme understatement, requiring patience and close attention from the observer.

If one looks at the dates of the works I have grouped and tried to place in a context, one finds that they fall mostly between 1962 and 1969. Of the sixty I consider, forty-two fall between those years, with twenty-five falling in the three years 1964, 1965, and 1966. These dates coincide, of course, with the two great exhibitions at the Albright-Knox Art Gallery, from which many of the works were acquired. It would be a mistake to assume that production of this kind of art was limited to these years. Quite the contrary, it has continued to increase. The reputation of the artists I have cited continues to grow and the number of recruits is enormous.

The aesthetic or critical evaluation of works of art is a dangerous venture. The view that these preconceived, constructed works are mechanical and dehumanized is at least as risky as to say that any one is a masterpiece. Paradoxically, these planned, contrived, meticulously executed works show an extraordinary diversity, while not in the least trying to be "different." With all their detachment, these artists nevertheless show a personal, highly differentiated, inventive imagination, in spite of the absence of "handwriting." It is in the energy of their mental activity, rather than in any uncensored impulse, that they show their humanity.

CALDER *The Cone* 1960
Steel and aluminum, 100 x 110 x 65 in. (254 x 279.4 x 165.1 cm.)
Gift of Seymour H. Knox   K61:24

Alexander Calder

In *The Cone*, 1960, Calder has combined a Stabile and a Mobile in a single work. The Stabile section consists of two black cone shapes, one placed asymmetrically over the other, each of which was cut to form a triangular void. The Mobile portion is formed by a rigid rod with a large red circle attached at one end and balanced by a freely moving arrangement of white circles suspended from the other. The connecting rod was welded to a separate small cone which rests on the apex of the Stabile, pivoting freely and presenting an ever changing composition. The white discs react to the slightest air movement, bouncing and swaying in an intricate pattern.

Also in the Gallery collection is *Conger*, c. 1950, a Mobile suspended from the ceiling, painted black except for the three vertical elements, which are red, yellow, and blue, suspended from a red wire. This Mobile was formerly in the collection of A. Conger Goodyear.

Alexander Calder was born in 1898 in Philadelphia. His father was Alexander Stirling Calder, a well-known sculptor; his mother was a painter; and his paternal grandfather was also a sculptor. Although his childhood was spent in an atmosphere of art, Calder graduated as a mechanical engineer from Stevens Institute of Technology in Hoboken, New Jersey, in 1919. After a number of short-lived engineering jobs, he began to study at the Art Students League in New York, 1923–26, working part-time as a freelance illustrator for the National Police Gazette.

In 1926, he went to Paris where he soon began his famous Circus, an interest that stemmed originally from a Gazette assignment. Calder fashioned miniature performers and animals of wire, wood, and miscellaneous materials, which he then guided through performances to the accompaniment of recorded music. The troupe was increased and the programs became more elaborate. The Circus introduced Calder to many of the artists in Paris who were to be influential to his career, and it served also as a laboratory in which he developed ideas and techniques used in his later work. The twisted-wire portions of these ingenious, tiny creations evolved into perceptive and amusing figurative sculptures and portraits, resembling line drawings in space.

In 1930, after a visit to Mondrian's studio, Calder abruptly abandoned representational sculpture in favor of abstract, geometrical constructions, involving primary colors, which Jean Arp labeled Stabiles. He gradually began to add movement (another factor of the Circus) to the sculptures, and these became known as Mobiles, named by Marcel Duchamp. The first of these were motorized or operated by hand cranks, which Calder soon found too repetitive and predictable; he then began to create works which were dependent solely on air currents for motion. To this free movement, he often added free-form, organic shapes similar to those of Miró and Arp. By 1934, he had arrived at the basic concepts of the Mobiles and Stabiles, which have constituted the major portion of his work. Usually constructed of sheet aluminum, these range from table size to monumental outdoor sculptures.

Since his first visit to Paris, Calder has divided his time between France and the United States, currently living in Sache and Roxbury, Connecticut.

CALDER *Conger* **c. 1950**
Iron and wire, 43 x 69 x 38 in. (109.2 x 175.2 x 96 cm.)
Gift of A. Conger Goodyear Trust 65:16

ALBERS *Homage to the Square: Terra Caliente* 1963
Oil on masonite, 48 x 48 in. (122 x 122 cm.)
Gift of The Seymour H. Knox Foundation, Inc.
and Evelyn Rumsey Cary Fund 68:7

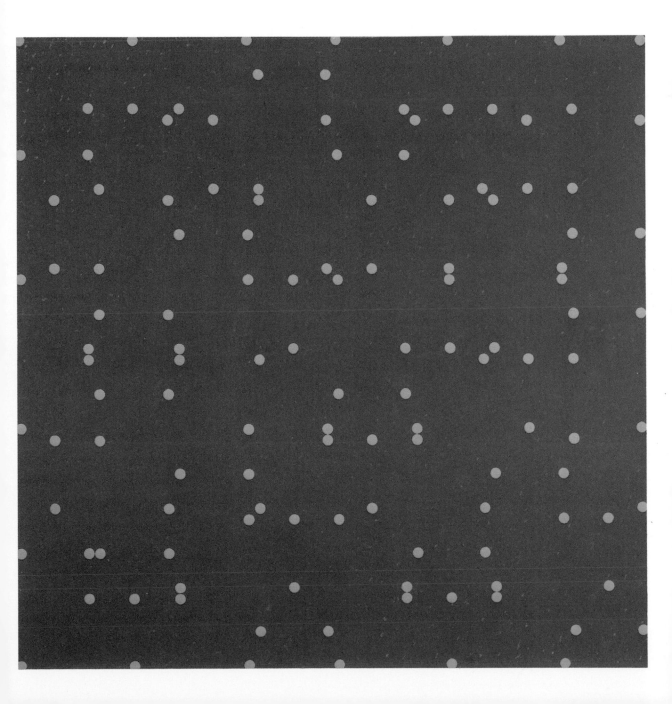

Josef Albers

"In their horizontal arrangement, the smallest square is in the center, and measures four by four units. For each of the three overlapping larger squares, there is an additional one unit to the right and left. In the vertical arrangement there are three half-units below the center square and three one-and-a half units above it. In this way, the spaces left and right, above and below the center balance out in axial extension. The downward shift gives additional weight, but also enhances movement." *

"Seeing several of these paintings next to each other makes it obvious that each painting is an instrumentation in its own. This means that they are all of different palettes, and, therefore, so to speak of different climates. Choice of colors used, as well as their order, is aimed at interaction—influencing and changing each other forth and back. Thus, character and feeling alter from painting to painting without any additional 'handwriting' or, so called, texture. Though the underlying symmetrical and quasi-concentric order of squares remains the same in all paintings—in proportion and placement—these same squares group or single themselves, connect and separate in many different ways. In consequence, they move forth and back, in and out, and grow up and down and far and near, as well as, enlarged and diminished. All this, to proclaim color autonomy as a means of plastic organization." †

Two paintings from this series are in the Gallery collection: *Homage to the Square: Terra Caliente*, 1963, and *Homage to the Square: Dedicated*, 1955, with a purple center, surrounded by two shades of gray and a yellow.

Josef Albers was born in 1888 in Bottrop, Westphalia, Germany. He studied at art schools in Berlin, Essen, and Munich from 1913 until 1920, when he enrolled at the newly founded Bauhaus. He taught at the Bauhaus from 1923 until the school was closed by the Nazi government ten years later. He then emigrated to the United States, teaching at Black Mountain College in North Carolina, 1933–49, and at Yale University, where he was Chairman of the Department of Design, School of the Fine Arts, 1950–59.

From the beginning of his career, Albers produced abstract works as well as conventional figurative compositions, which he soon abandoned completely. The first of his many serial works, a group of gouaches based on the motif of the treble clef, was begun in Germany and completed at Black Mountain. During the 1930's and 1940's, his compositions became increasingly simplified, texture was virtually eliminated, and the major emphasis was on a balance between relationships of color and form.

As an artist, a teacher, and a writer, Albers has been an important influence on the artists of several generations, including those later involved in widely divergent movements. His theories have affected a major portion of the painting of recent decades in which color is an important component.

---

* Albers, *Scrapbook*, vol. 9, Library of The Museum of Modern Art, New York.
† The artist, in *Josef Albers: Homage to the Square* (New York: The Museum of Modern Art, 1964), p. [16].

Larry Poons

Orange Crush, 1963, one of Poons's earliest optical paintings, is named for a popular soft drink of an unnatural, man-made color, reminiscent of the intense orange of the background. Although the blue-green dots appear to have been placed at random, Poons's designs for these paintings were carefully and mathematically planned; he made preparatory drawings, and in *Orange Crush* the penciled outlines of a grid and the revised placement of the small circles remain visible. The dots suggest musical notes aligned on staffs; they and their flashing after-images, induced by the use of complementary colors, activate the surface with a staccato rhythm of repeats and intervals. The lack of any central focus in the painting and the intensity of the color and the after-images force the eye to move quickly and constantly over the surface of the painting, thus introducing an element of time which further accentuates the comparison to music.

Larry Poons was born in Tokyo, Japan, in 1937, though his family returned to the United States the following year. He studied music at the New England Conservatory, Boston, 1955–57, and attended the Boston Museum School of Fine Arts for six months in 1958 before moving to New York. In his early works, he attempted to transcribe musical themes into visual geometric designs, shortly beginning to employ optical effects of color, particularly complementary colors which induce after-images. During the late 1960's, the small, ordered areas of color such as the circles in Orange Crush were replaced by more loosely painted ellipses in several colors, which appear to turn and flicker, moving within a larger and deeper space. In his more recent paintings, he pours acrylic paints directly on the canvases, building up heavy layers of paint which crack and blister in the drying process.

Victor Vasarely

In 1947, Vasarely vacationed at Belle-Île-en-Mer, an island off the coast of Brittany, where the sea and the pebbles and bits of glass polished by continuous exposure to the waves inspired a group of abstract paintings that the artist calls his Belle-Île series. Although *Mindanao* (named for the southernmost of the Philippine Islands) is of a later date, 1952–55, it is primarily related to that series. The elongated ovoid form was developed in the Belle-Île paintings and, in the artist's words, indicates the "oceanic feeling." The horizontal lines, angular and curving, a motif he frequently employed, undoubtedly suggest stylized waves, moving in several directions and overlapping. The muted color of the painting anticipates a series of black-and-white paintings executed in the late 1950's and early 1960's. *Bora III*, 1964, from that group, and *Vega-Nor*, 1969, a colorful "net" painting, are also in the Gallery collection.

The artist has written that the title of *Bora* refers to "a wind in Hungary which descends vertically from the Carpathian Mountains and always blows at night. *Bora III* is a vertical composition on a black ground with lines of accented forces." Of *Vega-Nor*, he stated, "Vega is a distant star well known by everyone. . . . This composition expresses the extension, the expansion of the Universe: the extreme of the great infinities of Nature. . . . Most of my expanding compositions have been called Vega but in order to differentiate them—aside from numbering—I add a small word." *

Victor Vasarely was born in Pecs, Hungary, in 1908. He studied medicine for two years before enrolling for a year at the Mühely Academy, a version of the Bauhaus that had been started in Budapest by Alexander Bortnyik. In 1930, he went to Paris where he earned a living for several years as a commercial artist. In 1945, he began to paint in a Surrealist style, turning to abstract art in 1947. Since that time, he has developed an optical art based on a repeat pattern of geometric units, modified by variations in shape and color—works that persent, simultaneously, a strong surface design and an impression of images actively moving in space. Vasarely has worked both in brilliant colors and with a palette limited to black and white. His production includes three-dimensional constructions, in addition to paintings and graphics. In recent years, he has confined himself to planning his works, which are then executed by assistants.

A prolific writer as well as graphic artist, Vasarely has had a wide influence on younger artists. Lately, he has been concerned primarily with the integration of all the arts and has established a foundation for that purpose.

---

* Letter from the artist, August 3, 1972.

VASARELY *Mindanao* **1952–55**
Oil on canvas, 63½ x 51⅛ in. (161.3 x 129.9 cm.)
Gift of Seymour H. Knox   K58:45

VASARELY *Bora III*   **1964**
Oil on canvas, 58 x 55½ in. (147.3 x 141 cm.)
Gift of Seymour H. Knox   K66:2

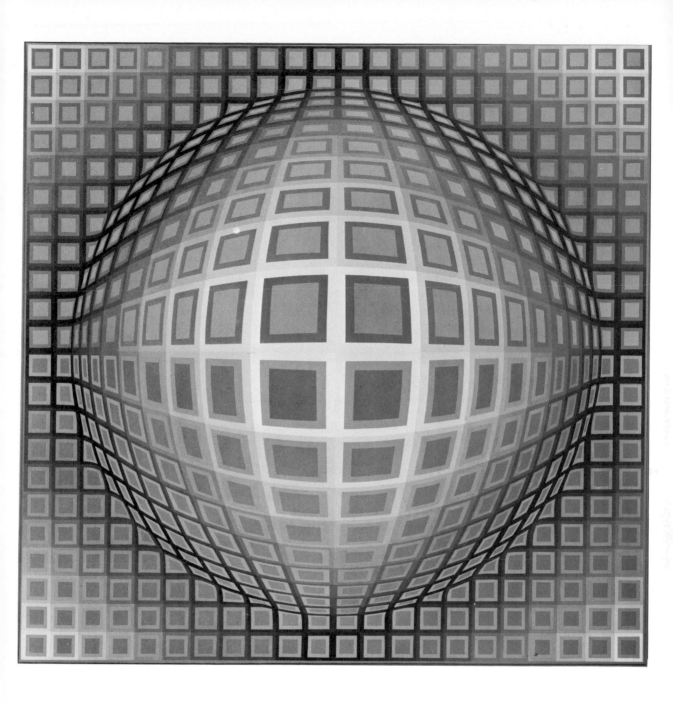

VASARELY *Vega-Nor* **1969**
Oil on canvas, 78¾ x 78¾ in. (200 x 200 cm.)
Gift of Seymour H. Knox   K69:29

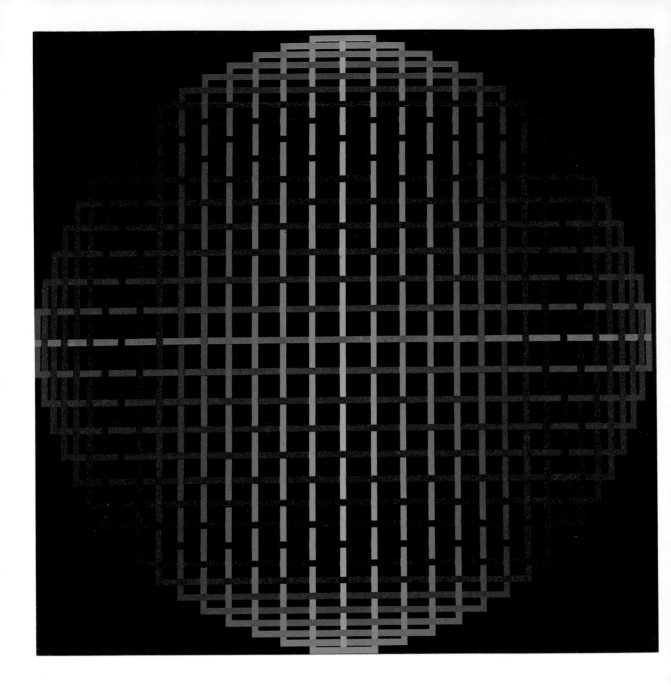

YVARAL *Polychromatic Diffraction* **1970**
Acrylic on canvas, 178½ x 178½ in. (199.4 x 199.4 cm.)
Gift of Seymour H. Knox K71:3

ANUSZKIEWICZ *Iridescence* **1965**
Acrylic on canvas, 60 x 60 in. (152.4 x 152.4 cm.)
Gift of Seymour H. Knox   K66:17

Yvaral

Yvaral's *Polychromatic Diffraction*, 1970, deliberately draws attention to paradoxical habits and peculiarities in human visual perception. For example, he constructs what is experienced as a volumetric sphere while relying entirely on straight lines and right angles. With means more economical than those used by his father, Vasarely, in his somewhat analogous painting *Vega-Nor* (p. 317), Yvaral manipulates value contrasts so that the light hues in the center of the canvas appear to push forward from the black ground. Yet equivalent hues at the four axial points not only are kept from the same apparent projection but are actually made to recede by means of the gradual diminution of the empty spaces between the parallel lines. Despite the undeniable spatial effect, however, the regular interweaving of the lines presupposes one flat plane. Yvaral exploits the optical effects which arise from the contrast of hues. The small squares formed at every point of intersection appear to jump and quiver before the retina.

The Gallery collection also includes Yvaral's *Acceleration #15 Series B*, a kinetic relief of 1962 in which vinyl cords interact with the black and white striped background.

Son of the painter Victor Vasarely, Jean-Pierre Yvaral was born in 1934. He studied graphic design and commercial art at the École des Arts Appliqués in Paris. In his late teens, he undertook his first experiments in abstract painting in the Constructivist vein and in 1955 made his first kinetic pieces. With Le Parc and Sobrino he was closely involved in the founding of the Groupe de Recherche d'Art Visuel in 1960. Throughout his prolific production of reliefs, free-standing sculptures, and paintings, he has consistently sought to clarify the act of artistic creation and to promote scientifically oriented experimental work. He describes his approach as an attempt to compile a primer of simple visual elements which can be combined, codified, and programed into situations that will actively educate and inform the spectator's visual perception.

Richard Anuszkiewicz

"My work is of an experimental nature and has centered on an investigation into the effect of complementary colors of full intensity when juxtaposed and the optical changes that occur as a result. Also, a study of the dynamic effect of the whole under changing conditions of light, and the effect of light on color." *

Iridescence, 1965, is dominated by series of precise lines, evenly placed, with every other line stopping short at measured intervals as the central square is approached. Because of the varying lengths of the lines, the composition consists of eight well-defined squares, and the effect of deep space is achieved. The red ground appears to change color according to the density of the alternating blue and green lines, which are not colored uniformly but change from blue to green, and vice versa, as they move from one square to the next.

Also in the Gallery collection are *Water from the Rock*, 1961–63 (the last painting in which Anuszkiewicz used oils, which he then replaced with acrylic paint), and an optical construction *Convex, Concave I Dimensional*, 1967.

Richard Anuszkiewicz was born in Erie, Pennsylvania, in 1930, and educated at the Cleveland Institute of Art, B.F.A., 1953; Yale University, M.F.A., 1955; and Kent State University, B.S. in Education, 1956.

At Yale, Anuszkiewicz studied with Josef Albers, who has been a formative influence on his work. Both painters compose around a central focal point and both make use of a square within a square. Albers's squares are placed asymmetrically, while Anuszkiewicz's are centered; Albers creates spatial levels by means of color and balances his asymmetries through the different weights of his colors, while Anuszkiewicz intensifies perspective and makes use of complementary colors, which cause the images to vibrate.

* Dorothy Miller, *Americans 1963* (New York: The Museum of Modern Art), p. 6.

Lucas Samaras

Lucas Samaras's box constructions were of modest dimensions until he re-created his bedroom, Room No. 1, in 1964. Room No. 2, later retitled *Mirrored Room*, was built in 1966. According to the artist, "The idea for a completely mirror-covered cube room occurred to me around 1963 when I incorporated the idea in a short story, *Killman*. The reason I used a cube rather than any other geometric shape was to minimize the number of planes that would reflect the space enclosed within them but still give a convincing illusion of perpendicular extension in every direction.

"The mirror room which is in a way a box (I had covered the inside of two boxes with mirror in 1960–61 but had also glued down tacks on the mirror partly to produce a pattern, partly to transform mirror into something else, and I also thought about the possibility of covering a box inside and outside with mirror but didn't do anything about it) is a continuation of the idea of enlargement or gigantism. I was primarily dealing with small carryable works and it wasn't until 1964 when I did the bedroom at the Green Gallery that I entered the territory of largeness. Also, since that bedroom had been a real, autobiographical room, I was searching for an idea to create some other kind of room, an abstract, geometric or theoretical room. As it developed, the *Mirrored Room* was such a thing. I included a table and chair, two important objects that can be found in a room, as a three-dimensional drawing you might say, a skeleton, a sculptural outline. A table and chair for someone to sit down and imagine or think or discover. In terms of my other work, mirror as a surface is related to silver paint and tin foil that I was using in the late 1950's." *

The *Mirrored Room* is composed of 24-inch-square mirrors, attached to a plywood frame with screws which are covered by glass balls. No interior lighting is incorporated; the single source of light is the open door. Preparatory drawings and photographs of the construction of *Mirrored Room* were published in *Letters from 31 Artists* (Albright-Knox Art Gallery, 1970).

Also in the Gallery collection is *Transformation: Boxes*, 1966–67, a group of twelve boxes of varying shapes and colors.

Lucas Samaras was born in 1936 in Kastoria, a small town in Northern Greece. His father immigrated to the United States in 1939, but the family could not join him until after World War II, when they moved to West New York, New Jersey, in 1948. The artist attended Rutgers University, 1955–59, where he was influenced by Allan Kaprow and George Segal, with whom he studied. From there, he went to Columbia University, studying with Meyer Schapiro, 1959–62. He was trained as a painter but also studied acting and participated in numerous Happenings.

In the early 1960's, when Samaras had settled in New York, he became increasingly involved with a three-dimensional box format, often employing pins, razor blades, tacks, or other sharp objects, menacingly placed and repellent to the touch. More recently, he has made extensive use of photographs, frequently of himself and sometimes painted.

---

* Letter from the artist, July, 1969.

322

SAMARAS *Mirrored Room* 1966
Mirrors on wooden frame, 8 x 8 x 10 ft. (243.9 x 243.9 x 304.8 cm.)
Gift of Seymour H. Knox   K66:15

Pol Bury

In *Nine Balls on Five Planes*, 1964, Bury has included balls of different sizes, set upon inclined, as well as horizontal, surfaces. Each ball moves independently at a speed unrelated to its size or the plane on which it rests. Attached by nylon threads, the balls move—so slowly as to be almost unnoticeable—to the edges of the planes. Then, just before they would normally fall, they roll back to the original position, again moving slowly.

The artist has said: "Between the immobile and mobility, a certain quality of slowness reveals to us a field of 'actions' in which the eye is no longer able to trace an object's journeys. . . . Thus, we can see that slowness not only multiplies duration but also permits the eye following the globe to escape from its own observer's imagination and let itself be led by the imagination of the traveling globe itself. The imagined voyage becomes imaginative." *

Pol Bury was born in 1922 in Haine Sainte-Pierre, Belgium, and attended the Académie des Beaux-Arts in Mons, 1938–39. He began his career as a painter, influenced by the Surrealists, particularly Magritte and Tanguy. In 1952, he saw an exhibition of Calder's work and soon began to experiment with geometric wooden shapes which could be moved by hand. These were followed by motorized and magnetized constructions made of plastics, metal, and rubber, as well as wood, and sometimes painted. His works from the early 1960's involved balls, cubes, and rods which moved slowly and irregularly. His most recent work continues to utilize slow movement, occasionally incorporating sound, and frequently made of polished metal.

* *Pol Bury* (Berkeley, Calif.: University Art Museum), p. 24.

BURY *Nine Balls on Five Planes* **1964**
Wood, motorized, 39⅜ x 8 x 16¾ in.
(100.3 x 20.3 x 42.5 cm.)
Gift of Seymour H. Knox K64:35

LE PARC *14 Series, No. 2* **1970**
Acrylic on canvas, 67 x 67 in. (170.2 x 170.2 cm.)
Gift of Seymour H. Knox   K71:5

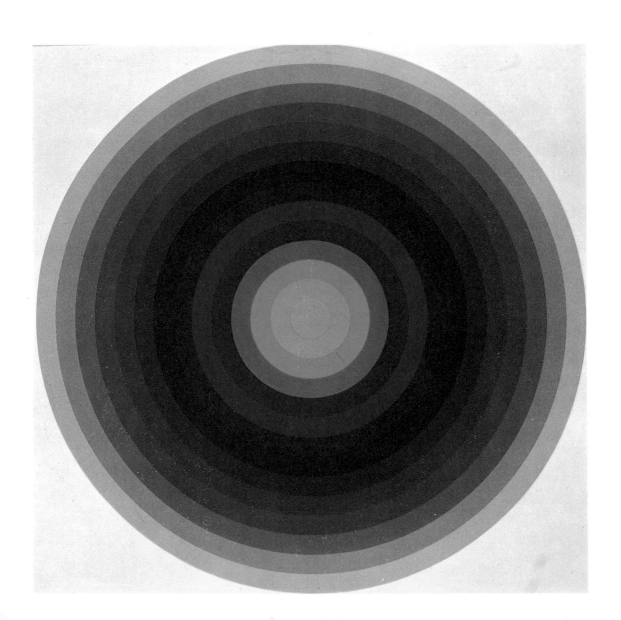

TADASKY *Untitled B 133* **1964**
Oil on canvas, 46½ x 46½ in. (118.1 x 118.1 cm.)
Gift of Seymour H. Knox K64:36

Julio Le Parc

Le Parc's earlier works were black, gray, and white, but he began to work in color in 1959, almost immediately after his arrival in Paris. Using a progressive gamut of fourteen colors from yellow through green, blue, violet, red, and orange, he began to construct increasingly complex compositions based on the regular repetition of the spectrum. Even though limiting himself to a vocabulary of circles and squares, he calculated that it would require 150 years to execute all the possible permutations of color and shape.

14 Series, No. 2 is one of a series of fourteen paintings which proceed in a rigorous order with each color in the spectrum serving successively as the central point of departure for the fourteen sequentially concentric circles. The adjoining color rings appear to move in and out and cause the flat configuration to be experienced as both a concave and a convex three-dimensional form. Whereas Tadasky restricted himself almost exclusively to straightforward primaries in his somewhat similar target painting (p. 327), Le Parc derives a particularly insistent visual effect for his thin and high-keyed decorator hues.

Although Le Parc is perhaps best known for his optical and kinetic reliefs, this painting nevertheless clearly illustrates his fundamental interest in the repeated unit, the programed composition, and, above all, in the instability of appearance.

Julio Le Parc was born in Mendoza, Argentina, in 1929. He entered the School of Fine Arts in Buenos Aires at the age of fifteen where he began to paint in a semi-abstract style. He was drawn to avant-garde ideas, particularly those of the Italian-Argentine Lucio Fontana, who advocated the elimination of traditional distinctions between painting and sculpture. In 1958 he went to Paris where he was attracted immediately by Victor Vasarely's experiments with both optical illusion and actual movement. In 1960, with Francisco Sobrino and a number of other young artists, he founded the Groupe de Recherche d'Art Visuel (GRAV). In reaction against Tachisme, or action painting, which was then dominant in France, this group advocated the elimination of any traces of the artist's hand and of all subjective composition. They dedicated themselves to an open-ended art of continuous research in which the spectator and teams of artists would collaborate in abolishing the idea of the unique art object produced by a solitary creator for a limited public. Le Parc has been primarily concerned with problems of transparency, movement, and light, often producing his works in multiple editions according to the basic tenets of GRAV. Between 1960 and 1968, he executed numerous Unstable-continual Lights, of which a version of about 1962 is in the Gallery collection.

Tadasky

Untitled B 133 of 1964 is composed of narrow concentric circles in four bright colors in a regular order in which red alternates repeatedly with yellow, blue, and green. Tadasky executed the paintings of this period by holding his brush upon a canvas which had been placed on a motorized revolving surface. In this manner he achieved a strict uniformity of width and an evenness of touch which, while far from mechanical, avoided any irregularities which would have interfered with the optical effects of the colors. The dominating color is red, which interacts violently with the complementary green stripes and again with the adjacent yellow and blue stripes, which tend to mix visually to produce green. The after-images generated by the contrast of complementary hues cause the colors to seem to shift outward and the disk to spin, thus undermining the stability of the target image.

In his more recent work, Tadasky has modified his characteristic circles and adopted sprayed acrylics to give the illusion of modeled three-dimensional form, as in *E-111* of 1969.

Tadasky (Tadasuke Kuwayama) was born in 1935 in Nagoya, Japan. He is from a family of skilled craftsmen; his father is a noted shrine-builder and his brother Tadaaki Kuwayama is a hard-edge painter currently working in this country. Tadasky came to the United States in 1961 to attend the Cranbrook Academy of Art in Michigan. He soon moved to New York and studied at the Art Students League and the Brooklyn Museum Art School. He came to public attention in 1965 when his first one-man show of target paintings coincided with widespread interest in optical art.

Rogelio Polesello

Rogelio Polesello's *Painting* of 1969 combines a rigidity achieved through an absolutely symmetrical design with dynamic rhythms of undulating line and vivid contrasts in color. Nine equal circles are arranged to form a diamond, the circles overlapping at fixed points along their circumferences in a pattern of linked ellipses around central diamonds with concave sides.

Although depth is implied in this apparent overlapping, the colors are chosen arbitrarily for their decorative and optical effect and do not result from the systematic combination of the two superimposed hues. The assertion of flatness is achieved despite the eye's tendency to experience various colors and shapes as alternately advancing and receding.

Rogelio Polesello was born in 1939 in Buenos Aires, Argentina, where he studied painting and engraving at the Escuela Nacional de Artes Visuales. The repeated geometric motifs and color experiments of Victor Vasarely, seen in a major exhibition in Buenos Aires in 1958, proved the formative influence on Polesello's painting style. Although briefly attracted to the Boa group, which advocated a kind of Surrealist abstraction, Polesello soon returned to an approach closer to simplified graphic design.

POLESELLO *Painting* **1969**
Acrylic on canvas, 51¼ x 51¼ in. (130.2 x 130.2 cm.)
Gift of Seymour H. Knox   K70:5

Jesús Rafael Soto

Wood—Iron Rods of 1964 is from the series called Vibration Structures, in which Soto suspended metal rods, usually against a striped background, to achieve visual movement, sometimes combined, as in this piece, with incidental actual movement from natural sources, such as air currents. Here, twenty thin black metal rods have been hung—at uneven intervals—by nylon threads from a "roof," which projects five inches in front of the black and white back panel. The rods are shaped into linear designs which suggest letters of an unknown alphabet. Some of the rods extend the entire length of the striped surface, while others are shorter; some are isolated in space, others overlap one another. As the spectator moves or a draft disturbs the rods, a shimmering pattern is created.

Jesús Rafael Soto was born in 1923 in Ciudad Bolivar, Venezuela. He had little formal education but, after studying drawing with a local artist, won a scholarship to the School of Fine Arts in Caracas, 1942–47. In 1950, he went to Paris, where he soon abandoned his Impressionist style and became interested in the works of Mondrian, particularly his last paintings, the Boogie Woogie series. He began making optical reliefs, using colored geometric shapes in a repeat design, followed by experiments with the spatial relationships between dots of the same size but of different colors. In 1954, he added a clear plastic sheet, placed several inches in front of the picture plane, both areas painted with dots so that as the viewer moves, the image changes. In the following year, after seeing Marcel Duchamp's Rotary Demisphere, he introduced a moiré effect—thin black and white lines form a background before which, at a distance, wire rods are suspended or metal squares mounted to form constructions, which again depend on the movement of the spectator to achieve the particular optical effect.

SOTO *Wood—Iron Rods* **1964**
Painted masonite and wire, 40¼ x 67¾ x 6¼ in. (102.2 x 172.1 x 15.9 cm.)
Gift of Seymour H. Knox   K65:2

Jean Tinguely

The artist has said, "for me the machine is above all an instrument which permits me to be poetic."

Cocktail au cheval, 1966, is an assemblage of salvaged rods, hooks, gears, bolts, a dangling metal leaf, and a silhouetted horse. Although the component parts of the composition were of flat or linear design originally, they have been assembled into a three-dimensional sculpture. As with all of Tinguely's work after early 1963, the assemblage is painted entirely in black, which unites the elements and disguises their assorted origins. When activated by electricity, the horse and a perforated plate revolve while a third element moves a small piston, each appearing to operate independently; the remainder of the sculpture is stationary. (For suggested explanation of the title, see p. 273.)

Also in the collection is an earlier work by the artist, *Peut-être No. 11*, c. 1959.

Jean Tinguely was born in Fribourg, Switzerland, in 1925, and his family moved to Basel three years later. At the age of fourteen, he constructed a sound-making mechanized "orchestra" of two dozen waterwheels attached to hammers which tapped various tone-producing jam jars. From 1941 to 1945, he attended, somewhat sporadically, the Basel School of Fine Arts. In 1945, he made his first constructions in wire, wood, paper, and even "edible" sculptures in grass. In 1951, he moved to Paris where he has continued to spend the major part of his time.

Soon after his arrival in Paris, he began to collect, assemble, and motorize an ever increasing variety of scrap metal and other discarded material. His sculptures are nonfunctional, ironically parodying the discipline, rhythm, and productivity of machines. He refers to his boisterous pseudo-machines as "metamechanics," since they transcend pure mechanics as metaphysics transcends physics. His motorized apparatus for making drawings, the various robot-like structures, and the self-destroying machines reflect and comment upon our technological environment.

TINGUELY   *Cocktail au cheval*   **1966**
Iron and wood, motorized
39 x 26 x 18 in. (99 x 66 x 45.8 cm.)
Gift of Seymour H. Knox   K70:10

Yaacov Agam

Agam describes his reliefs such as *Free Standing Painting*, 1971, as "contrapuntal . . . painted on a corrugated surface with one series of pictorial elements painted on one side of the ridges and another series on the other side. These paintings are based on the dynamic relationship and fusion of several independent themes, which are thereby completely transformed into a new pictorial event. The evolution of this relationship and fusion is revealed as the different sides of the corrugated surface of the painting come into view." * In *Free Standing Painting* the pictorial elements consist of a variety of geometrical shapes in flat, bright colors which offer a multiplicity of views on both sides either as the viewer moves around the relief or as the construction is rotated manually.

Ninth Power, 1970–71, is a spiral of stainless-steel, circular forms, posed beside an identical base composed of concentric circles. "They interchange like the number 8. They intercommunicate with one another, they evolve and concentrate, they are closed and open, follow one another like a spiral. Eight added to your one becomes the ninth power." †

In Agam's *Loud Tactile Painting* of 1962 (also in the collection), thirty-five shallow metal drums are attached to long slender springs. Small objects inside a number of the drums produce a delicate metallic rattle. When activated by the touch of the spectator's hand, the small disks produce a subtle variety of tones, grouped largely around B and E though varying by quarter, and less than quarter, tone differences. In addition to the sounds, the moving disks form a pattern of bobbing shadows.

Born in Israel, the son of a rabbi, Yaacov Gipstein studied industrial art briefly at the Bezaleal School in Jerusalem, his only formal art training. Among early influences, he cites Kandinsky's treatise On the Spiritual in Art *and the work of the Swiss artists Siegfried Gideon and Max Bill, which he came to know during two years in Zurich, 1949–51. He arrived in Paris in 1951 and adopted the name Agam two years later.*

From the beginning of his career, his interest has been in kinetic, movable, and transferable works. His various constructions rotate, slide, vibrate, emit different sounds, are rearrangeable, and can be viewed from a number of different angles. He has extended his experiments to include architecture, literature, music, and theater.

* *Yaacov Agam* (New York: Marlborough-Gerson Gallery, 1966), p. [10].
† *Transformables, Yaacov Agam* (New York: Galerie Denise René, 1971), p. [8].

AGAM *Free Standing Painting* 1971
Painted aluminum, wood, stainless steel
80 x 118 x 31½ in. (203.2 x 299.7 x 80 cm.)
Gift of Seymour H. Knox K71:18

335

AGAM *The Ninth Power* **1970–71**
Stainless steel, 5 ft. (154.3 cm.)
Gift of Seymour H. Knox   K72:9

George Rickey

"Since I was concentrating more and more on 'movement itself' I wanted to simplify the elements which moved. The lines have been an attempt to reduce the design to essentials. The line was tapered to allow for a counterweight and fulcrum near one end, with the remainder of the line (usually about 5/6) sweeping in a wide, slow arc.

"I was aware of the precedent of a tapered line in engraving and pen strokes. I often thought of my moving lines as a finite, but indeterminate, drawing in space.

"The combination of such lines permits great variety and I began to explore some of them, from a simple horizontal to clusters too numerous to be readily counted. . . .

"The kinetic sculpture *Five Lines* was one element among six which made up my *Peristyle I*. . . . The title of *Peristyle* is from a loose association with surviving rows of Greek columns. . . . This was made up in the fall and winter, 1963–64, and was shown in the Institute of Contemporary Art in Boston in March, 1964, in a one-man exhibition of my work.

"The sculpture comprised groups of vertical 'lines' (actually tapered needles of stainless steel 8' long) increasing in number from one to six, mounted on hard knife-edge bearings so that they swung in the wind across the long axis of the work, making a kind of kinetic fence of increasing density.*

"The lines are hollow, the section an equilateral triangle made of 8' long strips of stainless steel welded together. The counterweights are lead.

"The sculpture was originally designed only for indoor installation. But *Five Lines* was modified in 1968 by strengthening the bearings and adding a spring shock absorber so that it could be placed outside.

"*Peristyle* was intended to be a simple composition to be held intact. However, the possibilities of exhibiting it, entire, were few and it was shown piecemeal in various places in the United States and Europe which resulted in its being acquired piecemeal.

"The other five elements of *Peristyle I* are distributed as follows:

> *One:* destroyed
> *Two:* Private collection, Chicago
> *Three:* Private collection, Milwaukee
> *Four:* Art Gallery of Ontario, Toronto, Canada
> *Six:* Private collection, Dallas." †

George Rickey was born in South Bend, Indiana, in 1907, but in 1913 moved with his family to Scotland where he attended Trinity College, Glenalmond, 1921–26. He received a B.A. degree in modern history from Balliol College, Oxford, in 1929 and an M.A. in 1931. He studied also at the Ruskin School of Drawing, Oxford, 1928–29, and with André Lhote and at the Académie Moderne in Paris, 1929–30. He taught history in the United States, 1930–33; lived in Paris, 1933–34, and in New York, 1934–37; taught painting at colleges in Michigan, Illinois, and Pennsylvania, 1937–41; and served in the Air Force, 1942–45.

* Illustrated in *Letters from 31 Artists* (Albright-Knox Art Gallery, 1970) p. 34.
† Letters from the artist, October and December, 1968.

Rickey made his first mobile sculpture in 1945. After further study, he continued his work with kinetic objects, moved by hand or air currents, made of a variety of materials, and sometimes in color. His constructions during the 1950's became increasingly complex. After 1960, his works were simplified, color was eliminated, movement became solely dependent on natural forces, and planar elements were replaced by "lines" of hollow stainless-steel spars.

In addition to his sculpture, Rickey is an eminent critic and writer; he published a book on Constructivism: Origins and Evolution in 1967 and is the author of a number of articles on kinetic sculpture. Since 1960, he has lived and worked in East Chatham, New York.

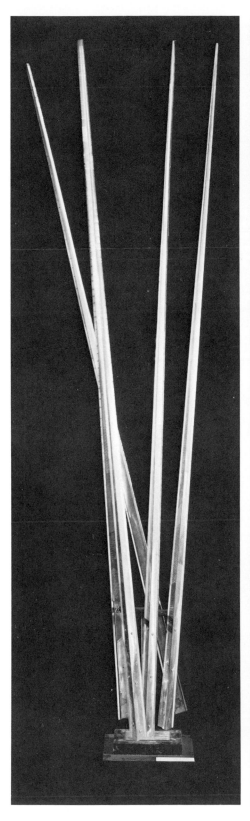
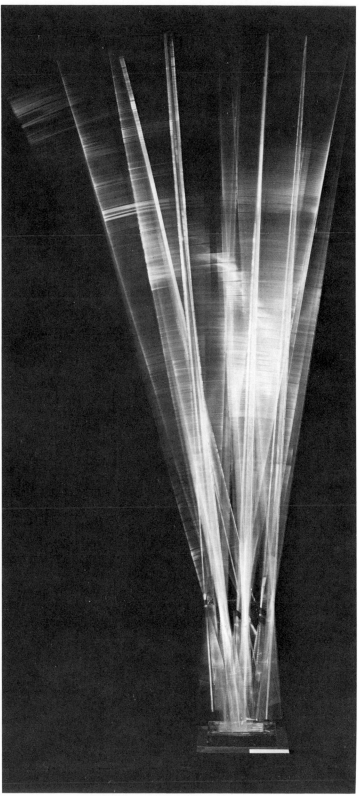

RICKEY *Peristyle: Five Lines* **1963–64**
Stainless steel, 100 x 10 x 13 in. (254 x 25.4 x 33 cm.)
A. Conger Goodyear Fund   65:8

Nicolas Schöffer

Spatiodynamic 22, 1954, a stationary work, was constructed during a transition period when Schöffer was simultaneously creating both moving and nonmoving sculptures. Completed in the same year as his first large tower, this sculpture of steel and aluminum is made up entirely of right angles, omitting the circular forms the artist frequently included. The strictly rectilinear design recalls Mondrian's paintings, as though rendered in three dimensions—the metal bars equating with the black lines and the aluminum sheets that reflect light reminiscent of the color areas in the paintings. Although Spatiodynamic 22 is small (50 inches high) in comparison to many of Schöffer's works, the structure casts shadows on the adjacent walls that suggest a far more monumental scale.

Nicolas Schöffer was born in Kalocsa, Hungary, in 1912 and studied at the Fine Arts Academy in Budapest before moving to Paris in 1936, where he attended the École des Beaux-Arts. By the late 1940's, he had developed his theories of spatiodynamism, "the dynamic integration of space into a plastic work" that should define, not confine, space. In 1954, he constructed his first large sound-equipped spatiodynamic and cybernetic tower in the Parc de Saint-Cloud, Paris, with the collaboration of the composer Pierre Henry and the technical assistance of Jacques Bureau, an engineer. In 1956, he produced his cybernetic sculpture CYSP I, a construction with an electronic "brain" that emits light and sound, moves at varied speeds, reacts to color and heat, and has performed with human dancers.

In 1957, Schöffer introduced luminodynamics, followed in 1960 by chronodynamics, which involved further use of light and music. In 1961, his 170-foot tower was constructed in Liège, Belgium, which creates an audiovisual spectacle with music by Henri Pousseur.

The actual construction of Schöffer's works is carried out by engineers and technicians. He is particularly interested in large works that become an integral part of the environment, a theme he has explored in a recent book, La Ville Cybernetique, 1969.

The first major presentation of Schöffer's work in the United States was at the Albright-Knox Art Gallery in the Art Today: Kinetic and Optic exhibition, 1965, in which seven of his constructions were shown.

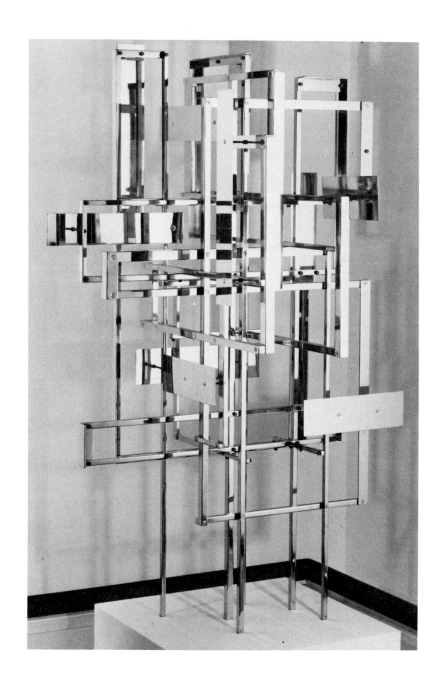

SCHÖFFER *Spatiodynamique 22* **1954**
Steel and aluminum, 49½ x 22¾ x 29¼ in.
(125.7 x 57.8 x 74.3 cm.)
A. Conger Goodyear Fund   65:11

American Painting Since 1960

Henry Geldzahler

Interest in painting in the 1960's was dominated both by a new wave of abstraction and by a series of relatively short-lived popular movements. The list of these movements includes Happenings and Environments, Minimal sculpture, Conceptual art, and the Earthworks. In painting as such, one is limited to Pop art, which, besides being traditionally collectible as canvases and objets d'art, emerged with the look of the new early in the decade and had the greatest impact. With the exception of a rather academic hard realism in the last years of the decade, there is little painting of interest that cannot be adequately described as recent abstraction or Pop art.

While the Albright-Knox Art Gallery has an excellent record in picking distinguished paintings by the best artists who emerged in the sixties, it is difficult to do justice to the decade without acknowledging the continuing contribution to high culture made by painters whose reputations were secure well before the decade began. In retrospect, the sixties will be known as much for what Hans Hofmann, Robert Motherwell, Mark Rothko, Barnett Newman, Willem de Kooning, and other masters of American abstraction achieved in these years as for the new abstraction of Morris Louis, Kenneth Noland, Jules Olitski, Helen Frankenthaler, and Frank Stella. In particular, Hans Hofmann, after he had turned eighty, closed his school and was able to devote his full and extraordinary energies to painting, producing his best work in what must be considered the most astonishing achievement of the decade.

Two dissimilar works by artists of earlier reputation, Adolph Gottlieb's *Dialogue I*, 1960, and Mark Tobey's *Coming and Going*, 1970, share an interest in personal calligraphy. Gottlieb's symbols reveal in their bravura the man who believes in his vision and seeks to reproduce it while the feeling is strong. The unfailing vitality of this aspect of Gottlieb's work suggests the value of continued interest in the ancient discipline of expressive brushwork that we know as action painting. It must be recognized that the pictographic waves in *Dialogue I* can be seen, as well as elements of a seascape, a fact that Gottlieb must long since have accepted and used to the advantage of his art. Much of what appeared to be pure abstraction in postwar American painting may also be considered a continuation of the romantic landscape tradition that pictured man's awe in the face of nature's majesty.

Mark Tobey developed his "white writing" in the 1930's by adapting Oriental cursive script to Western painting. In his over-all pictures, Tobey covers the page with a maze of running strokes, then repeats the process, adding layer upon layer until the image is manifested with enough authority to discourage thoughts of improvement. Whereas Gottlieb's pictures may also be seen as significant and forceful gestures on a pagelike surface, Tobey's use of calligraphy is entirely in the service of giving birth to his phantasmagoric imagery. For this reason, like most works of Surrealism, Tobey's is more interesting as illustration than as painting. Although Tobey stops working on his pictures before his calligraphy turns into mere rendering, the calligraphy itself has energy only within the context of its skillful use as a technique for materializing subject matter.

The major contribution of the sixties to abstract painting has surely been in the area of the color field, the successful attempt in the best paintings to retain the sense of an expansive field of vision as developed by Pollock and Newman, while at the same time using color, as did Matisse, for decorative as well as expressive effect. The advent of acrylic paints helped to make this development possible because they allowed artists working on raw canvas to obtain effects similar to those of watercolor on paper. Diluted acrylics soaked into raw canvas have a transparency and brilliance unobtainable from oil color. Oil on raw canvas leaves a stain, a telltale ring that surrounds the pigments and eventually rots the fiber. The stain of oil color on raw canvas tends also to appear dull and washed out. Pigment in an acrylic medium lends itself to being muted by the texture, absorbency, and buff tone of unbleached cotton.

The color-field painters developed techniques for laying down paint in such a way as to minimize or eliminate traces of the artist's hand, and they were careful to leave intact the uniform texture and reflective properties of the raw canvas. By painting in this manner and by following Newman's lead in eliminating overlapping lines and shapes, they were able to exploit the full possibilities of nonpictorial surface decoration. Yet, despite the severe painterly and design limitations involved, the use of acrylics as watercolor combined with the technique of cropping still provided the artist with sufficient means of leading the viewer to visualize an image.

To trace the history of this new sensibility one must first take into account some achievements of the 1950's. An often neglected precursor of color-field painting was Sam Francis, a California-based painter of international reputation; it sometimes seems he is more honored in Europe and Japan than in the United States. We see the development of his style in the three Albright-Knox paintings *Blue-Black*, 1952, *Untitled*, 1956, and *Whiteness of the Whale*, 1957. The white ground increasingly dominates the picture, while the color becomes more localized and more intense. In recent years, Sam Francis has painted pictures all in white except for narrowly brushed edges of color. Though Francis has never produced paintings that have distinctly separate and antagonistic qualities as object and as illusion, his sense of color in relation to ground, color isolated and heightened, places him as both a precursor and a practitioner of the color abstraction we associate with the 1960's.

Helen Frankenthaler began staining canvas in an inspired extrapolation of the qualities that impressed her in Jackson Pollock's later over-all paintings. But her sense of form continued to reflect the biomorphic landscapes and interiors of Arshile Gorky. While Frankenthaler's imagery is rarely specifically identifiable, it makes reference to a natural and imagined world that we recognize as her own. *Round Trip*, 1957, with its drawing in paint on canvas, also has certain qualities in common with the watercolors of John Marin and Arthur Dove, though it would be inaccurate to imply that she was particularly affected by them. Like many Americans, she has responded to the visionary aspect of French modernism rather than to its physicality.

The technical innovation of Frankenthaler's early painting is often cited as having influenced Morris Louis and Kenneth Noland. We must also recognize the impact of her daring to practice traditional drawing at a time when the progress of American painting was impeded by an insistence upon the single image as the sign of an artist's accomplishment. Through her willingness and ability to experiment in public in the early 1950's, Helen Frankenthaler's work influenced artists who were to achieve prominence in the next decade. At the same time, she was working toward the large-scale watercolors in acrylic on canvas that were to establish her as one of the better painters of her generation.

Morris Louis's *Alpha*, 1960, belongs to a series that has come to be called the Unfurleds. In these pictures, Louis worked with a panoramic format the center of which he left physically untouched. The only paint on the canvas is in the diagonal streams of color that fall away from one another, as do the curtains of a stage, to reveal an open expanse. Although *Alpha* is an Unfurled by reason of its composition, its central motifs, the black spouts and orange spatulas, are vestiges of Louis's previous series, the Alephs. The swashes of yellow, blue, and red at the peripheries of the canvas subsequently evolved into the rivulets Louis used exclusively in the fully developed Unfurleds.

Alpha has somewhat the look of a screen because the color is decoratively keyed and the paint is soaked in to a uniform density. Even when each is seen as a distinct entity, the poured colors with their respective shapes and directions seem to lie on one plane, almost as if they had been developed in a photographic emulsion; despite the opacity of the color, the acrylic emulsion retains its translucency. This is one reason the painting as a whole has great transparency. In addition, the atmospheric texture of the canvas comes through the paint, and the unpainted spaces that separate the poured figures allow one to see through their illusionistic unity as a fabric into the space beyond. The illusion of drapery is rendered by the attenuation of the verticals, both painted and unpainted, and it is heightened by a sense of light and shade resulting from the distribution of colors and values. The sweep of the drapery is indicated by the fall of the S-curves.

One may think of *Alpha* as a decorative abstraction because of its design quality. While the image remains subliminal, one's attention is drawn to the painted figures in themselves, first by the clarity of their color, then in awe of the skill with which they have been poured. But the greater amazement of the Unfurleds is due to the fact that Louis succeeded in giving full pictorial intensity to a stretch of unpainted canvas by forcefully engaging the viewer's peripheral vision. The raw canvas depicts the heart of the painting without being its center of focus.

The Unfurleds and the Alephs were preceded by a series of pictures known as the Veils. With the last of the Veils, Louis abandoned for the most part his earlier practice of painting variations on a theme. He continued to paint in series, but only insofar as he worked with the same idea over and over again in order to develop his basic conception and to master its execution. Louis's art reached its apogee with his last major series, the Pillars. The most accomplished Unfurleds, such as the Boston Museum of Fine Art's *Theta* and the Metropolitan Museum's *Alpha Pi*, are astonishing in their grandeur, but there remains a source of discomfort in the tendency of the streams of colors to outweigh the raw canvas format. Louis appears to have rejected the wall-sized panoramic format as being inimical to monumental imagery. While the Pillars are dramatic in their upsurge of parallel stripes, they do not involve the viewer in a sequence of perceptions that form a narrative, which in the case of the

344

Unfurleds is somewhat problematic. By focusing on a single dramatic event, the Pillars more perfectly celebrate Louis's technical and pictorial genius.

Kenneth Noland was first recognized in the late fifties for his loosely painted circles within circles. Within a few years the circles had become strictly concentric, but their target effect was simultaneously opened and animated by the juxtaposition of lovely and unexpected color jumps. Noland's subsequent series of Chevrons and Diamonds (*Yellow Half* is an example of the former) led to his parallel-line paintings of 1967–70, such as *Wild Indigo*, 1967, in which the unprimed canvas was used to new advantage as an active element.

In these later paintings the color, rather than being stained into the canvas, lies on the surface as painted bands. The canvas that is left unpainted separates one color from the next and allows the picture to breathe, as it does in Stella's painting; the raw canvas also functions as a colored band in its own right.

In previous color-field painting the raw canvas, at first sight, had read as background, the painted color as foreground. In Louis's *Alpha* it is only when the poured colors are seen as drapery that areas of raw canvas, because of their lighter value, come forward as highlighted folds. In Noland's parallel-line paintings, as in his Targets, some bands of raw canvas stand out, others recede. The raw canvas may also appear as a wider band on which the colored bands have been painted. However, in the parallel-line paintings, by introducing pastel colors of the same value as the unbleached cotton, the color of the cotton at key points ceases to be neutral. By this means Noland was able to mediate between the sharp polarities of the raw canvas's alternating roles as ground and figure. By contrasting the respective surface and texture of the painted and unpainted bands, and by using width, color, and value to control jumps in distance and changes in vibration among the bands, Noland produced a rich sense of expanse, atmosphere, and movement in paintings that also have the attraction of both schematic design and painted finish. *Yellow Half*, with its stained chevrons, is an emblematic picture. If we continue to be arrested it is by the clarity of the color. The later stripe paintings may be more ingratiating, but they also demand greater effort from the viewer; more decisions must be held in the memory to carry the picture away.

Whereas Morris Louis's Veils are washed onto raw canvas, and Helen Frankenthaler's shapes are stained, Jules Olitski sprays acrylic onto canvas that has already been bathed in a diluted ground. His brush is a spray gun. Olitski has made successful and original use of this technique; others have followed, as others followed Pollock a decade and a half earlier in pouring paint directly from the can. In both cases no one has used the new technique as convincingly as its originator.

Olitski's over-all pictures, alternately diaphanous and palpably textural, continue to fascinate ambitious younger artists. Of all the processes developed by the color-field painters, his has been the most scrutable; his painting is additive rather than schematic, and his palette eclectic. In the late sixties, he was the first of the prestigious color-field painters to introduce in his work an immediately visible illusion of depth, or more specifically in the case of the Albright-Knox's *Second Tremor*, 1969, an illusion of light radiating with such intensity as to form a mass of color that locates the picture plane at the forefront of a dense atmosphere.

Olitski's denigrators have failed to recognize that his highly romantic color and imagery, and the license taken to produce it, is balanced by severe formal restraint. Within limits Olitski can afford, one might say he is even compelled to delight in, ethereal mists of lush color because the atmosphere of his pictures is so heavily pressurized. In Louis's and Noland's work, suppression of feeling had reached such a degree that critics who were faithful to the paintings concentrated first on describing them in strictly formal terms that ruled out speculation as to what the forms "contain." In contrast, the emotion in Olitski's spray painting speaks for itself, but the force of his appeal is difficult to locate.

Recently, Kenneth Noland, Robert Motherwell, and a number of younger painters appear to have been seeking a less punishing alternative to the compulsive energy that has in the postwar years produced the most forceful American abstraction. This energy is generated by the kind of tension that continues to pervade Olitski's work alone. In releasing some of that tension, Noland, in his latest work, may be seen as having joined his younger colleagues in suffering the temporary setback of being without an adequate driving force.

An Olitski of the early 1960's, stained, pre-spray, with large, sumptuously rounded forms, would make an important addition to a collection of paintings that attempts to reveal the achievement of the sixties. Both Olitski and Noland dealt for a time with the problems of using invented shapes, but they soon abandoned the undertaking. As an alternative they adopted Newman's and Louis's conception of the picture as a charged panoramic expanse or, in terms of the vertical, a monumental extension of the spirit. From the standpoint of an artist's career, the decade of the sixties with its booming prosperity and cultural frenzy was not the time to grapple with apparently insoluble difficulties. A confrontation with the psychic dangers Pollock got into in the early fifties by reintroducing shape had to be bypassed. It was rather in the character of the time to move forward with a succession of impressively realized pictures.

Frank Stella is well represented in the collection with three paintings that span his career from *Jill*, 1959, painted a year after his graduation from Princeton, through *Fez*, 1964, yellow and green from the Moroccan series, to the large and many-colored "protractor" painting, *Lac Laronge III*, 1969. When Stella first started looking seriously at art in the mid-fifties, he was struck by what seemed to him to be an overconcern on the part of such admired artists as Willem de Kooning and Franz Kline with the central image. To Stella the corners of their paintings seemed left over. Like the Cubists whom these artists were heirs to, they started at the center and worked their way out. The edges and the corners of their paintings seemed arbitrarily finished and unfinished. In a Rembrandt where the spotlight is on a portrait bust, this centrality seems logical. But given the modernist aesthetic of flatness as a presupposition, there had to be a way of giving equal and total attention to the entire painted surface. At Princeton, Stella became aware through a course in medieval art history of the tradition of manuscript illumination in which one decorated the page from the border in. This helped him to arrive at the revolutionary format of his "black" series, of which *Jill* is a prime example. While the focus of the painting is obviously the central diamond, everything in the painting works from corner to center, as well as from center to edge. Similarly in *Fez* by subdividing the painting into four equal squares, Stella controls the entire surface. In the horizontal *Lac Laronge III*, total symmetry has been abandoned in favor of an image-and-a-half. The color has been chosen according to intuition and sensibility rather than any strict plan in order to counterbalance the rigorous structure.

Although Stella has shared the color-field painters' interest in the canvas as a design format, having in fact at one point in the early sixties influenced Noland, his paintings have rarely suggested pictorial illusion; as decorative devices they do not evoke a sense of light and space. Rather, the image is symbolic; the designs themselves seem to have a mystical significance.

As a student and critic of two-dimensional decorative design, Stella has been highly ambitious and successful. In addition to his study of manuscript illumination, the more recent paintings reflect original insights into Islamic art, the geometry of Frank Lloyd Wright, and Art Deco. His compositions of interwoven concentric circles are an unexpected resurrection of Orphism, the French school of abstract design that was initiated by the Delaunays and Frank Kupka in the second decade of the century. These paintings are enlargements of ornamental details. Hanging dramatically on the walls of austere white rooms, they serve one of the traditional functions of architectural ornamentation: the depiction of cosmological symbols in decorative patterning.

Both Larry Poons's *Orange Crush*, 1963, and Darby Bannard's *Harbor View #1*, 1970, are the products of painting systems that involve the use of a grid. Poons's system employed the geometric logic that was Stella's contribution to the art of the early 1960's. The Bannard exhibits the rococo sensibility of the late sixties and early seventies that his paintings foreshadowed and continue to epitomize. Poons, too, in his recent work has turned to pale color and integumental surface, which owes much to the example of Jules Olitski and, through him, to Monet's late water-lily paintings. Edward Avedisian is represented in the Albright-Knox collection by an early picture, *West #2*, 1962. Avedisian's development has been quixotic and fascinating, always profoundly painterly. Although his recent pictures have qualities in common with those of his peers, they bespeak an exceptional opinion as to the substance and future of American abstraction.

To many young artists in the mid-1950's, it seemed that the expressionist abstraction of Willem de Kooning and Franz Kline indicated the high road in recent American art. The second generation, or Tenth Street painters, as they were known after the concentration of galleries that first showed their work, painted pictures that seemed vibrant at the time; now, in retrospect, only the best of these painters may be said to have achieved more than an academic competence. Alfred Leslie moved from energetically painted abstractions in the mid-fifties, his best pictures, to paintings influenced by his own collages, such as *Hialeah*, 1961, in which he used a *trompe l'œil* effect simulating pasted paper with brushwork. Since the mid-sixties he has painted disturbing, Byzantine portraits in a grayed palette. Leslie's ink-wash cloudscapes in the collection of The Museum of Modern Art impressively demonstrate what he has learned from the study of nineteenth-century English and American watercolors. *George Went Swimming at Barnes Hole*, 1957, is typical of Joan Mitchell's work. She continues to be a steadily capable and undervalued painter. Michael Goldberg's *Summer House*, 1958, with its deep spatial hole in the middle of the canvas and its hectic brushing typifies another and more additive manner within the second generation. Ray Parker's *Untitled*, 1959, like Edward Avedisian's *West #2*, 1962, plays with large areas of dark and light, brushed in the Parker, stained and brushed in the Avedisian. The monolithic post and lintel Parker, with its deft brushwork and lucid monumentality, is a happy surprise in the Albright-Knox collection.

Jack Tworkov, James Brooks, Conrad Marca-Relli, and Theodoros Stamos among the older painters produced lovely works that secured them positions within the dominant abstract style. Many of these artists, untouched by the changing impetus in the sixties, continued to paint characteristic pictures that are often under-appreciated by a profession and public attracted to novelty at the expense of more modest excellence.

Jack Tworkov's *East Barrier*, 1960, is typical of his best paintings, which are drawn and hatched with the quality of a palimpsest. There is deliberation in his expressionism that removes it from the more active and even frenzied work of many of his contemporaries.

Both James Brooks's *Cooba*, 1963, and Kenzo Okada's *White and Gold*, 1961, play successfully with lightly anchored shapes in a curious fusion of American abstraction and the aesthetic of the Japanese painted screen. Okada's blocks of impasto at times remind us of Nicolas de Staël's thicker abstractions of the early fifties, but the charm of his pictures lies in the successful harmonization of impasto with thinly painted, almost gold-leafed areas. James Brooks, whose work continues to look strong and effectively decorative, floats and anchors his forms with the nicest possible sense of balance. Many of his best paintings are autumnal in color range, sober without falling into somberness.

As a movement, Pop art was most effective during the years 1959 to about 1965, after which it became more sensible to consider such artists as Claes Oldenburg and Andy Warhol as individuals rather than members of a group. The original generation of Pop artists—Warhol, Lichtenstein, Rosenquist, Oldenburg, Dine, Wesselmann, Indiana, Marisol—became visible in New York studios and downtown galleries as early as 1959 and 1960 but were not recognized by the major art galleries and museums until 1962. While this does not seem a long time for a movement to lie neglected, it did, at the time, appear as if Pop art was finding more opposition than it warranted. In late 1962, The Museum of Modern Art held a symposium in which four of the six panelists as well as the moderator felt that Pop was not art and that, even if it was, it was coming on too fast. Discussions about how quickly an art movement should be accepted and at what rate new art should enter permanent museum collections reached the point of inanity. The conservatism of dealers, critics, curators, and trustees needs no encouragement when called upon to balance the desire on the part of the art world to rush in and support the new without weighing its merits. Most people eager to discuss the proper time sequence for the acceptance of the new are merely treading water while they allow their taste and intelligence to become accustomed to a shifting of gears. This is neither reprehensible nor remarkable; merely a bore, when treading water is seen as a brave moral position.

The forerunners of Pop art, Robert Rauschenberg and Jasper Johns, are represented in the Albright-Knox collection by paintings that make clear their role as mediators between the rich painterly abstraction of the later fifties and the sparely rendered Pop art of the sixties. Rauschenberg's

Painting with Red Letter S, 1957, is an abstract collage with thickly painted passages on an open ground. The paisley fragment and the letter S of the title indicate that a change in subject matter is around the corner. With the introduction of his Target paintings in the middle fifties, Jasper Johns joined Rauschenberg and in some ways surpassed him in the attempt to use Abstract Expressionist techniques to legitimize the illustration of literal images. The numbers in Johns's *Numbers in Color*, 1959, are rendered in such a way as to seem embodied in the clotted paint of an apparently nonobjective manner.

The blatant and at times shocking superficiality of Rauschenberg's and Johns's subject matter—letters, collage material, and photographs in Rauschenberg; numbers, maps, targets, and flags in Johns—licensed a generation of artists to indulge their love of the familiar representation without the fear of seeming academic. However, in contrast to the Pop artists, Johns and Rauschenberg in different ways continued to paint thickly and loosely through the sixties, leaving decisions to the act of painting. Robert Rauschenberg's *Ace*, the large five-panel composition of 1962, is, if anything, more improvised, more broadly brushed and radically collaged than his earlier *Painting with Red Letter S*. A rectangle of paint, at the right, is mimicked by a cardboard carton splayed open and glued to the surface above it; the dripped paint in the lefthand panel is as "accidental" and raw as anything in second-generation Abstract Expressionism. As in many of Rauschenberg's works of these years, *Ace* has objects that protrude from the surface of the canvas, militating against the modernist dictum of flatness, which both he and Johns, who used similarly three-dimensional devices in these years, might well have felt to be doctrinaire and limiting.

Larry Rivers, too, through the fifties and into the sixties painted objects received from popular culture in a loose and painterly manner. *The Final Veteran*, 1960, is an abstracted commentary on a photograph of the last Civil War veteran. Larry Rivers's role in keeping alive the possibility of representing the familiar and the recognizable during the dominance of abstract art is well documented. His *Washington Crossing the Delaware*, destroyed by fire at The Museum of Modern Art, was a key painting based on the popular and often reproduced textbook painting by the mid-nineteenth-century German-American painter Emanuel Leutze. Rivers's work in this respect suggested a number of possibilities such as those definitively realized in Warhol's Soup Cans and Lichtenstein's Comic Strips.

Roy Lichtenstein's *Head—Red and Yellow*, 1962, is in the flat, simplified comic-book style that seemed so shocking in the early sixties when he first applied the familiar printing technique to canvas. One theme in the history of twentieth-century art is the new techniques that have been legitimized by artists of imagination in attempts to reinvigorate traditional subject matter. The French continually borrowed techniques from the art of exotic peoples, children, the insane, and the drugged. Braque's use of collage was inspired by his experience as a house painter and paper hanger. In Roy Lichtenstein's paintings, the flattened pattern and Ben Day dots stenciled on canvas looked raw and uncivilized at first. We soon, however, came to see their closeness in spirit with the Purism of Ozenfant and Le Corbusier, the machinelike Légers of the twenties and later, and the syncopated urban design of Stuart Davis. Not that Lichtenstein's comic-strip paintings look like any of these; it was the impulse that was familiar and legible beyond the shock of the enlarged and seemingly mechanical rendering. It was also clear that the adjustments Lichtenstein made in translating the advertisements and comic panels he uses as his found sketches were always toward clarity and immediacy and away from inelegant drawing and unnecessary detail. In recent years he has worked away from the figuration of these early works toward a semi-abstraction in wordless but posterlike paintings based on the Art Deco designs of the twenties and thirties, and in schematic representations of Monet's Haystacks and Cathedrals, based as always on the challenging limitations of line-cut printing.

Andy Warhol has provided one of the most fascinating chapters in the social life of the sixties. He invented, projected, and recorded a style so much in tune with the decade that his work sums up its gaiety and tragedy; Andy Warhol's Soup Cans and his underground movies are the Charleston and goldfish-swallowing of the sixties. Warhol's career, which stretches to include his successful stint as a fashion illustrator in the fifties and his recent adventures as a movie director and producer, makes essential social history as well as art history. His personal collections have always been fascinating and compulsive: Surrealism in the fifties, abstract art in the sixties, Art Deco and American Indian handicrafts in the late sixties, and always the odd and the beautiful people, the superstars, who are his true and most personal collection.

The argument about Pop art from the beginning was: Does it celebrate American affluence, or does it denigrate it? The Germans wittily call the movement Capitalist Realism and they collect it at high prices. Gertrude Stein said that America was the oldest country in the world because it entered the twentieth century first. Thus, to the Germans, who entered after World War II, our culture is an old one and Pop art epitomizes it. Being neither totally negative nor totally accepting, it essentializes and describes a system of values with which all consumer-oriented industrial countries must come to terms. Andy Warhol's stacks of beef-noodle soup cans, *100 Cans*, 1962, is both an image of abundance in the supermarket and a handsome decorative panel. If we are accustomed to homemade soup, it might seem depressing. If we are used to no soup at all, it represents plenty. The Campbell soup can has become the most familiar Pop art image, an image that Warhol has repeated and varied many times. He has magically turned the humble soup can into a superstar of the decade.

Nomad, the seventeen-foot-long painting by Jim Rosenquist, is a good example of the Surrealist montage he has preferred to the Pop artist's penchant for the single image. *Nomad*, like so many of Rosenquist's best paintings, is concrete in its subject matter and dreamlike in its interrelations; we see legs, a soap package, a picnic table, grass, spaghetti and meatballs, an oversize light bulb, and more. There is a rightness about the "story" that they cumulatively tell, but the poetry is dislocated. Although the free association of ideas in these paintings refers back to Surrealism, the multiplicity of focal points is derived from postwar over-all painting, specifically, the Cubism of De Kooning is interpreted by Rauschenberg, whose larger compositions also pull our eye this way and that, defying us to take in everything at once.

In much work of the sixties, a single image dominated the picture. One thinks of Warhol, Stella, Noland, and Lichtenstein. But another current was apparent in the work of Rauschenberg, Olitski, Poons, and Rosenquist where no central image carries the burden. Although the emblematic pictures have greater memorability, the sense of time and of story in these other paintings is more complex. Both strains interweave and add richness to the painting of the sixties.

A drier and less complex painting related to Pop art but without its shock value was produced in the early 1960's by such artists as Jim Dine, Tom Wesselmann, and Robert Indiana, all of whom are well represented in the Albright-Knox collection. Wesselmann's *Still Life #20* combines collage with actual objects in a punning play on the ambiguity between depiction and reality—a color poster advertisement in conjunction with an actual faucet and kitchen cabinet, all of them equally dislocated from their familiar context in a composition that looks only like a Wesselmann. Indiana's Whitman quotation, *Year of Meteors*, 1961, is designed and laid out, stenciled in circles within a square, not so much a departure from commercial techniques as a quotation from them. Jim Dine's *Child's Blue Wall*, 1962, is a sweetly poetic evocation that stretches our eye across a wall of stars and dots from the light switch at the left to the crenellated toy guard house with its light-bulb moon at the lower right. Although the level of ambition in *Child's Blue Wall* is mild, the mood is unforgettable. With the exception of this particular picture, Dine's most impessive contribution has been his graphics.

In point of richness and variation in paint quality, two artists deserve to be considered: Wayne Thiebaud, who paints in northern California, and Ron Kitaj, a Midwesterner active in London. Thiebaud's *Yo-Yos*, 1963, uses Pop art subject matter, the lowly yo-yo, but in a thickly brushed impasto that relates directly to the West Coast figuration of David Park and Richard Diebenkorn rather than to the cool painted-out handwriting of New York Pop art. Ron Kitaj's illustrative and cinematic composition, *Walter Lippmann*, 1966, with its opposition of fully painted to lightly sketched-in areas, is additive in a more deeply spatial, traditional composition than we see in the extended horizontality of Rosenquist and Rauschenberg. The images seem sequential in time, as in superimposed stills from an imaginary movie.

The final tendency within the sixties that must be considered is hard-edge painting. As an extension of Neo-Plasticism and Concrete Abstraction, it is the latest development of a movement that has had a longer continuous history than any in the twentieth century. A major consequence of the abstracting tendencies of Picasso and Braque in their Cubist paintings after 1907, paintings that were still derived from recognizable, if somewhat disguised, subject matter, were the Russian and Dutch inventions of what appeared at the time to be total abstraction, the Suprematism of Malevich and the Neo-Plasticism of Mondrian. These styles continue to awe and to influence artists who concentrate in their work on a careful adjustment of formal elements that parallels and echoes nature. Rather than transform the recognizable, they attempt to invent a sense of order that affirms man's ability to wrest form from chaos.

Ilya Bolotowsky in *Scarlet Diamond*, 1969, and Fritz Glarner in *Relational Painting #93*, 1962, adjust neo-Mondrianesque elements in series of paintings to which they have each devoted decades of careful balancing and weighing. Glarner's slight tilting of the angles in his paintings is a successful device that earns him a place in the continuing development of the Neo-Plastic vision. Burgoyne Diller's paintings of the early sixties, of which

First Theme, 1963–64, is a fine example, isolated and monumentalized simple elements in a way that influenced younger Minimal artists. Ludwig Sander has avoided the primary reds, yellows, and blues, blacks and whites of the more orthodox Neo-Plasticists. His compositions of rectangles, such as *Untitled*, 1963, separate, contrast, and harmonize seemingly vulgar colors with skill and clarity, so as to make them the keynote of a style that is at once crude and refined. In *Number 2* and *Number 3*, both painted in 1963 and both of equal size, Rollin Crampton set himself the problem of reversing grounds, black on white and white on black in identical compositions. The result has surprising force beyond obvious decorative success.

Josef Albers's contribution to American painting since his arrival from Germany in 1933 is a major one. The chapters in his career are well known: his years as student and master at the Bauhaus, his teaching career at Black Mountain College in North Carolina (1933–50) and at Yale (1950–60). His patient experiments in sand-blasted glass, formica, and masonite are part of the visual memory of all who are interested in modern art, and his series Homage to the Square, to which *Terra Caliente*, 1963, belongs, has been of primary interest since the early fifties. Like Hofmann, another important teacher, Albers has done his greatest painting since his retirement. The range in mood he has been able to project within what is only apparently a severely limited discipline makes him a poet as well as a painter of the concrete.

Ellsworth Kelly's somewhat atypical *New York, N.Y.*, 1957, abstracts and enlarges the initials N and Y almost to the verge of nonrecognizability. Many of his paintings of the fifties and early sixties, for all their look of invented abstraction, were based on the observation of nature, a man's shirt and tie, the negative space between a pair of legs, even architectural elements. In recent years, however, as in *Blue, Yellow and Red*, 1968, Kelly has produced abstractions that for the moment defy literary description. Often the canvas is shaped, nonrectangularly as here, or, more recently, by adding separate rectangles and squares of color to form additive paintings of nicely calculated weight. The uniqueness and complexity of his imagination place him in a happily anomalous position, neither quite color-field abstraction nor simply a tiller in the Neo-Plastic field. His work forces us to consider it in its own terms.

Jack Youngerman's *Delfina*, 1961, is a successful decorative composition. It at once brings to mind both the projected images of Ellsworth Kelly and the torn paper edge mocked in paint that we associate with Clyfford Still. Both Kelly and Youngerman were influenced by Matisse's late paper cutouts.

Alfred Jensen's *The Great Mystery II*, 1960, with its arcane, hieroglyphic numerology embedded in a thick expressionist impasto, marks him as an original and underrated painter. We do not need to understand the exact meaning of his symbols to be moved by his compacted vision. George Ortman in *Aton*, 1964, sets his hard-edged circles, hearts, arrows, triangles, and squares, mounted on wood in sections, flush with the flat surface of the canvas. The lightened palette and smooth facture give his work a sweeter and more modest look than Al Jensen's.

Nicholas Krushenick and Al Held, in his recent work, design strongly linear images based on Cubist drawing. Krushenick's *Lotus Europa*, 1969, calls to mind a primitive step architecture, Mexican or Assyrian, flattened on canvas by an artist of the sixties. Al Held's *B/WX*, 1968, is a thickly and strictly drawn black-and-white accumulation of primary architectonic forms. This type of picture represents a departure for Held from the enormous and heavily painted color abstractions with which he was previously identified.

Mark Tobey

Red Man–White Man–Black Man, 1945, originally exhibited with a group of paintings on the theme of Indians, reflects in its title the spirit of the Bahá'í faith, which teaches the unity of mankind and advocates the elimination of all social barriers, particularly racial discrimination. Building up innumerable directional strokes and lines, Tobey creates an abstract space charged with the spirit and energy of human activity to the extent that the painting seems to generate its own special illumination. Through the devices of "multiple space" and "moving focus," the spectator's eyes are kept constantly moving, penetrating and exploring the space at many levels. Intimate in scale, Tobey's paintings invite and reward careful scrutiny.

This earlier painting is complemented by *Coming and Going*, 1970. Here calligraphic strokes of red, yellow, green, black, and white intermesh in a spatial field energized from the center. Painted in Tobey's eightieth year, it represents a somewhat enlarged format for the artist and demonstrates a masterly sureness of conception and execution.

Mark Tobey was born in Centerville, Wisconsin, in 1890 and spent his childhood years in Trempealeau, Wisconsin, and Hammond, Indiana, where he commuted to Chicago to attend Saturday classes at the Art Institute for a brief period. Although he had little formal art education, he became a successful fashion designer and portrait painter in both Chicago and New York. In 1918 he became a convert to the Bahá'í World Faith, which teaches a mystical, ecumenical doctrine based on the Oneness of Mankind and on the eventual unification of all peoples in a single, peaceful, progressive world state. In the twenties and thirties, he taught periodically at the Cornish School in Seattle and Dartington Hall, Devonshire, England, otherwise dividing his time between Seattle, Chicago, and New York, and traveling extensively in Europe and the Near East. In 1934 he visited China and Japan, spending a month in a Zen monastery in Kyoto studying calligraphy, painting, and poetry. It was after this trip, in 1935, that he painted a group of pictures that first utilized his "white writing," a linear and calligraphic structuring of space in which line is identified with both light and movement. Recognition came to him late in life, and more in Europe than in the United States. In 1958, he won the first prize for painting at the 29th Venice Biennale, the first American to do so since Whistler. Tobey has lived in Basel, Switzerland, since 1960.

TOBEY *Red Man—White Man—Black Man* 1945
Oil and gouache on cardboard
27½ x 24½ in. (69.8 x 62.2 cm.)
Room of Contemporary Art Fund   RCA46:4

TOBEY *Coming and Going* **1970**
Tempera on cardboard
39½ x 27¼ in. (100.3 x 69.2 cm.)
Charles Clifton Fund   70:10

Morris Louis

Alpha, 1960, belongs to the series known as Unfurleds, which Louis considered his most ambitious statement. The colors—orange, black, yellow, blue, and red—flow diagonally down the sides of the painting, balancing and activating the bare white central section and reversing the compositional format of the veils. *Alpha* is an early work of the series, a transition piece: the forms are more vertical, recalling the Veils, and start from the top of the painting instead of the sides as in later Unfurleds. The colors are fewer, more transparent, and have softer edges than the later, more optical paintings.

Morris Louis was born Morris Louis Bernstein in Baltimore, Maryland, in 1912. He moved to the Washington, D.C., area in 1947. In 1952, while an instructor at the Washington Workshop Center, he became friends with fellow teacher Kenneth Noland. In April, 1953, Louis and Noland, together with critic Clement Greenberg, visited the New York studio of Helen Frankenthaler, where they saw her recently completed Mountains and Sea, a painting utilizing the poured-stain technique. This greatly impressed both artists. For Louis, it proved to be the turning point in his career. He said later of Frankenthaler, "She was a bridge between Pollock and what was possible." *

Borrowing from Pollock a greater freedom in paint handling and an enlarged format, Louis explored the possibilities of the stain technique by soaking thin veils of pure color into unprimed cotton duck canvas. The resulting series of softly overlapping color configurations with sensuous, evocative outlines came to be known as the Veil paintings. Louis was not concerned with gesture, with the artists' "handwriting" that was so important to the Abstract Expressionists. Instead of impasto and emphasis on paint quality, he employed color that, soaked into the raw canvas, became a part of the fabric.

In 1959 Louis had his second one-man show in New York, and a succession of exhibitions followed in the next three years. During this period he painted the series known as Florals, the Unfurleds, and the Stripe paintings. Although he received some critical acclaim before his death in 1962, extensive public recognition has come to him posthumously.

* G. Nordland, *The Washington Color Painters* (Washington Gallery of Modern Art, 1965), p. 12.

LOUIS *Alpha* **1960.** Acrylic resin paint on canvas, 105½ x 145½ in. (268.3 x 369.8 cm.)
Gift of Seymour H. Knox K64:5

Kenneth Noland

Yellow Half, 1963, an early example of the chevron motif, marks an important development in Noland's artistic self-critique, which involves a constant reevaluation and clarification of pictorial organization. No longer dependent on concentricity, he nevertheless retains symmetry as a mode of organizing the picture surface. The two upper corners are bisected at 45-degree angles by the chevron, the tip of which touches the bottom framing edge, effectively dividing the surface into zones of color that relate to one another and to the shape of the canvas in an explicit and logical manner. As opposed to the earlier target paintings, where Noland utilized a great deal of raw canvas as a field on which the circles floated, the surface of Yellow Half is completely covered with paint, tending to emphasize its flatness. Uneven paint application and the presence of "accidental" splatters attest to Noland's lack of concern with a pristine finish. Although the edges of the chevrons are sharp and clean, the stain technique gives the surface a matte, softened appearance.

Wild Indigo, 1967, is an early painting from Noland's initial horizontal stripe series which was characterized by attenuated bands of many intense hues, stretching tautly across a canvas of monumental dimensions. The horizontal extension of the bands allows maximum surface contact between colors, resulting in an intense optical quality. This is tempered by Noland's sensitive articulation of twenty-nine different hues, which enables the painting to maintain unity. The "breathing spaces" of raw canvas permit the colors to expand and appear to come forward and suffuse the space between the canvas and the spectator. These paintings determine the distance from which they are most successfully viewed by the relationship of the parts to the whole: in order to distinguish the individual stripes of color, the viewer is drawn close to the painting; while to perceive it as a whole, he must see it from a considerable distance. The over-all patterning of directional lines does not allow the eye to rest, but forces it to constantly scan back and forth over the image. As was the case with many paintings of the sixties, the execution is impersonal and mechanistic, the artist being responsible primarily for the conception of the work and remaining relatively detached from the actual painting process.

Kenneth Noland was born in 1924 in Asheville, North Carolina. He studied at Black Mountain College, 1946–48, with Ilya Bolotowsky, and with Ossip Zadkine in Paris in 1940. He returned to the United States in 1959 to teach at the Institute of Contemporary Art in Washington, D.C., and at the Washington Workshop Center, where he became friends with Morris Louis. After a visit to the New York studio of Helen Frankenthaler in 1953, Noland and Louis spent weeks working together attempting to overcome their preconceived assumptions about painting by eliminating recognizable structure, and experimenting with new techniques such as the poured-stain method deriving originally from Jackson Pollock.

In 1957–58 Noland first utilized the center of the canvas as a structuring device. In the resulting paintings, pinwheels and concentric color bands, the depicted forms related to the shape of the canvas through a shared central axis. Such a schematic arrangement, which automatically excluded the

NOLAND *Yellow Half* **1963**
Acrylic resin on canvas, 70 x 70 in. (177.8 x 177.8 cm.)
Gift of Seymour H. Knox   K64:6

possibility of involvement in arbitrary formal decisions (he called them self-canceling structures), freed Noland's use of color. In 1963–64 he developed the chevron motif and by 1967 had reduced the format of his painting to horizontal color stripes, often on canvases of monumental proportions.

Noland moved to New York in 1961. He taught at Bennington College, Bennington, Vermont, 1967–68.

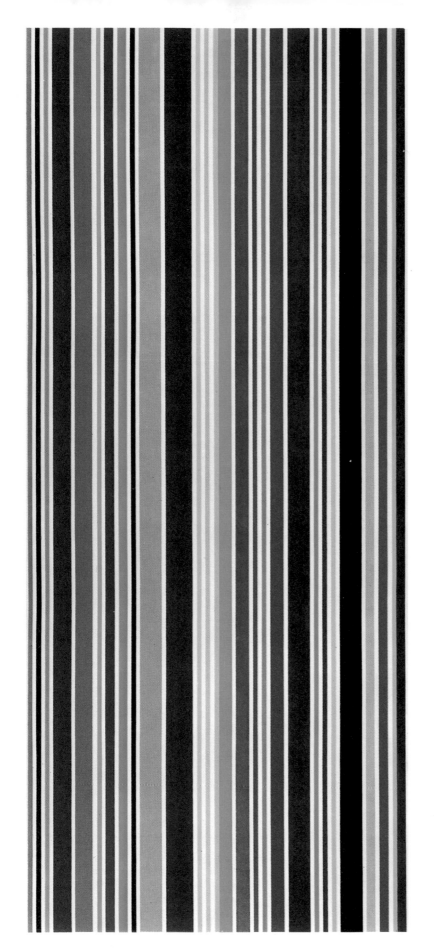

NOLAND *Wild Indigo* **1967.** Acrylic on canvas, 89 x 207 in. (226 x 527.7 cm.)
Charles Clifton Fund   72:5

Robert Rauschenberg

Ace, 1962, is composed of five separate panels originally intended for another work, a sound collage with radio loudspeakers behind the canvas, operated by remote control. Though electronic problems caused the project to be abandoned, the piece retains a high level of complexity. As the artist stated, "5 is the first complicated number; it's not two pairs, three or a couple." *

Apparently, this is Rauschenberg's last major work to combine found objects with brushed passages of heavy pigment. Except for the crumpled metal at the center and a small suspended can, the attached objects were already either entirely flat, as with the cardboard, paper, and umbrella fragment, or perceptually flattened by the bold two-dimensionality of the letters and the arrow. This separation of flat surface and appendage (and the hint of an illusion of depth created by the gradations in value at the far left) is significant in Rauschenberg's later work. Henceforth, the complex texture and rhythm of contemporary life, as well as the sudden shifts in subject and focus, would be conveyed entirely through floating and overlapping silkscreened images or transferred photographs, moving from the particular object to the abstracted picture of it. Recently he has made a series of collage prints, using flattened corrugated cardboard cartons similar to the one in *Ace*, which he calls Cardbirds.

In *Painting with Red Letter S*, 1957, fabric and paper collage were applied to unsized canvas, with areas of gesso and oil paint added in a predominantly rectangular patterning. The three-dimensionality achieved by the use of found objects, which was characteristic of Rauschenberg's "combines," is suggested in this painting by small areas of thick pigment. *Painting with Red Letter S* was the first of the artist's works to enter a public collection.

Born in 1925 in Port Arthur, Texas, Rauschenberg studied briefly at the Kansas City Art Institute and the Académie Julien in Paris. Dissatisfied with his inability to break away from the colorful and sensual qualities of pigment, he returned to the United States in 1948 to study under Josef Albers at the avant-garde Black Mountain College in North Carolina. During the next two critical years, he not only absorbed Albers's characteristic restraint and discipline but also began what was to be a continuing involvement with photography, music, and modern dance.

Rauschenberg has lived in New York since 1949, when he studied for a year at the Art Students League. In the early fifties, he designed sets and costumes for the Merce Cunningham Dance Company and worked closely with the composer John Cage and the painter Jasper Johns. During this period he developed his "combines," bringing together on the canvas freely brushed areas and increasingly assertive three-dimensional objects. By the late fifties, Rauschenberg became interested in a number of graphic techniques—rubbing, silkscreen, and lithography—that influenced his subsequent work.

* Alan Solomon, *Oracle* (New York: Leo Castelli Gallery, 1965).

RAUSCHENBERG   *Painting with Red Letter S*   **1957**
  Oil and collage on canvas, 51 x 52 in. (129.5 x 132 cm.)
  Gift of Seymour H. Knox   K59:16

RAUSCHENBERG *Ace* **1962.** Oil, wood, metal, cardboard on canvas, 108 x 240 in. (274.3 x 609.6 cm.)
Gift of Seymour H. Knox   K64:15

Jasper Johns

"I am concerned," Johns said in 1964, "with a thing's not being what it was, with its becoming something other than what it is, with any moment in which one identifies a thing precisely and with the slipping away of that moment, with at any moment seeing and saying and letting it go at that." *

The artist's statement, although made a few years after *Numbers in Color* of 1959, is an accurate description of the painting. The numbers are there, legible, set forth in sequence whether read from the right or from the top, and yet the images blur, sometimes are almost effaced and again are accented. While the viewer, from habit, tends to follow the numbers as such, simultaneously his eye is equally attracted to the over-all surface by the bright colors that appear at irregularly repeated intervals and the rich texture created by the wax medium with the addition of paper and canvas collage, sometimes cut out to shape the numbers and sometimes freely applied. The result is a tantalizing visual experience in which the numbers appear and disappear, constantly shifting and ambiguous.

Born in Georgia in 1939, Jasper Johns grew up in South Carolina and attended the state university for a year and a half. After service in the army, he went to New York in 1952 where friendships with the avant-garde composer John Cage and the painter Robert Rauschenberg, with whom he shared a studio, were influential to his development as an artist. At that time, Abstract Expressionism dominated the New York art world, although Geometric Abstraction and American Realism were also in evidence. From each of these opposing movements, Johns chose certain elements that he shaped to his own uses. He elected to employ real and commonplace subject matter, pre-existing and inherently flat motifs such as the American flag, targets, maps, letters of the alphabet, and numbers which he placed in carefully ordered compositions, retaining the flat surface, and rendered with painterly brushwork akin to that of the action painters.

Johns has produced a limited amount of sculpture and is a particularly distinguished printmaker, his innovations and sensibility marking him as one of the most accomplished and influential American artists ever to work in this field.

* John Russell, "Jasper Johns," *Réalités*, October, 1971, p. 74.

JOHNS *Numbers in Color* **1959**
Encaustic and newspaper on canvas, 66½ x 49½ in. (168.9 x 125.7 cm.)
Gift of Seymour H. Knox K59:10

Frank Stella

Eliminating color to concentrate on structure, Stella stressed a pictorial organization deduced from the shape of the canvas. The resulting paintings were large emblematic designs composed of parallel bands of black enamel and thin "breathing" spaces of raw canvas. They divide roughly into two groups: in the first, the bands are rectilinear and parallel the framing edge; in the second, to which *Jill* belongs, the bands run parallel to the diagonal axes of the picture field. The first tends to be centripetally arranged, the second, centrifugally. When first exhibited publicly, the Black paintings appeared particularly mute, inert, even nihilistic.

Jill, 1959, in keeping with the downbeat titles of the Black pictures, was named after a girl involved with black, deviate nightclubs. It is one of the simplest compositions in which concentric bands echo the central diamond shape, and the modular repetition implies an extension beyond the picture's edge. It demonstrates Stella's holistic approach to painting and recalls his goal to "see the whole idea without any confusion." Like the other Black pictures, *Jill* was painted freehand and reveals the irregular edges and personal paint handling absent from most geometric painting, and modified in Stella's later work.

"My main interest has been to make what is popularly called decorative painting truly viable in unequivocal abstract terms. Decorative, that is, in a good sense, in the sense that it is applied to Matisse. . . . I would like to combine the abandon and indulgence of Matisse's *Dance* with the over-all strength and sheer formal inspiration of a picture like his *Moroccans*." *

Fez, 1964, is from Stella's Moroccan series, the titles of which derive from Moroccan cities. It combines Stella's new interest in color experimentation with a deceptively simple, yet sophisticated structure. Fluorescent Day-Glo paint applied in a thin layer results in a luminosity and transparency unprecedented in his work. The surface is divided into equal quadrants that relate to one another through the repetition and direction of alternating green and yellow stripes; green in the upper left and lower right squares corresponds to yellow in the lower left and upper right squares. A powerful tension exists between the central axis, marked by both + and × forms, and the diagonally opposed squares, which tend to unite as spatially active fields. Stella reduced the number of stripes from twenty-six per quarter in the original drawing to twenty in the final painting.†

Lac Laronge III, 1969, is part of the Saskatchewan series that Stella started in the summer of 1967 in Canada, where, being unable to obtain shaped canvases, he adapted his Protractor series to a rectangular format. It is related to the schema *Gur*, one of the twenty-seven variations planned by Stella for the Protractor series, and the internal design is that of the interlaced protractor shapes (as opposed to the rainbow and fan motifs). A significant departure for Stella is the introduction of a figure-ground relationship, absent in earlier Protractor paintings where the depicted shape was identified with the shape of the canvas. While the strong color and

---

* William S. Rubin, *Frank Stella* (New York: The Museum of Modern Art, 1970), p. 148.

† *Ibid.*, p. 160.

curvilinear surface patterning induces a powerful kinesthesia, this effect is kept in check by Stella's use of a strict and pervasive geometry.

Born in Malden, Massachusetts, in 1936, Frank Stella attended Phillips Academy, Andover, 1950–54, and Princeton University 1954–58, where he majored in history and studied painting under William Seitz and Stephen Greene. After exploring the then-dominant Abstract Expressionist style while at the university, Stella moved in 1958 to New York, where he produced a series of "transitional" paintings influenced by Jasper Johns's flags and targets. In the winter of that year, he began the Black series, three of which were selected by Dorothy Miller to appear in the Sixteen Americans exhibition at The Museum of Modern Art in December, 1959.

Stella's approach to pictorial problems has been systematic, rigorously formal, and radically innovative. Early in 1960 he pioneered the shaped canvas with his Aluminum series by cutting notches in the canvases to eliminate "leftover spaces" in the design. Even more extreme shaping took place with the Copper series, which followed that summer. In 1961 he began his first color series (called Benjamin Moore, after the trade name of the house paint he used), still continuing, however, with the monochrome canvas. Not until the winter of 1962–63 did he begin to paint multicolored canvases—the Concentric Squares and Mitered Mazes. With the Irregular Polygons of 1965, Stella moved away from the self-imposed restriction of stripes to large geometric areas of unbroken color. In 1967, curvilinear designs were introduced for the first time in the Protractor series, Stella's most monumental works to date.

STELLA *Jill* **1959**
Enamel on canvas, 90¾ x 78¾ in. (230.5 x 200 cm.)
Gift of Seymour H. Knox   K62:1

368

STELLA *Fez* **1964**
Fluorescent alkyd on canvas, 77 x 77 in. (195.5 x 195.5 cm.)
Gift of Seymour H. Knox   K64:38

STELLA *Lac Laronge III* **1969.** Polymer paint on canvas, 9 x 13½ ft. (274.3 x 411.4 cm.)
Gift of Seymour H. Knox   K70:8

Ellsworth Kelly

Kelly's use of black and white in *New York, N. Y.,* 1957, differs markedly from the earlier black-and-white paintings that appeared in France and the United States in the late forties and early fifties. In these paintings, Hartung, Soulages, De Kooning, Motherwell, Kline, Pollock, and others explored the expressive and symbolic properties of a limited palette in which black was used in a gestural way, calligraphically as a sign, or as deep space.

The black in *New York, N. Y.* functions optically rather than spatially, the extreme value contrast imbuing it with the impression of color. The smooth unmodulated surface and mechanistic handling cause the forms to appear more as a design than as an expressive gesture, even though they share the heroic scale of the Abstract Expressionist works, which they seem almost to parody (as compared, for instance, to Franz Kline's painting *New York,* 1953, also in the collection of the Albright-Knox Art Gallery). Kelly also is concerned with the sign-making aspects of painting to the extent that he employs the letters N Y, but in this work it is the white negative forms that carry the message. His literal interpretation of a sign relates *New York, N. Y.* to Pop imagery rather than to the calligraphy of the previous generation.

Kelly rejected the hard-edge designation in 1964 when he stated: "I'm not interested in edges, I'm interested in the mass and color. . . . The edges happen because the forms get as quiet as they can be. I want the masses to perform." *

In *Blue, Yellow and Red,* 1968, the three fully saturated primary colors are juxtaposed on a one-to-one basis in equal-sized, parallel bands that extend the length of the painting, thus avoiding the spatial effect of figures in a field. Kelly's concern with flatness is also emphasized by his pristine surfaces and immaculate execution. As opposed to his modular paintings, where each color reads as a separate unit, the elongated parallelogram establishes itself as one shape, the inclined angle giving the forms a dynamic rather than static quality.

Ellsworth Kelly was born in 1923 in Newburgh, New York. After serving in the army, 1943–45, he attended the Boston Museum School for two years and in 1948 went to France to study art, returning to the United States in 1954 to live in New York.

In Paris, Kelly assimilated influences from Matisse and Arp (whom he met in 1950) and the Réalités Nouvelles group, creating an art that was purist and formal in intent. As early as 1950–51, he was painting modular and serial panel paintings of adjacent color rectangles, anticipating these developments in the United States by a decade.

After his return to this country, Kelly painted two-color biomorphic images with a strong figure-ground tension. These were often derived from natural forms such as the plants he observes and records in delicate drawings. In 1963, he returned to rectilinear forms and his earlier interest in modular and spectral painting as a vehicle of expression for his vibrant, fully saturated colors. Since 1959, he has also been involved in making sculpture.

* *Art International,* February, 1964, p. 47.

KELLY *New York, N.Y.* **1957.** Oil on canvas, 73¾ x 90 in. (187.3 x 228.6 cm.)
Gift of Seymour H. Knox   K59:11

KELLY *Blue, Yellow and Red* **1968**
Oil on canvas, 101½ x 30 in. (258 x 76.2 cm.)
Gift of Seymour H. Knox K69:3

Jules Olitski

Olitski establishes a surface that achieves the illusion of depth and expansive space while simultaneously reaffirming flatness and materiality. Olitski is said to have remarked that he would like to make paintings that would consist of nothing but some color sprayed into the air and remaining there. This statement is revealing of his art in two ways: first, it demonstrates Olitski's belief in the primacy of *paint* in painting; and second, it suggests Olitski's approach to structure, which he feels should be an outgrowth of color.

In *Second Tremor*, 1969, the heavy paint surface of Olitski's early spray paintings gives way to a much lighter, more ethereal treatment. Two framing borders are left partially unpainted and, throughout the surface, bare canvas shows through as a kind of atmospheric field in which the colors float. Although the primary impression is of a diagonal gradation from yellow in the lower right to violet in the upper left, blue, green, white, and gold pigments are also blended in with a light and sure touch. Not unlike Seurat, Olitski uses a stippled, painted border as a device to call attention to the painted space. Olitski's border, however, forms only a partial frame, and in its fractured, slightly tilted, form it makes the relationship to the space ambivalent rather than fixed.

Born in Gomel, Russia, in 1922, Jules Olitski came to the United States at the age of two. He studied at the National Academy of Design, New York, 1939–42, and attended the Ossip Zadkine School and the Académie de la Grande Chaumiére, Paris, 1949–50. He received B.A. and M.A. degrees from New York University.

Originally a portrait painter, Olitski started in the fifties to paint abstractions in a heavy impasto. Around 1960 he abandoned this style in favor of the stain technique developed by Helen Frankenthaler and Morris Louis.

A technical innovation, the spraying of acrylic paint onto an unsized and unprimed canvas with electrically powered spray guns, enabled Olitski in 1965 to explore the problems of modern painting in a highly individual way, and thereby establish his mature style.

OLITSKI *Second Tremor* **1969.** Acrylic on canvas, 105 x 81 in. (266.7 x 203.2 cm.)
Gift of Seymour H. Knox   K70:17

Andy Warhol

When questioned as to why he chose to paint soup cans, Warhol said, "Because I used to drink it. I used to have the same lunch every day for twenty years, I guess. The same thing over and over again." * Between 1962 and 1967, Warhol depicted the cans in every condition: pristine, opened, crushed; individually placed and in stacks; portrayed sketchily or precisely rendered; enlarged to varying degrees; presented in both realistic and fanciful colors, and in different media.

100 Cans, 1962, is one of the last of the "painted by hand" series. Pencil lines are discernible beneath the thin oil paint; the red is somewhat lighter than in the standard label; the "gold" seal has become a yellow circle. The word "Campbell's" is usually carefully lettered in script while the lettering of the other words varies in preciseness. The fleurs-de-lis are often randomly placed. The cans in the painting are almost double actual size—seven inches as compared with four. The multiple presentation, interrupted at the lower part of the canvas by partial cans, suggests endless stacks of cans of which only a small portion is seen.

"I never give my background and anyhow I make it all up different every time I'm asked." Andy Warhol was born in either Philadelphia or Pittsburgh, Pennsylvania, about 1930, the son of Czech emigrants named Warhola. He attended art school at the Carnegie Institute of Technology in Pittsburgh and went to New York in 1949, where he soon became a successful commercial artist. Around 1960, he began paintings of enlarged versions of comic strips, similar to Lichtenstein's work of that time. This subject was followed by Campbell's soup cans, Coca-Cola bottles, paper money, and other commonplace objects, all presented in an objective and reportorial manner. During 1962–63, he used a silkscreen technique, producing works in which the same image—or, sometimes, variations of the image—was repeated. These repetitions frequently resemble a strip of motion picture film, an art form Warhol began to use in 1963 and to which he has turned his attention increasingly in recent years.

* Gene Swenson, *Art News*, November, 1963, p. 26.

WARHOL *100 Cans* **1962**
Oil on canvas, 72 x 52 in. (182.9 x 132.1 cm.)
Gift of Seymour H. Knox   K63:26

Roy Lichtenstein

Head—Red and Yellow, 1962, is one of the first of a large series of paintings of women, adapted from banal, glamorized commercial photographs or comic strips. Even without a comparison with the original source, the stylization of line exaggerated into a play of negative and positive shapes and the asymmetrical composition make clear the number and importance of Lichtenstein's own changes. Color is limited to the bold effect of two primary hues.

The painting well demonstrates the paradoxes at the basis of Lichtenstein's art. Not only does he manage to convey the brazen stridency of the image by apparently dispassionate means, but he also capitalizes on the pseudomechanical manufacture to draw attention specifically to those formal elements: simplification, exaggeration, isolation, and enlargement, which remind the spectator of the process of personal artistic choice.

Roy Lichtenstein, born in New York in 1923, studied with Reginald Marsh at the Art Students League (1939) and, after three years with the army in Europe, 1940–43, at Ohio State University, where he received B.F.A. and M.F.A. degrees. He lived in Cleveland, 1951–57, painting scenes from the history of the American West. While teaching at the New York State College at Oswego, 1957–60, he worked in a nonfigurative, Abstract Expressionist style. Toward the end of this period, his interest in cartoon images, which he drew for his children and incorporated into his own pictures, led to the painting of a vastly enlarged bubble-gum wrapper. By the summer of 1961, the breakthrough to his mature style was complete. After teaching at Rutgers University, 1960–63, Lichtenstein moved to New York. His prolific production includes sculpture, drawing, graphics, ceramics, and enamels, in addition to paintings.

LICHTENSTEIN *Head—Red and Yellow*   **1962**
Oil on canvas, 48 x 48 in. (121.9 x 121.9 cm.)
Gift of Seymour H. Knox   K62:15

James Rosenquist

"In *Nomad*, I'm concerned with the scale and speed of recognition of ordinary things. It has to do with what I have to bring with me into the future. Generally I'm trying to prove to myself what I remember." *

This 1963 painting dates from the period when Rosenquist had begun to attach three-dimensional objects to his canvases. In the upper left corner, a plastic bag with drips of pigments that it presumably once contained is suspended directly over a fragile wood-and-metal construction on the floor upon which paint has been dripped and spattered. The unusual collection of commonplace images in the painting is related by repeated design motifs—the x of the Oxydol powdered soap label, the legs of the ballet dancer, and those of the picnic table and bench; the O of the label and the bulbous forms of meatballs, olives, and a light bulb.

The effect of the painting is that of a composite billboard, providing no central focal point; the eye of the viewer tends to wander over the surface, attracted first to one area and then another, like the nomad of the title.

James Rosenquist was born in Grand Forks, North Dakota, in 1933. He attended the University of Minnesota, 1953–55, where he studied painting and art history with Cameron Booth. During this time, he became interested in the Mexican muralists Orozco and Rivera, whose large-scale works and flattened images were adapted by Rosenquist in his later paintings. In 1955, he won a scholarship to the Art Students League in New York, where he studied until 1958. At the age of nineteen, Rosenquist began working as a commercial painter and he continued to earn a living at this trade in New York, where he painted billboards, later transferring that technique to his own paintings. During the late fifties, he was influenced by Abstract Expressionism, but he soon developed his own version of Pop art in enormous, collage-like paintings in which portions of commonplace objects are depicted, often in distorted size and in unexpected combinations.

* Letter from the artist, June 1, 1969.

ROSENQUIST *Nomad* **1963**
Oil on canvas, plastic and wood
90 x 141 in. (228.5 x 358 cm.)
Gift of Seymour H. Knox   K63:25

Robert Indiana

The title *Year of Meteors*, 1961, is also that of a poem by Walt Whitman, dated 1859–60, from the "Birds of Passage" section in *Leaves of Grass*:

> Nor forget I to sing of the wonder, the ship as she swam
> up my bay,
> Well-shaped and stately the Great Eastern swam up my bay,
> she was six hundred feet long,
> Her moving swiftly surrounded by myriads of small craft
> I forget not to sing;
> Nor the comet that came unannounced out of the north flaring
> in heaven,
> Nor the strange huge meteor-procession dazzling and clear
> shooting over our heads,
> (A moment, a moment long it sail'd its balls of unearthly light
> over our heads,
> Then departed, dropt in the night, and was gone;) . . .

Indiana's interest in American literature and history, combined with the location of his studio near Coenties Slip, by which the *Great Eastern* probably sailed into New York, contributed to the inspiration for this painting. His designs and colors recall street signs and hex signs; the lettering within circles suggests commemorative medals. In *Year of Meteors*, the colors are the blue and green of water and the white of cresting waves. The eight-pointed motif lends itself to a multiplicity of interpretations: points of the compass, a ship's wheel, a star, or—simply—an emblematic device to relate the two circles.

Also in the Gallery collection is an assemblage, *Star*, 1960–62 (p. 291).

Biography of the artist, p. 290.

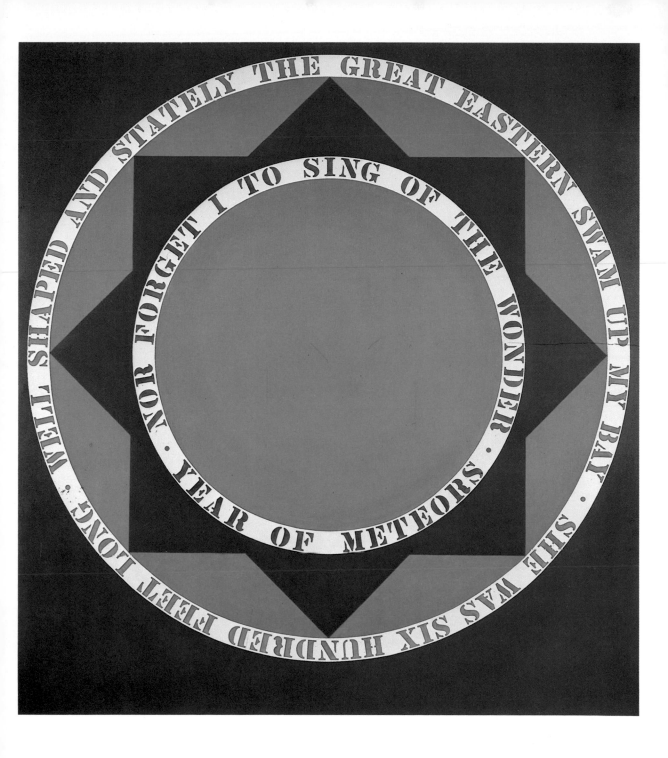

INDIANA *Year of Meteors* **1961**
Oil on canvas, 90 x 84 in. (228.5 x 213.3 cm.)
Gift of Seymour H. Knox K62:13

Jim Dine

In *Child's Blue Wall*, 1962, the painted surface can be variously interpreted as a painting of a wall covered with starred wallpaper, the pale star-filled sky of early evening or dawn, possibly seen through a window, or an imagined or remembered scene. These multiple references occur often in Dine's work, which is always highly personal, often poetic, and frequently auto-biographical. The field of color is limited suddenly by the attached lamp, which introduces a further ambiguity in that the lamp may be turned on or off, changing the appearance of the painting.

Jim Dine, born in Cincinnati, Ohio, in 1935, graduated from Ohio University in 1957 with a B.F.A. degree. In 1959, he went to New York where, with Allan Kaprow and Claes Oldenburg, he participated in some of the early Happenings. During 1960, he returned to painting but retained a theatrical quality in his work in the dramatic placement of actual objects, either attached to the painted surface or placed before it to set up an interaction among the elements. Although he has been called a Pop artist, his aesthetic is far more within the tradition of Abstract Expressionism, Dada, and the Neo-Surrealists. The objects he uses are either personal, such as his own clothes, or newly purchased, as in the case of shovels or wrenches. Nor is the object presented as an entity, as with Warhol's Soup Cans; instead, Dine places it within a painterly environment that has personal connotations for him. In the mid-sixties, he made a number of free-standing cast aluminum sculptures and, in recent years, has produced graphics, as well as watercolors and some environmental works.

DINE *Child's Blue Wall* **1962.** Oil on canvas, and mixed media, 60 x 72 in. (152.4 x 182.9 cm.)
Gift of Seymour H. Knox K63:1

385

Ilya Bolotowsky

Bolotowsky describes his art as "based on the relationship of the right angle and of the straight lines which result in rectangles. Associations, images, literature do not belong in this style. It depends for its effects strictly on the tensions and rhythms created by the neutral, non-associative, pure, plastic elements. The aim is to realize a feeling of timeless harmony and dynamic equilibrium." *

In *Scarlet Diamond*, Bolotowsky uses a shape ("a square standing on one corner") that he favors because "a diamond format creates a feeling of a larger and freer space than a square shape the same size." † The diamond format opens up the edges of the painting, allowing the horizontal and vertical elements to extend seemingly beyond the space of the painting. The diagonal of the edge against the vertical and horizontal forms inside creates a dynamic tension without undermining the basic rectangular relationships of the composition. The composition in Bolotowsky's painting is always asymmetrical, a part of his De Stijl heritage, and is dependent on his use of color for balance—in this case, fully saturated red, yellow, and blue.

Born in St. Petersburg, Russia, in 1907, Ilya Bolotowsky emigrated with his parents during the Russian Revolution, first living in Istanbul, and finally settling in the United States, where he has been a citizen since 1929.

He studied at the National Academy of Design in New York, 1924–30, and was painting in a semi-abstract style until 1933, when he first saw Mondrian's paintings in an exhibition of the Gallatin Collection at New York University. Since that period, his style has evolved from paintings influenced by Miró and the Russian Suprematists to an increasingly thorough and complex investigation of the Neo-Plastic aesthetic originated by Mondrian and the De Stijl artists.

Bolotowsky was one of the cofounders of the American Abstract Artists Association in 1936, and he was Acting Chairman of the art department at Black Mountain College, 1946–48. A noted teacher and lecturer, Bolotowsky has also written plays and produced experimental films.

* Lawrence Campbell, *Art News*, February, 1970, p. 40.
† Letter from the artist, September 12, 1970.

BOLOTOWSKY *Scarlet Diamond* **1969**
Oil on canvas, 48 x 48 in. (122 x 122 cm.)
Gift of Seymour H. Knox K69:10

Fritz Glarner

Adopting two of Mondrian's basic assumptions about painting—that it must be an abstract two-dimensional experience and that equilibrium is established through opposition—Glarner has created an art of dynamically balanced planes. *Relational Painting #93*, 1962, displays his characteristic use of a subtle variety of grays to bind together and accentuate the primary colors, red, blue, and yellow. By breaking up his rectangles with a slanted line, Glarner has created equalized shapes that read on the same plane, yet are never static.

Born in Zurich in 1899 of Swiss and Italian parents, Fritz Glarner lived primarily in Naples from 1904 to 1922 where he received a thorough grounding in academic painting during six years of study at The Royal Institute of Fine Arts. Having lived in France periodically as a youth, he moved to Paris in 1923, where he met many artists including Van Doesburg, Mondrian, Vantongerloo, and Leger. He exhibited in the first Abstraction-Création show in 1930. Glarner moved to New York in 1936 and established a close relationship with Mondrian and his American followers in the last two years of Mondrian's life, 1942–44. After Mondrian's death, he went through a period of self-searching, devoted himself to drawing for a year, and emerged with his first paintings whose space he termed "organized." Since 1945, all of his works have been titled Relational Painting.

Glarner has painted mural-sized works for the Time-Life Building, 1958–59, and for the Dag Hammarskjöld Library at the United Nations in New York, 1958–61. He died in Switzerland in 1972.

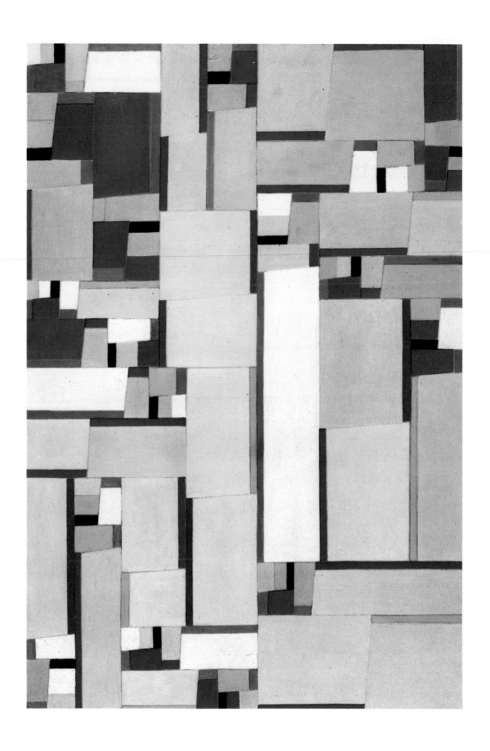

GLARNER *Relational Painting #93* **1962**
Oil on canvas, 66⅞ x 44 in. (169.9 x 111.8 cm.)
Gift of The Seymour H. Knox Foundation, Inc.
66:8

Burgoyne Diller

Diller's search for a means of constructing a volume on a two-dimensional surface was classified into three categories that he called "tangential development on three visual themes."

"First Theme" involves the placing of an element (usually one or more rectangles) in a relationship of dynamic intensity to the surface of the picture plane through relating shape, color, position, brightness, and size. In "Theme Two," the original free element becomes submerged in a system of planes redefining the surface. In "Theme Three," the free element is completely destroyed and the entire picture surface becomes active and complex. In his later years, Diller returned more frequently to Theme One, where "he notes something grand and elemental which he has lost in Themes Two and Three." *

First Theme (Estate Number 9), 1963–64, is a simplified composition that depends completely on size and color relationships to express the feeling of volume with which Diller was concerned. Black, white, red, and yellow are used exclusively to provide maximum contrast. While the Neo-Plastic emphasis on the right angle is retained, the symmetrical, heraldic composition demonstrates a distinct departure from his De Stijl beginnings.

Born in New York in 1906, Burgoyne Diller grew up in Michigan and studied at the State College in Lansing. Already painting at this time, he hitchhiked on weekends to the Chicago Art Institute, where he admired Seurat's La Grande Jatte and Cézanne's paintings. In 1926 he returned to New York to study at the Art Students League.

Diller's early work was influenced by Cubism, but he soon became one of a small group of Americans painting in the Neo-Plastic style of Van Doesburg and Mondrian, a style he was to develop for the next thirty years. In the thirties, Diller became director of the mural division of the Works Projects Administration for the New York area, where he worked actively for the cause of abstraction. Stuart Davis and Arshile Gorky were among the artists who painted murals under his supervision.

For the last twenty years of his life, Diller lived and worked in virtual seclusion, highly respected by a number of artists, critics, and curators but relatively unknown to the general public. He died in 1965.

* Lawrence Campbell, Art News, May, 1961, p. 57.

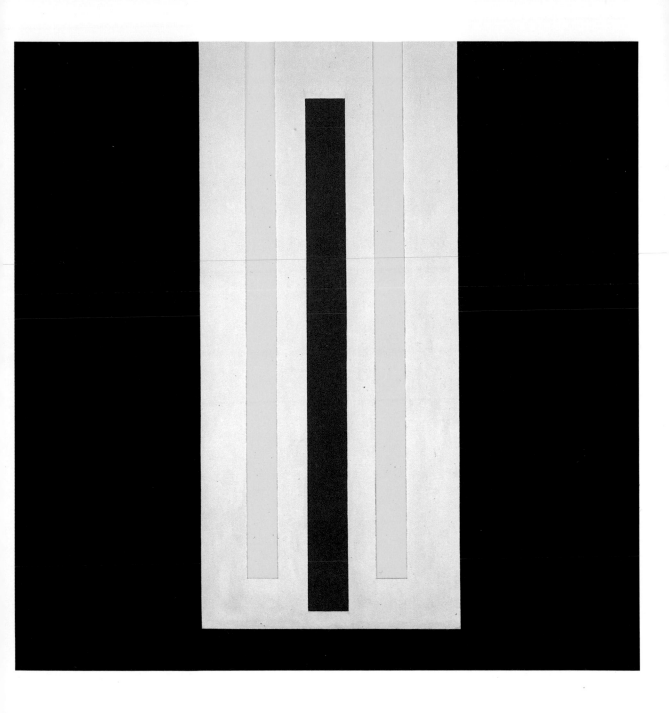

DILLER *First Theme* **1963–64**
Oil on canvas, 71¾ x 71½ in. (182.2 x 181.6 cm.)
Gift of Seymour H. Knox   K69:13

Ludwig Sander

Sander's is an art of relational color planes. He likes to "exhaust" the possibilities of a color by painting series of variations on a single or limited combination of hues, avoiding pure primary colors. *Untitled*, 1963, explores a range of yellows and greens, subtly combined and balanced. Sander's method is intuitive. Although his format is basically geometric, in fact derived from De Stijl concerns, it is not hard-edge, since the lines separating planes are of varying and uneven widths. His surfaces are usually painted in several layers, the color adjusted as the painting develops, so that the lingering presence of earlier hues comes through as underpainting and sometimes is visible along the edges of planes.

Also in the Gallery collection is *Composition-Blue*, 1960.

Born in New York in 1906, Ludwig Sander began painting in 1925. In 1927, he studied at the Art Students League, traveled in Germany and Switzerland, and upon his return to New York became a pupil of Alexander Archipenko. In 1931, he spent time in Paris with Nakian and other American artists before going to Munich to become a pupil of Hans Hofmann. He studied there for two semesters and continued his relationship with Hofmann after the latter moved to New York. In 1946, Sander studied art history at New York University. Although he was in close contact with other artists of the New York School during this period, his own style was more closely related to that of Mondrian. He was a founding member of The Club in 1950, an association of New York artists that was a focal point of Abstract Expressionist activity.

SANDER *Untitled* **1963**
Oil on canvas, 60 x 54 in. (152.4 x 137.2 cm.)
Gift of Seymour H. Knox   K64:9

Jack Youngerman

"For me shape is the central issue in painting. . . . People seem to have noticed my surfaces, edges, etc., but not my primary concern which is finding and inventing new shapes. I am working for something organic and lyrical. I like the expressiveness of locked, meshed or tension-provoking shapes in opposition, a union in combat." *

In *Delfina*, 1961, the interplay of positive and negative forms was derived ultimately from Matisse's cutouts and the art of Jean Arp, although Youngerman has found inspiration in sources as diverse as the cave paintings of Lascaux and blue-and-white Arabic tiles. The patterning of shapes determines the character of the other elements in the painting—the colors, the surface qualities, and the size and proportions of the canvas. The sharp and jagged contours recall *papier-collé* and are suggestive of topographical formations caused by natural forces.

Also in the Gallery collection is *Roundabout*, 1970.

Jack Youngerman was born in Louisville, Kentucky, in 1926. He studied at the University of North Carolina, Chapel Hill, 1944–46, and received a B.A. degree from the University of Missouri, Columbia, in 1947. In 1947–48 he studied at the École des Beaux-Arts in Paris, where he was drawn to the hard-edge Constructivism of the Réalités Nouvelles artists. He eventually found this style incompatible with his lyrical and romantic vision, and since 1953 he has developed a more personal expression. Before his return to the United States in 1956, he traveled extensively in Europe and the Orient.

* Youngerman, *Artform*, January, 1966, p. 30.

YOUNGERMAN *Delfina* **1961**
Oil on canvas, 106 x 80 in. (274.4 x 203.2 cm.)
Gift of Seymour H. Knox   K61:26

Nicholas Krushenick

Krushenick has a vocabulary of forms and shapes that he "is in love with," which he feels must be dynamic and not literal. "They have to have a certain kind of mystery, so you can't identify them, but they suggest many forms." * This is true of *Lotus Europa*, 1969, which can be seen in one of two ways: as a convex white shape cutting diagonally across a background of blue and orange stripes, or as a concave space dividing step-like forms that appear to descend in the upper left and ascend in the lower right. The ambiguity of the linear structure is further complicated by Krushenick's color, confined within black lines to increase vibrancy, which brings all the action back to the surface of the canvas. Thus, any suggestion of spatial illusion is negated.

Nicholas Krushenick was born in the East Bronx, New York, in 1929. He studied in 1948–50 at the Art Students League and in 1950–51 with Hans Hofmann, for whom he had great personal respect. In 1958, with his brother John, he opened the cooperative Brata Gallery on Tenth Street, which they operated until 1962, showing the work of Al Held, Ronald Bladen, George Sugarman, and other now well-known artists.

After working with shaped collages in 1959, Krushenick started painting with acrylics to achieve the clear, hard colors now characteristic of his work. About the same time, he introduced rigid black outlines, which have caused his work to be compared with Roy Lichtenstein's comic-strip painting. Although his paintings are nonobjective, his outlines, commercial colors, and animated forms have linked him with Pop art.

* *Art in America*, May–June, 1969, p. 68.

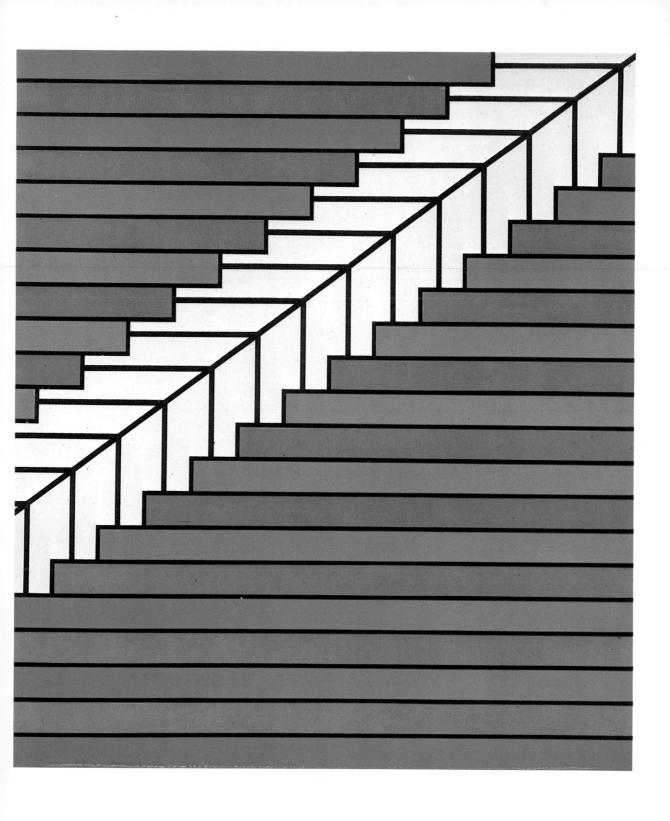

KRUSHENICK *Lotus Europa* **1969**
Acrylic on canvas, 84 x 74 in. (213.3 x 188 cm.)
Gift of Seymour H. Knox   K69:23

Nassos Daphnis

"*11-67* was the eleventh painting of the year 1967. . . . All my works since 1950 are numbered in the order of their execution for each year. The study for this painting was done in 1966 . . . when I was introducing the curved line or arch to the straight line of the earlier paintings. This painting, as well as all my works done since 1950, does not have any subject matter. They only deal with matter in a planar space organized in a way where both elements coexist in harmony with each other.

"*11-67* was painted on canvas, sprayed on with epoxy paint which I started to use in 1963 [when] I was looking for a paint to give me the vibrant quality of color and the durability of the surface. After the design was put on the canvas, each area to be sprayed was taped and masked . . . until all the colors were painted. . . .

"The significance of this painting, I feel, is the order that exists between the two elements, matter and space. In this period of time and in the world of today, I think it is very important to try and achieve a balance of coexistence." *

Also in the Gallery collection are two paintings of 1960 and 1961, a plexiglass sculpture, 1963, and an early painting dated 1938.

Nassos Daphnis was born in Krokeai, Greece, in 1914. He immigrated to the United States in 1930 and began painting five years later. A self-taught artist, his earliest paintings were lyrical landscapes and figurative works in a naïve style. A Surrealist influence is evident in his landscapes and underwater images painted after World War II. In the early fifties, after two years of travel and study in Europe, he developed the principles of form— a striving for purity and natural order—and pure color on which he based all his subsequent abstract, geometric paintings and constructions. By juxtaposing intense and recessive colors, as defined by his Color-Plane theory (in which black is rated most intense, followed by blue, red, yellow, and white), he created tension and subtle optical effects, anticipating the optical art of the sixties. Daphnis's paintings of the mid-fifties were quite complex in design, consisting of primary colors and black and white arranged in hard-edge blocks and grids. By the late fifties, he had simplified the compositions with the result that these paintings resemble enlarged versions of segments of earlier works.

* Letter from the artist, September 2, 1970.

DAPHNIS *11–67* **1967**
Epoxy on canvas, 98 x 77 in. (249 x 195.6 cm.)
Gift of Seymour H. Knox   K69:14

DAVIS *Plane Sawtooth* **1970.** Polyester resin and fiberglass, 60 x 140 in. (152.4 x 355.6 cm.)
Gift of Seymour H. Knox K71:6

Ron Davis

Davis's intense exploration of spatial illusionism has been heightened by his pioneering use of new materials and techniques. Working with polyester resin and fiberglass, he paints his forms in reverse on a working surface from which they are removed once the compound has hardened. These "plastic colored" paintings are all shiny surface, in a deliberate contradiction to the pronounced three-point perspective of his depicted shapes.

Davis's use of perspective creates the effect of monumental volumes, distorting their actual distance from the spectator and transforming the wall into an abstract spatial field. His pictorial manipulation of transparency and opacity in *Plane Sawtooth*, 1970, causes the piece to appear weightless and makes a visual pun on the transparent nature of plastic, which in this case is an illusion.

Ron Davis was born in 1937 in Santa Monica, California, and grew up in Cheyenne, Wyoming. He studied engineering at the University of Wyoming, Laramie, 1955–56, and worked as a radio announcer, 1958–59. He studied at the Yale University–Norfolk Summer School of Music and Art in 1962.

Davis's early paintings were hard-edge, shaped canvases, some of which made use of the wall as part of the composition. In 1966 he started painting with acrylic or polyester resin and fiberglass, developing a unique style in which color, surface, and support are one.

He lives and works in Los Angeles.

Larry Rivers

The Final Veteran, 1960, is one of several paintings by Rivers that were based on photographs related to the death of Walter Williams, the last Civil War soldier, reproduced in Life magazine January 11, 1960. In the original photograph, the aged veteran in uniform is shown in a flag-draped coffin with an honor guard at attention and wreaths of flowers in the background. In this painting, one of the earliest in the series and also one of the most abstract, broad, sweeping brushstrokes convey a generalized and blurred impression of the scene—the fragmentary heads of the veteran and the guard, and the Confederate flag are recognizable, as is the sketched outline of a tilted cross at the upper left, repeating the design of the flag. Rivers has said that "the important thing in painting is . . . condensed passion, and I decided not to worry about borders, sidelines and accessories. . . . If I can get the main impact right, I'm not concerned about surrounding details and sometimes they weaken the principle image." *

Larry Rivers was born in 1923 in the Bronx, New York, of Eastern European immigrant parents. After being discharged from the army in 1943, he studied music for one year and played saxophone in a number of jazz bands. He began painting in 1945 and studied at the Hans Hofmann School in New York and Provincetown, 1947–48. During the fifties he gradually arrived at his characteristic style in which fragmentary and blurred images were rendered in thin paint and transparent washes. At a time when most advanced painting was unquestionably abstract, Rivers persisted in painting the human figure, frequently nude. His work has been seen to constitute a link between the painterly techniques of Abstract Expressionism and the interest in figuration and commercial imagery of Pop art. More recently, he has created increasingly complex and elaborate three-dimensional assemblages often based on sociological or historical themes.

* Sam Hunter, Larry Rivers (New York: Abrams, 1969), p. 25.

RIVERS *The Final Veteran* **1960.** Oil on canvas, 81⅜ x 51 in. (206.7 x 129.5 cm.)
Gift of The Seymour H. Knox Foundation, Inc.   K61:3

Georgia O'Keeffe

"In 1929 I saw an old broken down house with a walled garden. It was a large pigpen. The house had a patio with that green door in a long wall on one side. The walled garden and the long wall with the green door made me decide that it was going to be my house. It took another ten years to get the place but I finally got it from the church and now I live in it.

"I have painted the door many times." *

O'Keeffe's painting of her adobe house in Abiquiu, New Mexico—Green Patio Door, 1955—is one of her sparest compositions, consisting only of three bands—the sky, the wall with the centered rectangle of the door, and the ground. Based on reality, as are all her paintings, it is a distillation, a purification of visual experience, personal, and delicately painted. During the forty years she has lived in the New Mexico desert, she has consistently found her subject matter there in the contours of the land, the flowers, and the bleached bones of animals. The desert has been her source of inspiration, both artistic and spiritual, complementing her private and mystical vision.

Georgia O'Keeffe spent her childhood on a farm near Sun Prairie, Wisconsin, where she was born in 1887. She moved with her family to Williamsburg, Virginia, in 1902. After studying at The Art Institute of Chicago, 1905–6, and the Art Students League, New York, 1907–8, she became disenchanted with the academic mode and decided to give up painting. She worked in commercial art and taught until her interest in painting was renewed by the teaching of Arthur Dow, whose inspiration derived from the flat patterning of Oriental art. She studied with Dow at Teachers College, Columbia University, 1914–15. In the autumn of 1915, while teaching in Columbia, South Carolina, she sent a group of drawings to a friend in New York, with the admonition to show them to no one. Instead, her friend took them to Alfred Stieglitz, who exhibited them at his 291 Gallery, the beginning of a long relationship that resulted in their marriage in 1924, and lasted until Stieglitz's death in 1946. O'Keeffe's style developed early and has alternated between precise realistic rendering verging on Surrealism, and equally meticulous but simplified abstractions often derived from the same subject matter. In the twenties, O'Keeffe painted in New York and at Lake George and received almost yearly exhibitions planned by Stieglitz at the Anderson Galleries and later at the Intimate Gallery, where Demuth, Dove, Marin, and Hartley were also represented. From 1929, she spent her summers in New Mexico and, after Stieglitz's death, moved there permanently.

* Letter from the artist, October 24, 1968.

404

O'KEEFFE *Green Patio Door, 1955* **1955**
Oil on canvas, 30 x 20 in. (76.2 x 50.9 cm.)
Gift of Seymour H. Knox   K58:13

Appendix

Exhibition and publication references
for paintings and sculpture, pp. 11–405.

Afro (Basaldella)
Fear of the Night (La Paura del buio), **1952**
Inscribed l.r. "Afro 52"

Exhibitions

XXVI Biennale di Venezia, June 14–October 19, 1952, #18

Albright Art Gallery, Buffalo, May 15, 1957–February 15, 1958, *Contemporary Art—Acquisitions 1954–1957*, #28, ill. p. [40]

The Mills College Art Gallery, Oakland, Calif., April 13–May 11, 1958, *Afro*, checklist, #5

The Cleveland Museum of Art, November 11–December 31, 1958, *Some Contemporary Works of Art*, #1, ill. p. [22]

Museo Nacional de Bellas Artes, Buenos Aires, October 23–November 30, 1969, *109 obras de Albright-Knox Art Gallery*, #43, p. 54, ill.

Albright-Knox Art Gallery, Buffalo, July 21–August 27, 1972, *Continental Painting and Sculpture, 1942–1972, in the Albright-Knox Art Gallery*, checklist, #[2]

Yaacov Agam
Free Standing Painting, **1971**
Inscribed l.r. "Agam 71"

Exhibitions

Galerie Denise René, New York, April 29–June 8, 1971, *Transformable Sculpture and Recent Painting by Yaacov Agam*, h.c.

Albright-Knox Art Gallery, Buffalo, March 4–April 9, 1972, *Movement, Optical Phenomena and Light: Kinetic and Optic Painting and Sculpture in the Albright-Knox Art Gallery*, checklist, #[2]

Yaacov Agam
The Ninth Power, **1970–71**
Inscribed inside largest circle "Agam"

Exhibitions

Galerie Denise René, New York, May, 1971, *Transformable Transformables Yaacov Agam*, ill. p. [25]

Reference

M. V[ictor] A[leper], "Images: Agam at Denise René," *Arts Magazine*, vol. 45, no. 8, Summer, 1971, p. 48, ill.

Josef Albers
Homage to the Square: Terra Caliente, **1963**
Inscribed l.r. "A.63." Inscribed on reverse u.r. "Homage to the Square: /'Terra Caliente'/ Albers 1963." Inscribed on reverse u.l. "48 × 48" /=121.5 × 121.5 cm."

Exhibitions

Sidney Janis Gallery, New York, April 10–May 4, 1968, *New Work by Josef Albers*

Albright-Knox Art Gallery, Buffalo, June 17–September 1, 1969, *Contemporary Art—Acquisitions 1966–1969*, #65

Museo Nacional de Bellas Artes, Buenos Aires, October 23–November 30, 1969, *109 obras de Albright-Knox Art Gallery*, #69, p. 80, ill.

Sidney Janis Gallery, New York, October 5–31, 1970, *Paintings by Joseph Albers*

Pierre Alechinsky
Greet the North, Greet the South (Salut le nord, salut le sud), **1962**
Inscribed l.l. "Alechinsky II 1962"

Exhibitions

Upton Gallery, State University College, Buffalo, April 30–May 13, 1964, *Outstanding Art Collections of Greater Buffalo*, checklist, #11

The Arts Club of Chicago, February 26–March 27, 1965, *Pierre Alechinsky*, #31, ill. p. [13]; traveled to: The University Gallery, University of Minnesota, Minneapolis, April 7–May 4; The Jewish Museum, New York, May 15–June 15

Albright-Knox Art Gallery, Buffalo, September 30–October 30, 1966, *Contemporary Art—Acquisitions 1962–1965*, #1

National Gallery of Art, Washington, D.C., May 19–July 21, 1968, *Paintings from the Albright-Knox Art Gallery*, ill. p. 79

Museo Nacional de Bellas Artes, Buenos Aires, October 23–November 30, 1969, *109 obras de Albright-Knox Art Gallery*, #50, ill. p. 61

Albright-Knox Art Gallery, Buffalo, July 21–August 27, 1972, *Continental Painting and Sculpture, 1942–1972, in the Albright-Knox Art Gallery*, checklist, #[3]

Richard Anuszkiewicz
Iridescence, **1965**
Inscribed on reverse "© 101/Richard Anuszkiewicz/ 1965"

Exhibitions

Sidney Janis Gallery, New York, November 3–27, 1965, *New Paintings by Anuszkiewicz*, #11, ill. p. [14]

Albright-Knox Art Gallery, Buffalo, March 3–April 14, 1968, *Plus by Minus: Today's Half-Century*, #6, ill. p. [29]

National Gallery of Art, Washington, D.C., May 19–July 21, 1968, *Paintings from the Albright-Knox Art Gallery*, ill. p. 90

Albright-Knox Art Gallery, Buffalo, June 17–September 1, 1969, *Contemporary Art—Acquisitions 1966–1969*, #1, ill. p. 18

Museo Nacional de Bellas Artes, Buenos Aires, October 23–November 30, 1969, *109 obras de Albright-Knox Art Gallery*, #86, p. 97, ill.

Albright-Knox Art Gallery, Buffalo, March 4–April 9, 1972, *Movement, Optical Phenomena and Light: Kinetic and Optic Painting and Sculpture in the Albright-Knox Art Gallery*, checklist, #[6]

Karel Appel
Flight (La Fuite), 1954
Inscribed l.r. "K. Appel 54"

Exhibitions

Martha Jackson Gallery, New York, December 6–31, 1954, *Karel Appel*, checklist, #5

Albright Art Gallery, Buffalo, May 15, 1957–February 15, 1958, *Contemporary Art—Acquisitions 1954–1957*, #26, ill. p. [39]

Walker Art Center, Minneapolis, April 5–May 17, 1959, *School of Paris 1959—The Internationals*, #4, p. 19, ill. p. 18

Yale University Art Gallery, New Haven, April 27–September 24, 1961, *Paintings and Sculpture from the Albright Art Gallery*, checklist, #1

Albright-Knox Art Gallery, Buffalo, July 21–August 27, 1972, *Continental Painting and Sculpture, 1942–1972, in the Albright-Knox Art Gallery*, checklist, #[4]

Jean Arp
Constellation-Punctuation, 1956
Not inscribed

Exhibitions

Sidney Janis Gallery, New York, January–February 1960, *Arp—Mondrian*, #9, ill.

Sidney Janis Gallery, New York, January 8–February 9, 1969, *Masterpieces of 20th Century Art*, checklist, #48

Albright-Knox Art Gallery, Buffalo, June 17–September 1, 1969, *Contemporary Art—Acquisitions 1966–1969*, #116, ill. p. 56

Albright-Knox Art Gallery, Buffalo, July 21–August 27, 1972, *Continental Painting and Sculpture, 1942–1972, in the Albright-Knox Art Gallery*, checklist, #[10]

Jean Arp
Classical Figure (Figure classique), 1964
Not inscribed

Exhibitions

Albright-Knox Art Gallery, Buffalo, September 30–October 30, 1966, *Contemporary Art—Acquisitions 1962–1965*, #182, ill. p. 79

Albright-Knox Art Gallery, Buffalo, July 21–August 27, 1972, *Continental Painting and Sculpture, 1942–1972, in the Albright-Knox Art Gallery*, checklist, #[11]

Francis Bacon
Man with Dog, 1953
Not inscribed

Exhibitions

The Hanover Gallery, London, June–July 1954, *Francis Bacon*
Martha Jackson Gallery, New York, October 12–November 6, 1954, *3 British Artists / Hepworth / Scott / Bacon*, #17, ill. p. [3]

Albright Art Gallery, Buffalo, May 15, 1957–February 15, 1958, *Contemporary Art—Acquisitions 1954–1957*, #18, ill. p. [28]

Yale University Art Gallery, New Haven, April 27–September 24, 1961, *Paintings and Sculpture from the Albright Art Gallery*, checklist, #[2]

The Tate Gallery, London, May 24–July 1, 1962, *Francis Bacon*, #25, ill. p. 28

The Agnes Etherington Art Centre, Queen's University, Kingston, Ontario, Canada, October 25–November 25, 1962, *Constable to Bacon*, #50, p. [14], ill. p. [15]

The Solomon R. Guggenheim Museum, New York, October 17, 1963–January 12, 1964, *Francis Bacon*, #24, p. 27, ill. p. 47; traveled to: The Art Institute of Chicago, January 24–February 23, 1964

Upton Gallery, State University College, Buffalo, April 30–May 13, 1964, *Outstanding Art Collections of Greater Buffalo*, #10, p. [17], ill.

Albright-Knox Art Gallery, Buffalo, October 27–November 29, 1964, *Contemporary British Paintings and Sculpture*, #7, p. 10, ill. p. 12; traveled to: Addison Gallery of American Art, Andover, Mass., January 5–February 15, 1965

The University Art Museum, University of New Mexico, Albuquerque, February 11–April 24, 1968, *The Animal Kingdom*, #17

National Gallery of Art, Washington, D.C., May 19–July 21, 1968, *Paintings from the Albright-Knox Art Gallery*, ill. p. 81

Museo Nacional de Bellas Artes, Buenos Aires, October 23–November 30, 1969, *109 obras de Albright-Knox Art Gallery*, #60, p. 71, ill.

Galeries nationales du Grand Palais, Paris, October 26, 1971–January 10, 1972, *Francis Bacon*, #15, p. 46, ill. p. 100; traveled to: Kunsthalle, Düsseldorf, Germany, March 7–May 7

Albright-Knox Art Gallery, Buffalo, June 13–July 16, 1972, *English Painting and Sculpture, 1942–1972, in the Albright-Knox Art Gallery*, checklist, #[6]

Reference

Ronald Alley, *Francis Bacon*, Thames and Hudson, London, 1964, #58, pp. 70–71, ill. p. [183]

Mary Bauermeister
Four Quarters, 1964–65
Inscribed u.r. on frame "4 Quarts 1964"

Exhibitions

Galeria Bonino, New York, April 13–May 8, 1965, *Mary Bauermeister*, #27, detail ill. p. [20]

Albright-Knox Art Gallery, Buffalo, June 17–September 1, 1969, *Contemporary Art—Acquisitions 1966–1969*, #32, ill. p. 41

Albright-Knox Art Gallery, Buffalo, March 4–April 9, 1972, *Movement, Optical Phenomena and Light: Kinetic and Optic Painting and Sculpture in the Albright-Knox Art Gallery*, checklist, #[8]

Willi Baumeister
Growing, 1952
Inscribed l.r. "Baumeister 3 52." Inscribed on reverse

"W. Baumeister/Weidler/'Wachstum' 1952/ 100 x 130/ Baumeister"

Exhibitions

Carnegie Institute, Department of Fine Arts, Pittsburgh, October 16–December 14, 1952, *The 1952 Pittsburgh International Exhibition of Contemporary Painting*, #14; traveled to: California Palace of the Legion of Honor, San Francisco, January 30–March 1, 1953

Albright-Knox Art Gallery, Buffalo, July 21–August 27, 1972, *Continental Painting and Sculpture, 1942–1972, in the Albright-Knox Art Gallery*, checklist, #[14]

Reference

"Room of Contemporary Art Collection" (letter from the artist), *Gallery Notes*, The Buffalo Fine Arts Academy, vol. XVII, nos. 2 and 3, June, 1953, p. 10, ill.

William Baziotes
White Bird, 1957
Inscribed l.l. "Baziotes"

Exhibitions

Whitney Museum of American Art, New York, November 20, 1957–January 12, 1958, *Annual Exhibition/ Sculpture, Painting, Watercolors*, #50, p. 8

Kootz Gallery, New York, February 18–March 8, 1958, *Baziotes*, checklist, #5

Universal and International Exhibition, Brussels, April 17–October 18, 1958, *American Art/Four Exhibitions: Seventeen Contemporary American Painters*, #114, p. 60

U.S. Information Service Library, London, October 31–November 21, 1958, *Seventeen American Artists + Eight Sculptors*, checklist, #2, ill.

World House Galleries, New York, December 15, 1958–January 17, 1959, *Brussels '58/Contemporary American Art*, checklist, #2

Memorial Art Gallery of the University of Rochester, January 15–March 5, 1961, *Paintings and Sculpture from the Albright Art Gallery*

Yale University Art Gallery, New Haven, April 27–September 24, 1961, *Paintings and Sculpture from the Albright Art Gallery*, checklist, #3

The Solomon R. Guggenheim Museum, New York, February 4–March 21, 1965, *William Baziotes, A Memorial Exhibition*, #35, p. 12, ill. p. [36]; traveled to: Cincinnati Art Museum, April 2–May 2; Reading (Pa.) Public Museum and Art Gallery, May 23–June 27; Santa Barbara (Calif.) Museum of Art, July 13–August 22; Milwaukee Art Center, September 9–October 10; Rose Art Museum, Brandeis University, Waltham, Mass., November 1–30; Munson-Williams-Proctor Institute, Utica, N.Y., December 11–January 11, 1966; The Columbus (Ohio) Gallery of Fine Arts, January 27–February 28; The Corcoran Gallery of Art, Washington, D.C., March 15–April 15; The Minneapolis Institute of Arts, May 15–June 15; Dallas Museum of Fine Arts, July 4–August 4; Fort Worth Art Center, August 25–September 25; Akron (Ohio) Art Institute, October 10–November 14, 1966.

National Gallery of Art, Washington, D.C., May 19–July 21, 1968, *Paintings from the Albright-Knox Art Gallery*, ill. p. 51

Museo Nacional de Bellas Artes, Buenos Aires, October 23–November 30, 1969, *109 obras de Albright-Knox Art Gallery*, #64, p. 75, ill.

Marlborough Gallery, New York, February 11–March 6, 1971, *William Baziotes' Late Work 1946–1962*, #18, p. 11

Albright-Knox Art Gallery, Buffalo, January 19–February 20, 1972, *Abstract Expressionism: The First and Second Generations in the Albright-Knox Art Gallery*, checklist, #[1]

References

J[ames] M[ellow], "Baziotes," *Arts*, vol. 32, No. 6, March, 1958, p. 60

F[airfield] P[orter], "William Baziotes," *Art News*, vol. 57, no. 1, March, 1958, p. 13

Max Beckmann
Hotel Lobby, 1950
Inscribed l.r. "Beckmann/N.Y. 50"

Exhibitions

Albright Art Gallery, Buffalo, April 15–May 14, 1950, *Bosch to Beckmann*, #22, ill. p. 43

Colorado Springs Fine Arts Center, July 2–September 4, 1950, *New Accessions USA, 1950*, #3, ill. p. [20]

Carnegie Institute, Department of Fine Arts, Pittsburgh, October 19–December 21, 1950, *The Pittsburgh International Exhibition of Paintings*, #70, ill. p. [100]

John Herron Art Institute, Indianapolis, January 7–February 4, 1951, *63rd Annual Exhibition / Contemporary American Paintings*, checklist, #3; traveled to: Dayton (Ohio) Art Institute, February 9–March 4

Haus der Kunst, Munich, Germany, June–July, 1951, *Max Beckmann*, #174; traveled to: Charlottenburg Schloss, Berlin, August–September; Basel, Switzerland, October; Stedelijk Museum, Amsterdam, The Netherlands, December–January, 1952, #84

Albright Art Gallery, Buffalo, May 10–June 29, 1952, *Expressionism in American Painting*, #22, p. 57, ill. p. 33

The Denver Art Museum, January 11–February 15, 1953, *Origins and Trends of Contemporary Art*, checklist, #5

Canadian National Exhibition, Toronto, Canada, August 28–September 12, 1953, checklist, #141, p. 17

Kunsthaus, Zurich, Switzerland, November 22, 1955–January 8, 1956, *Max Beckmann*, #143; traveled to: Kunsthalle, Basel, Switzerland, January 14–February 12, #131; Gemeentemuseum, The Hague, The Netherlands, March 14–May 7, #110

Pomona College, Art Department, Claremont, Calif., October 25–November 23, 1957, *German Expressionist Painting 1900–1950*, #3 ill. p. [12]; traveled to: University of California, Berkeley, December 3–December 18

Museum of Fine Arts, Boston, October 1–November 15, 1964, *Max Beckmann*, #74; traveled to: The Museum of Modern Art, New York, December 14–January 31, 1965; The Art Institute of Chicago, March 12–April 11

National Gallery of Art, Washington, D.C., May 19–July 21, 1968, *Paintings from the Albright-Knox Art Gallery*, ill. p. 41

Museo Nacional de Bellas Artes, Buenos Aires, October 23–November 30, 1969, *109 obras de Albright Knox Art Gallery*, #39, p. 50, ill.

Albright-Knox Art Gallery, Buffalo, July 21–August 27, 1972, *Continental Painting and Sculpture, 1942–1972, in the Albright-Knox Art Gallery*, checklist, #[15]

References

P[atrick] J. K[elleher], "Additions to the Room of Contemporary Art/*Hotel Lobby* by Max Beckmann," *Gallery Notes*, The Buffalo Fine Arts Academy, vol. XV, no. 1, January, 1951, pp. 15–16, ill. p. 10

H. W. Janson, "Max Beckmann in America," *Magazine of Art*, vol. 44, no. 3, March, 1951, pp. 90, 92, ill. p. 90

Max Bill
Construction from a Ring, 1942–63
Not inscribed

Exhibitions

Albright-Knox Art Gallery, Buffalo, September 30–October 30, 1966, *Contemporary Art—Acquisitions 1962–1965*, #184, ill. p. 74

Expo '67, Montreal, Canada, April 28–October 27, 1967, *International Exhibition of Contemporary Sculpture*, p. 115, ill. p. 63

Albright-Knox Art Gallery, Buffalo, March 3–April 14, 1968, *Plus by Minus: Today's Half-Century*, #15

Albright-Knox Art Gallery, Buffalo, July 21–August 27, 1972, *Continental Painting and Sculpture, 1942–1972, in the Albright-Knox Art Gallery*, checklist, #[18]

Max Bill
Field of 32 Parts in 4 Colors, 1965
Inscribed on reverse u.r. "Bill/1965"

Exhibitions

IBM Gallery, New York, November 13–December 9, 1967, *Concrete Art of Zurich*

Albright-Knox Art Gallery, Buffalo, March 3–April 14, 1968, *Plus by Minus: Today's Half-Century*, #19

Albright-Knox Art Gallery, Buffalo, June 17–September 1, 1969, *Contemporary Art—Acquisitions 1966–1969*, #4, color ill. p. 33

Museo Nacional de Bellas Artes, Buenos Aires, October 23–November 30, 1969, *109 obras de Albright-Knox Art Gallery*, #70, p. 81, ill.

Albright-Knox Art Gallery, Buffalo, July 21–August 27, 1972, *Continental Painting and Sculpture, 1942–1972, in the Albright-Knox Art Gallery*, checklist, #[20]

Ilya Bolotowsky
Scarlet Diamond, 1969
Inscribed l.r. "Ilya Bolotowsky/69"

Exhibitions

Albright-Knox Art Gallery, Buffalo, June 17–September 1, 1969, *Contemporary Art—Acquisitions 1966–1969*, #5, ill. p. 66

Museo Nacional de Bellas Artes, Buenos Aires, October 23–November 30, 1969, *109 obras de Albright-Knox Art Gallery*, #88, p. 99, ill.

University of Colorado, Boulder, March 22–April 26, 1970, *Ilya Bolotowsky, Paintings and Columns*, #32, p. 12 (organized by University Art Museum, University of New Mexico, Albuquerque, where exhibited June 14–July 16)

Lee Bontecou
Untitled, 1960
Inscribed l.r. "Bontecou 1960"

Exhibitions

The Museum of Modern Art, New York, May 20–August 18, 1963, *Americans 1963*, ill. p. 14; traveled to: The National Gallery of Canada, Ottawa, November 8–December 1; Artists Guild of St. Louis, December 18, 1963–January 15, 1964; Toledo (Ohio) Museum of Art, February 1–March 2; Ringling Museum of Art, Sarasota, Fla., March 18–April 15; Colorado Springs Fine Arts Center, March 1–29; San Francisco Museum of Art, June 16–July 14; Seattle Art Museum, September 16–October 15; Detroit Institute of Arts, November 4–29

Städtisches Museum, Leverkusen, Germany, March 1–April 7, 1968, *Lee Bontecou*, #7, p. [29], ill.; traveled to: Museum Boymans-van Beuningen, Rotterdam, The Netherlands, April 19–June 3, #8, p. [7], ill. p. [19]; Gesellschaft für Bildende Kunst, Berlin, June–July

Museum of Contemporary Art, Chicago, March 25–May 7, 1972, *Lee Bontecou*, #[10], ill. p. [8]

James Brooks
Cooba, 1963
Inscribed l.l. "J. Brooks"

Exhibitions

Kootz Gallery, New York, October 20–November 7, 1964, *James Brooks—New Paintings*, checklist

Colorado Springs Fine Arts Center, July 7–September 18, 1966, *New Accessions USA*, #1, p. [3], ill. p. [14]

Albright-Knox Art Gallery, Buffalo, September 30–October 30, 1966, *Contemporary Art—Acquisitions 1962–1965*, #4, p. 5, ill. p. 57

National Gallery of Art, Washington, D.C., May 19–July 21, 1968, *Paintings from the Albright-Knox Art Gallery*, color ill. p. 48

Museo Nacional de Bellas Artes, Buenos Aires, October 23–November 30, 1969, *109 obras de Albright-Knox Art Gallery*, #100, p. 111, ill.

Albright-Knox Art Gallery, Buffalo, January 19–February 20, 1972, *Abstract Expressionism: The First and Second Generations in the Albright-Knox Art Gallery*, checklist, #[3]

Dallas Museum of Fine Arts, May 10–June 25, 1972, *James Brooks*, #27, ill. p. 28

References

Ursula N. Eland, "James Brooks," *Gallery Notes*, The Buffalo Fine Arts Academy, vol. XXVII, no. 2, Spring, 1964, p. 14, color ill. p. 15

N[atalie] E[dgar], "James Brooks," *Art News*, vol. 63, no. 8, December, 1964, p. 17

"Letters from 31 Artists," *Gallery Notes*, The Buffalo Fine Arts Academy, vol. XXXI, no. 2, and vol. XXXII, no. 2, Spring, 1970, p. 9, ill.

Pol Bury
Nine Balls on Five Planes, 1964
Inscribed on back "Pol Bury Neuf Boules sur cinq plans Juillet 1964"

Exhibitions

Lefebre Gallery, New York, October 12–November 7, 1964, *Pol Bury*, ill. p. [9]

Albright-Knox Art Gallery, Buffalo, February 27–April 11, 1965, *Art Today: Kinetic and Optic*, #10, p. [7], ill. p. [5]

Instituto Torcuato di Tella, Buenos Aires, August 27–November 8, 1965, *Premio Nacional e Internacional Instituto Torcuato di Tella, 1965*, p. 52, ill. p. 53

The University Art Museum, University of California at Berkeley, March 21–May 2, 1966, *Directions in Kinetic Sculpture*, #10, ill. p. 31; traveled to: Santa Barbara (Calif.) Museum of Art, June 4–July 10

Albright-Knox Art Gallery, Buffalo, September 30–October 30, 1966, *Contemporary Art—Acquisitions 1962–1965*, #[49], p. 9, ill. p. 56

The University Art Museum, University of California at Berkeley, May 10–July 12, 1970, *Pol Bury Retrospective Exhibition*, #7, pp. 60, 6, ill. p. 13; traveled to: Walker Art Center, Minneapolis, August 1–31; Museum of Art, University of Iowa, Iowa City, September 20–October 31; The Arts Club of Chicago, November 25–January 2, 1971; Rose Art Museum, Brandeis University, Waltham, Mass., January 25–March 7; The Solomon R. Guggenheim Museum, New York, April 1–May 15; Albright-Knox Art Gallery, Buffalo, July 24–September 6, 1971, *¿Kid Stuff?*, checklist, #7

Albright-Knox Art Gallery, Buffalo, March 4–April 9, 1972, *Movement, Optical Phenomena and Light: Kinetic and Optic Painting and Sculpture in the Albright-Knox Art Gallery*, checklist, #[13]

References

Simon W. Taylor, "Pol Bury Clinamen in Art," *Studio International*, vol. 168, no. 866, June, 1965, p. 238, ill.

Tom L. Freudenheim, "Kinetic Art," *Gallery Notes*, The Buffalo Fine Arts Academy, vol. XXIX, no. 2, Autumn, 1966, p. 11, ill. p. 12

Reg Butler
Torso, c. 1950
Not inscribed

Exhibitions

Institute of Contemporary Arts, New Burlington Galleries, London, March 7–April 4, 1950, *London/Paris: New trends in painting and sculpture*, checklist #60

Middelheim Sculpture Park, Antwerp, Belgium, July–September, 1950, *Internationale tentoonstelling in de open lucht van beeldhoukunst 1900–1950*, #17, ill. #12

Battersea Park, London, May–September, 1951, *Sculpture* (presented by the London County Council in association with the Arts Council of Great Britain), #7, ill.

Curt Valentin Gallery, New York, May 26–June 19, 1953, *Reg Butler, Bruno Cassinari, Jan Cox, Irving Kriesberg, Alton Pickens*, checklist, #1

Curt Valentin Gallery, New York, December 22, 1953–January 24, 1954, *Sculpture and Sculptor's Drawings*, #6

Curt Valentin Gallery, New York, January 11–February 5, 1955, *Reg Butler*, checklist, #3

Albright Art Gallery, Buffalo, May 15, 1957–February 15, 1958, *Contemporary Art—Acquisitions 1954–1957*, #43, ill. p. [48]

Carnegie Institute, Department of Fine Arts. Pittsburgh, October 27, 1961–January 7, 1962, *The 1961 Pittsburgh International Exhibition of Contemporary Painting and Scultpure, Reg Butler*, #469

Albright-Knox Art Gallery, Buffalo, October 27–November 29, 1964, *Contemporary British Painting and Sculpture*, #9, p. 10; traveled to: Addison Gallery of American Art, Andover, Mass., January 5–February 15, 1965

Albright-Knox Art Gallery, Buffalo, June 13–July 16, 1972, *English Painting and Sculpture, 1942–1972, in the Albright-Knox Art Gallery*, checklist, #[8]

References

Robert Melville, "Personages in Iron," *The Architectural Review*, vol. 108, no. 645, September, 1950, pp. 148, 151, ill. p. 150

R[obert] R[osenblum], "Fortnight in Review: Reg Butler," *Arts Digest*, vol. 29, no. 8, January 15, 1955, p. 25

Alexander Calder
Conger c. 1950
Not inscribed

Exhibitions

Albright-Knox Art Gallery, Buffalo, April 30–June 5, 1966, *Paintings, Sculpture, Drawings, Prints collected by A. Conger Goodyear*, #43

Albright-Knox Art Gallery, Buffalo, September 30–October 30, 1966, *Contemporary Art—Acquisitions 1962–1965*, #89, ill. p. 45

Alexander Calder
The Cone, 1960
Inscribed on white disc "CA"

Exhibitions

Carnegie Institute, Department of Fine Arts, Pittsburgh, October 27, 1961–January 7, 1962, *The 1961 Pittsburgh International Exhibition of Contemporary Painting and Sculpture*, #54

Albright-Knox Art Gallery, Buffalo, July 25–September 6, 1971, *¿Kid Stuff?*, checklist, #8

Albright-Knox Art Gallery, Buffalo, March 4–April 9, 1972, *Movement, Optical Phenomena and Light: Kinetic and Optic Painting and Sculpture in the Albright-Knox Art Gallery*, checklist, #[15]

Anthony Caro
Georgiana, 1969–70
Not inscribed

Exhibitions

André Emmerich Gallery, New York, May 2–21, 1970, *Anthony Caro*, ill. inside cover

Albright-Knox Art Gallery, Buffalo, June 13–July 16, 1972, *English Painting and Sculpture, 1942–1972, in the Albright-Knox Art Gallery*, #[10]

Reference

John Russell, "Closing the Gaps," *Art News*, vol. 69, no. 3, May, 1970, p. 39, ill. pp. 38–39

John Chamberlain
Kroll, 1961
Inscribed "Chamberlain 61"

Exhibitions

Albright-Knox Art Gallery, November 19–December 15, 1963, *Mixed Media and Pop Art*, #7, p. 5

Norton Union, State University of New York at Buffalo, April 5–10, 1965, *The Arts in Contemporary America*, #6

The Solomon R. Guggenheim Museum, New York, December 23, 1971–February 20, 1972, *John Chamberlain: A Retrospective Exhibition*, p. 3, #21, ill. p. 52

Corneille (Cornelis van Beverloo)
Beginning of Summer (Ouverture sur l'été), 1962
Inscribed u.r. "Corneille 62." Inscribed on reverse u.r. "Ouverture sur /l'ete'Corneille 62"

Exhibitions

Lefebre Gallery, New York, March 27–April 21, 1962, *Corneille*

Albright-Knox Art Gallery, Buffalo, September 30–October 30, 1966, *Contemporary Art—Acquisitions 1962–1965*, #6, color ill. p. 53

Stedelijk Museum, Amsterdam, The Netherlands, October 21–December 18, 1966, *Corneille*, #50, ill. p. [45]; traveled to: Kunsthalle, Düsseldorf, Germany, January 28–March 5, 1967, #19, ill. p. [41]

National Gallery of Art, Washington, D.C., May 19–July 21, 1968, *Paintings from the Albright-Knox Art Gallery*, color ill. p. 49

Museo Nacional de Bellas Artes, Buenos Aires, October 23–November 30, 1969, *109 obras de Albright-Knox Art Gallery*, #49, p. 60, ill.

Albright-Knox Art Gallery, Buffalo, July 21–August 27, 1972, *Continental Painting and Sculpture, 1942–1972, in the Albright-Knox Art Gallery*, checklist, #[32]

Joseph Cornell
Soap Bubble Set (Ostend Hotel), c. 1958
Inscribed on reverse "soap bubble set"—"shell interior"

Exhibition

Albright-Knox Art Gallery, Buffalo, April 17–May 28, 1972, *Joseph Cornell—Collages and Boxes*

Nassos Daphnis
11-67, 1967
Inscribed on reverse u.l. "#11-67 Nassos Daphnis"

Exhibitions

Albright-Knox Art Gallery, Buffalo, March 9–April 13, 1969, *Nassos Daphnis/Work Since 1951*, #47; traveled to: Everson Museum of Art, Syracuse, N.Y., May 1–June 29

Albright-Knox Art Gallery, Buffalo, June 17–September 1, 1969, *Contemporary Art—Acquisitions 1966–1969*, #7, ill. p. 20

Museo Nacional de Bellas Artes, Buenos Aires, October 23–November 30, 1969, *109 obras de Albright-Knox Art Gallery*, #87, p. 98, ill.

Alan Davie
Female, Male (formerly *No. 12*), 1955
Inscribed on reverse u.r. "Alan Davie." Inscribed on reverse u.l. " ⑫ 60 x 78"

Exhibitions

Catherine Viviano Gallery, New York, March 27–April 21, 1956, *Alan Davie*, checklist, #12

Albright Art Gallery, Buffalo, May 15–February 15, 1958, *Contemporary Art—Acquisitions 1954–1957*, #19, ill. p. [29]

St. Catharines and District Arts Council, Rodman Hall Arts Centre, St. Catharines, Ontario, Canada, February 1–March 3, 1963, *Contemporary Paintings from the Permanent Collection of the Albright-Knox Art Gallery*

Albright-Knox Art Gallery, Buffalo, June 13–July 16, 1972, *English Painting and Sculpture, 1942–1972, in the Albright-Knox Art Gallery*, checklist, #[15]

References

Patrick Heron, "London," *Arts*, vol. 30, no. 7, April, 1956, p. 12, ill. p. 13

Alan Bowness, *Alan Davie*, Percy Lund, Humphries & Co. Ltd., London, 1967, pp. 172–73, ill. p. 36

Ron Davis
Plane Sawtooth, 1970
Not inscribed

Exhibitions

Leo Castelli Gallery, New York, January 16–February 6, 1971, *Ron Davis, New Paintings*

Albright-Knox Art Gallery, Buffalo, October 5–November 14, 1971, *Six Painters*, #24, p. 13, color ill. p. 59; traveled to: The Baltimore Museum of Art, December 11–January 23, 1972; Milwaukee Art Center, February 12–March 26

Reference

John Elderfield, "New Paintings by Ron Davis," *Artforum*, vol. 9, no. 7, March, 1971, p. 34, ill. p. 33

Sonia Delaunay
Colored Rhythm, No. 698 (Rythme Coloré), 1958
Inscribed l.l. "Sonia Delaunay"

Exhibitions

Städtisches Kunsthaus, Bielefeld, Germany, September 14–October 26, 1958, *Sonia Delaunay*, #248

Galerie Chalette, New York, March 31–June 14, 1960, *Construction and Geometry in Painting*, #48; traveled to: The Contemporary Arts Center of the Cincinnati Art Museum, July 5–October 9; The Arts Club of Chicago November 11–December 30; Walker Art Center, Minneapolis, January 14–February 25, 1961

Galerie Denise René, Paris, December 15, 1961–February 10, 1962, *Structure*, ill. p. 16

Salon des Réalités Nouvelles, Paris, April, 1962

Galleria d'Arte il Cavallino, Venice, Italy, September 8–21, 1962, *Sonia Delaunay*, ill. p. 2

Albright-Knox Art Gallery, Buffalo, September 30–October 30, 1966, *Contemporary Art—Acquisitions 1962–1965*, #9, ill. p. 42

National Gallery of Art, Washington, D.C., May 19–
July 21, 1968, *Paintings from the Albright-Knox Art Gallery*, ill. p. 72

Museo Nacional de Bellas Artes, Buenos Aires, October
23–November 30, 1969, *109 obras de Albright-Knox Art Gallery*, #21, p. 32, ill.

Albright-Knox Art Gallery, Buffalo, July 21–August 27,
1972, *Continental Painting and Sculpture, 1942–1972, in the Albright-Knox Art Gallery*, checklist, #[38]

Richard Diebenkorn
Woman in a Window, 1957
Inscribed l.r. "R. Diebenkorn/D 57"

Exhibitions

Poindexter Gallery, New York, February 24–March 22,
1958, *Recent Paintings—Richard Diebenkorn*

Albright Art Gallery, Buffalo, December 8, 1958–January
18, 1959, *Contemporary Art—Acquisitions 1957–1958*,
#4, ill. p. [15]

State University of Iowa, Department of Art, Iowa City,
May 26–August 7, 1960, *Main Currents of Contemporary American Painting*, #14, p. 8, p. 12, ill.

Pasadena (Calif.) Art Museum, September 6–October 6,
1960, *Richard Diebenkorn*, #29

California Palace of the Legion of Honor, San Francisco,
October 22–November 27, 1960, *Recent Paintings by Richard Diebenkorn*, #5

William Rockhill Nelson Gallery of Art. Kansas City,
Mo., January 19–February 26, 1961, *The Logic of Modern Art*, #49, ill. p. 35

St. Catharines and District Arts Council, Rodman Hall
Arts Centre, St. Catharines, Ontario, Canada, February
1–March 3, 1963, *Contemporary Paintings from the Permanent Collection of the Albright-Knox Art Gallery*

The Washington (D.C.) Gallery of Modern Art, November 6–December 31, 1964, *Richard Diebenkorn*, #27, p.
17, color ill. p. [42]; traveled to: The Jewish Museum,
New York, January 13–February 21, 1965; Pavilion Gallery, Newport Beach, Calif., March 14–April 15.

Lytton Center of the Visual Arts, Los Angeles, October
1–November 30, 1967, *California Art Festival*, #16, ill.
p. [17]

Albright-Knox Art Gallery, Buffalo, January 19–February
20, 1972, *Abstract Expressionism: The First and Second Generations in Albright-Knox Art Gallery*, checklist, #9

References

"The Singing Colors and Evocative Scenes of Richard
Diebenkorn," *Ameryka*, no. 82, 1965, U.S. Information
Agency, distributed in Poland, p. 44, color ill. p. 48

"The Singing Colors and Evocative Scenes of Richard
Diebenkorn," *America Illustrated*, no. 110, 1965, U.S.
Information Agency, distributed in U.S.S.R., p. 14, color
ill.

Matthew Baigell, "American Abstract Expressionism and
Hardedge: Some Comparisons," *Studio International*, no.
171, January, 1966, p. 12, ill. p. 11

Burgoyne Diller
First Theme (Estate Number 9), 1963–64
Not inscribed

Exhibitions

Galerie Chalette, New York, March 2–31, 1964, *Burgoyne Diller*

Kassel, Germany, June 27–October 6, 1968, *4. Documenta, Burgoyne Diller*, #4, p. 68, ill. p. 71

Albright-Knox Art Gallery, Buffalo, June 17–September
1, 1969, *Contemporary Art–Acquisitions 1966–1969*, #11,
ill. p. 26

The Metropolitan Museum of Art, New York, October
18, 1969–February 1, 1970, *New York Painting and Sculpture: 1940–1970*, #71, p. 44, ill. p. 144

Walker Art Center, Minneapolis, December 12, 1971–
January 16, 1972, *Burgoyne Diller*, #40, ill. p. 21

Reference

Jane Harrison, "New York Exhibitions: In the Galleries—
Burgoyne Diller," *Arts Magazine*, vol. 38, no. 9, May–
June, 1964, p. 33, ill.

Jim Dine
Child's Blue Wall, 1962
Inscribed on reverse u.r. "Child's Blue Wall Jim Dine
1962"

Exhibitions

Sidney Janis Gallery, New York, February 4–March 2,
1963, *New Paintings by Jim Dine*, #11

Albright-Knox Art Gallery, Buffalo, November 19–December 15, 1963, *Mixed Media and Pop Art*, checklist, #51

Albright-Knox Art Gallery, Buffalo, September 30–October 30, 1966, *Contemporary Art—Acquisitions 1962–
1965*, #10, ill. p. 40

The Art Gallery of Ontario, Toronto, Canada, January
14–February 12, 1967, *Dine, Oldenburg, Segal, Painting/
Sculpture*, #8, ill. p. 22; traveled to: Albright-Knox Art
Gallery, Buffalo, February 24–March 26

Whitney Museum of American Art, New York, February
27–April 19, 1970, *Jim Dine*, #35, ill. p. [43]

Albright-Knox Art Gallery, Buffalo, July 25–September 6,
1971, *¿Kid Stuff?*, checklist, #12

Akron (Ohio) Art Institute, September 27–November 7,
1971, *Celebrate Ohio*, ill. p. [34]

References

Lawrence Alloway, "Notes on Five New York Painters,"
Gallery Notes, The Buffalo Fine Arts Academy, vol.
XXVI, no. 2, Autumn, 1963, p. 16, ill. p. 17

John Russell, "Pop Reappraised," *Art in America*, vol.
57, no. 4, July–August, 1969, p. 89, color ill.

Jean Dubuffet
M. Plume, Portrait of Henri Michaux, 1947
Inscribed on reverse u.l. "J. Dubuffet"

Exhibitions

The Baltimore Museum of Art, July–September, 1952,
The Rosen Collection

The Baltimore Museum of Art, February 23–March 17,
1957, *Modern Art for Baltimore*, #[11]

The Baltimore Museum of Art, March 15–April 15, 1958,
Primitive Influences in Contemporary Art

Sidney Janis Gallery, New York, October 3–November 5, 1960, *XXth Century Artists*, #12, ill. p. [20]

Sidney Janis Gallery, New York, March 3–April 4, 1964, *2 Generations: Picasso to Pollock*, #58

Sidney Janis Gallery, New York, January 3–27, 1967, *2 Generations: Picasso to Pollock*, #40, ill. p. [15]

National Gallery of Art, Washington, D.C., May 19–July 21, 1968, *Paintings from the Albright-Knox Art Gallery*, ill. p. 80

Albright-Knox Art Gallery, Buffalo, June 17–September 1, 1969, *Contemporary Art—Acquisitions 1966–1969*, #67, ill. p. 48

Albright-Knox Art Gallery, Buffalo, July 21–August 27, 1972, *Continental Painting and Sculpture, 1942–1972, in the Albright-Knox Art Gallery*, checklist, #[40]

Jean Dubuffet
Borne au logos VII, 1967
Inscribed at right near base "J.D./67"

Exhibitions

The Pace Gallery, New York, April 13–May 18, 1968, *Dubuffet/New Sculpture and Drawings*, #11, color ill. p. 16

Albright-Knox Art Gallery, Buffalo, June 17–September 1, 1969, *Contemporary Art—Acquisitions 1966–1969*, #81, color ill. p. 49

Albright-Knox Art Gallery, Buffalo, July 21–August 27, 1972, *Continental Painting and Sculpture, 1942–1972, in the Albright-Knox Art Gallery*, checklist, #[42]

Herbert Ferber
Green Sculpture II, 1954
Inscribed "Ferber 54"

Exhibitions

Kootz Gallery, New York, January 25–February 12, 1955, *Ferber/New Sculpture*

Whitney Museum of American Art, New York, May 11–August 7, 1955, *The New Decade*, p. 93, ill. p. 25

Albright Art Gallery, Buffalo, January 5–27, 1957, *Contemporary Americans*, checklist, [8]

Albright-Knox Art Gallery, Buffalo, May 15, 1957–February 15, 1958, *Contemporary Art—Acquisitions 1954–1957*, #38, ill. p. [44]

The Cleveland Museum of Art, October 4–November 4, 1960, *Paths of Abstract Art*, #105, ill. p. 70.

Memorial Art Gallery of the University of Rochester, January 15–March 5, 1961, *Paintings and Sculpture from the Albright Art Gallery*

Yale University Art Gallery, New Haven, April 27–September 24, 1961, *Paintings and Sculpture from the Albright Art Gallery*, checklist, #94

Walker Art Center, Minneapolis, April 15–May 27, 1962, *The Sculpture of Herbert Ferber*, #108, p. 59; traveled to: Des Moines (Iowa) Art Center, June 24–July 29; San Francisco Museum of Art, September 6–October 21; Dallas Museum for Contemporary Arts, November 17–December 29; Santa Barbara (Calif.) Museum of Art, January 22–March 3, 1963; Whitney Museum of American Art, New York, April 13–May 12

Reference

Eugene Goosen, "Ferber," *Three American Sculptors*, Grove Press, New York, 1959, p. 12, ill. p. [22] (French translation: *Trois sculpteurs américains*, Jean Cathelin, Le Musée de Poche, Paris, 1959)

Sam Francis
The Whiteness of the Whale, 1957
Inscribed on reverse u.r. "Sam/Francis/57"

Exhibitions

Seattle Art Museum, April 24–May 17, 1959, *Sam Francis*, #1, p. [3]

Kunsthalle, Berne, May 28–July 17, 1960, *Sam Francis*, #41, ill. p. [19]

William Rockhill Nelson Gallery, Kansas City, Mo., January 19–February 26, 1961, *The Logic of Modern Art*, #44, ill. p. 34

National College of Art, Dublin, August 1–September 15, 1963, *Irish Exhibition of Living Art*, #78, ill. p. 17

The Museum of Fine Arts, Houston, October 11–November 19, 1967, *Sam Francis*, #28, pp. 17, 25, ill. p. 48; traveled to: The University Art Museum, University of California at Berkeley, January 15–February 18, 1968

National Gallery of Art, Washington, D.C. May 19–July 21, 1968, *Paintings from the Albright-Knox Art Gallery*, ill. p. 58

Museo Nacional de Bellas Artes, Buenos Aires, October 23–November 30, 1969, *109 obras de Albright-Knox Art Gallery*, #108, p. 119, ill.

Albright-Knox Art Gallery, Buffalo, January 19–February 20, 1972, *Abstract Expressionism: The First and Second Generations in the Albright-Knox Art Gallery*, checklist, #[13]

Albright-Knox Art Gallery, Buffalo, September 11–October 15, 1972, *Sam Francis*, #39, p. 68, color ill.

References

Dore Ashton, "Art," *Arts and Architecture*, vol. 76, no. 2, February, 1959, p. 32, ill. p. 10

Franz Meyer, "Sam Francis," *Quadrum*, no. 10, 1961, p. 125, color ill.

Priscilla Colt, "The Painting of Sam Francis," *Art Journal*, vol. XXII, no. 1, Fall, 1962, pp. 5–6, fig. #7, ill. p. 5

Gail Scott, *Sam Francis/Recent Paintings*, Los Angeles County Museum of Art, 1970, p. [2]

Helen Frankenthaler
Round Trip, 1957
Inscribed l.r. "Frankenthaler/57"

Exhibitions

Tibor de Nagy Gallery, New York, January 6–25, 1958, *Helen Frankenthaler*

Albright Art Gallery, Buffalo, December 8, 1958–January 18, 1959, *Contemporary Art—Acquisitions 1957–1958*, #51, ill. p. [46]

Whitney Museum of American Art, New York, February 20–April 6, 1969, *Helen Frankenthaler*, #12, p. 60, ill. p. 24; traveled to: Whitechapel Art Gallery, London, May 6–June 22; Orangerie Herrenhausen, Hanover, Germany, August 20–September 20, #9; Kongresshalle, Berlin, October 2–21, #9, p. [36]

Albright-Knox Art Gallery, Buffalo, January 19–February 20, 1972, *Abstract Expressionism: The First and Second Generations in the Albright-Knox Art Gallery*, checklist, #[14]

Reference

E[laine] G[ottlieb], "In the Galleries/Helen Frankenthaler," *Arts*, vol. 32, no. 4, January, 1958, p. 55

Naum Gabo
Linear No. 2, Variation, 1962–65
Not inscribed

Exhibitions

Albright-Knox Art Gallery, Buffalo, September 30–October 30, 1966, *Contemporary Art—Acquisitions 1962–1965*, #146, p. 17, ill. p. 69

Albright-Knox Art Gallery, Buffalo, March 2–April 14, 1968, *Naum Gabo*, #18, p. 14, cover ill.

Albright-Knox Art Gallery, Buffalo, July 21–August 27, 1972, *Continental Painting and Sculpture, 1942–1972, in the Albright-Knox Art Gallery*, checklist, #[47]

References

Charlotte Buel Johnson, "Gabo," *School Arts*, vol. 66, no. 6, 1967, p. 52, ill.

"Some Old Soldiers Live. . . ." *The Architectural Forum*, vol. 128, no. 3, April, 1968, p. 94, ill.

Alberto Giacometti
Man Walking, 1960 (third in an edition of six)
Inscribed base front "Alberto Giacometti 3/6"

Exhibitions

Carnegie Institute, Department of Fine Arts, Pittsburgh, October 27, 1961–January 7, 1962, *The 1961 Pittsburgh International Exhibition of Contemporary Painting and Sculpture*, #126, p. [35]

Pierre Matisse Gallery, New York, December 12–30, 1961, *Giacometti*, #3, cover ill.

The Phillips Collection, Washington, D.C. February 7–March 18, 1963, *Alberto Giacometti*, #35, p. [10], ill. p. [7]

The Solomon R. Guggenheim Museum, New York, October 20, 1967–February 4, 1968, *Guggenheim International Exhibition 1967/Sculpture from Twenty Nations*, pp. 28–29, ill.; traveled to: The Art Gallery of Ontario, Toronto, Canada, February–March; The National Gallery of Canada, Ottawa, April–May; Montreal Museum of Fine Arts, Montreal, Canada, June–August

Albright-Knox Art Gallery, Buffalo, July 21–August 27, 1972, *Continental Painting and Sculpture, 1942–1972, in the Albright-Knox Art Gallery*, checklist, #[48]

Reference

S. Frigerio, "Exposition internationale de Pittsburgh et les prix de l'Institut Carnegie," *Aujourdhui*, no. 34, December, 1961, p. 62, ill.

Fritz Glarner
Relational Painting #93, 1962
Inscribed on reverse u.r. "Fritz Glarner/Relational Painting #93 1962"

Exhibitions

Whitney Museum of American Art, New York, December 11, 1963–February 2, 1964, *Annual Exhibition 1963/Contemporary American Painting*, #40, ill. p. [28]

The Institute of Contemporary Arts, Washington, D.C., February 22–March 28, 1964, *American Paintings*, #14

Krannert Art Museum, University of Illinois, Champaign, March 7–April 11, 1965, *Contemporary American Painting and Sculpture*, #49, ill. p. 209

The Pennsylvania Academy of Fine Arts, Philadelphia, January 21–March 6, 1966, *One Hundred and Sixty-first Annual Exhibition of American Painting and Sculpture*, #246

National Gallery of Art, Washington, D.C., May 19–July 21, 1968, *Paintings from the Albright-Knox Art Gallery*, ill. p. 67

Albright-Knox Art Gallery, Buffalo, June 17–September 1, 1969, *Contemporary Art—Acquisitions 1966–1969*, #68, ill. p. 50

Museo Nacional de Bellas Artes, Buenos Aires, October 23–November 30, 1969, *109 obras de Albright-Knox Art Gallery*, #37, p. 48, ill.

San Francisco Museum of Art, November-December, 1970, *Fritz Glarner*, #10, p. 5, ill. p. 14; traveled to: Institute of Contemporary Art, University of Pennsylvania, Philadelphia, January–February, 1971; University of Iowa, Iowa City, March-April

Arshile Gorky
The Liver is the Cock's Comb, 1944
Inscribed u.l. "A Gorky 44"

Exhibitions

Julien Levy Gallery, New York, November 16–December 4, 1948, *Arshile Gorky, 1905–1948*, checklist, #3

Whitney Museum of American Art, New York, January 5–February 18, 1951, *Arshile Gorky Memorial Exhibition*, #33, p. 33, ill. p. 31; traveled to: Walker Art Center, Minneapolis, March 4–April 22; San Francisco Museum of Art, May 9–July 9

The Art Museum, Princeton University, Princeton, N.J., October 6–26, 1952, *Arshile Gorky*, checklist, #10

Sidney Janis Gallery, New York, February 16–March 14, 1953, *Arshile Gorky in the Final Years*, checklist, #5

Albright Art Gallery, Buffalo, May 15, 1957–February 15, 1958, *Contemporary Art—Acquisitions 1954–1957*, #6, ill. p. [20]

The Cleveland Museum of Art, November 11–December 31, 1958, *Some Contemporary Works of Art*, #20, p. [15], ill. p. [31]

Museum Fredericianum, Kassel, Germany, July 11–October 11, 1959, *11. documenta, Arshile Gorky*, #2, p. 30.

Bennington College, Bennington, Vt., April 7–29, 1960, *Surrealist Art, an Exhibition of Paintings and Sculpture 1913–1946*, #14, p. [2]

The Museum of Fine Arts, Houston, October 20–December 11, 1960, *From Gauguin to Gorky*, #25, ill. pp. [22–23]

Carnegie Institute, Department of Fine Arts, Pittsburgh, January 10–February 19, 1961, *Paintings from the Albright Art Gallery*, checklist, #[15]

Yale University Art Gallery, New Haven, April 27–September 24, 1961, *Paintings and Sculpture from the Albright Art Gallery*, checklist, #26

XXXI *Biennale di Venezia*, June 16–October 7, 1962, *Arshile Gorky*, #13, p. 114

The Museum of Modern Art, New York, December 17, 1962–February 12, 1963, *Arshile Gorky, Paintings, Drawings, Studies*, #68, p. [32], color ill. p. [32a]; traveled to: The Washington (D.C.) Gallery of Modern Art, March 12–April 14, 1963

The Minneapolis Institute of Arts, November 27, 1963–January 19, 1964, *Four Centuries of American Art*, p. [45], ill. p. [46]

City Art Museum of St. Louis, April 1–May 31, 1964, *200 Years of American Painting*, p. 51, ill.

The Tate Gallery, London, April 2–May 2, 1965, *Arshile Gorky: Paintings and Drawings*, #53, p. [33], color ill. frontispiece; traveled to: Palais des Beaux-Arts, Brussels, May 22–June 27; Museum Boymans-van Beuningen, Rotterdam, The Netherlands, July 24–September 5, *Arshile Gorky*, #69, color ill. p. [44]

Whitney Museum of American Art, New York, September 28–November 27, 1966, *Art of the United States 1670–1966*, #108, ill. p. 124

M. Knoedler & Co., Paris, October 18–November 25, 1967, *Six peintres américains*, p. [8], color ill. p. [9]

The Museum of Modern Art, New York, March 27–June 9, 1968, *Dada, Surrealism and Their Heritage*, #137, pp. 173–74, ill. p. 172

National Gallery of Art, Washington, D.C. May 19–July 21, 1968, *Paintings from the Albright-Knox Art Gallery*, color ill. p. 49

The Art Institute of Chicago, October 19–December 8, 1968, *Dada, Surrealism and Their Heritage*, #137, pp. 173–74, ill. p. 172

Pasadena (Calif.) Art Museum, November 24, 1969–January 11, 1970, *Painting in New York: 1944 to 1969*, #1, p. 20, ill.

Albright-Knox Art Gallery, Buffalo, January 19–February 20, 1972, *Abstract Expressionism: The First and Second Generations in the Albright-Knox Art Gallery*, checklist, #[17]

References

Sidney Janis, *Abstract and Surrealist Art in America*, Reynal & Hitchcock, New York, 1944, p. 89, ill. p. 120

André Breton, *The Eye-Spring/Arshile Gorky*, Julien Levy Gallery, New York, March, 1945, p. 2

Elaine de Kooning, "Gorky: Painter of His Own Legend," *Art News*, vol. XLIX, no. 9, January, 1951, p. 65, ill. p. 41.

James Fitzsimmons, "The Late Gorky," *Art Digest*, vol. 27, no. 11, March 1, 1953, p. 16

Ethel K. Schwabacher, *Arshile Gorky*, Macmillan Co., New York, 1957, pp. 98, 99, 102, 107, color ill. p. 64 (a)

Gordon M. Smith, "The Brave Buffalo," *Art News*, vol. 56, no. 3, May, 1957, p. 70, ill. p. 32

Marcel Jean, *Histoire de la peinture surréaliste*, Editions du Seuil, Paris, 1959, p. 328, ill. p. 329

Harold Rosenberg, *Arshile Gorky/the Man, the Time the Idea*, Horizon Press, New York, 1962, pp. 114, 122, color ill. pp. 18–19

Robert Reiff, "The Late Works of Arshile Gorky," *Art Journal*, vol. XXII, no. 3, Spring, 1963, pp. 149–50, ill. p. 150

William Rubin, "Arshile Gorky, Surrealism and the New American Painting," *Art International*, vol. VII, no. 2, February 25, 1963, p. 34, ill. p. 33

Julien Levy, *Arshile Gorky*, Harry N. Abrams, Inc., New York, 1966, p. 20, color ill. p. [119]

Thomas M. Messer, "Kandinsky en Amérique," XXe *Siècle*, no. 27, December, 1966, p. 116, ill. p. 117

Barbara Rose, *American Art Since 1900, A Critical History*, Frederick A. Praeger, Inc., New York, 1967, p. 171, color ill.

René Passeron, *Histoire de la peinture surréaliste*, Librairie Le Livre de Poche, Paris, 1968, p. 245, ill. p. 244

Erwin O. Christensen, *A Guide to Art Museums in the United States*, Dodd, Mead & Co., New York, 1968, pp. 102–103, ill. p. 103

H. H. Arnason, *History of Modern Art—Painting, Sculpture, Architecture*, Harry N. Abrams, Inc. New York, 1968, p. 497, color ill. p. 489

William S. Rubin, *Dada and Surrealist Art*, Harry N. Abrams, Inc., New York, 1969, pp. 402–404, color ill. p. 403

Sarane Alexandrian, *L'Art surréaliste*, Fernand Hazan, Paris, 1969, p. 176, ill. p. 175

Adolph Gottlieb
Dialogue I, 1960
Inscribed on reverse "Adolph Gottlieb/Dialogue I, 66″ x 32″/1960"

Exhibitions

Sidney Janis Gallery, New York, November 7–December 3, 1960, *Gottlieb/New Paintings*

Walker Art Center, Minneapolis, April 28–June 9, 1963, *Adolph Gottlieb*, #37, p. [18], ill. p. [37]; traveled to: VII Bienal, São Paulo, Brazil, September 1–December 31, #37, p. 221

The Minneapolis Institute of Arts, November 4, 1965–January 2, 1966, *50th Anniversary Exhibition, 1915–1965*, #[25], p. [11]

Whitney Museum of American Art, New York, February 14–March 31, 1968, *Adolph Gottlieb*, #81, p. 22, ill. p. 86

National Gallery of Art, Washington, D.C., May 19–July 21, 1968, *Paintings from the Albright-Knox Art Gallery*, p. 63, ill.

Museo Nacional de Bellas Artes, Buenos Aires, October 23–November 30, 1969, *109 obras de Albright-Knox Art Gallery*, #105, p. 116, ill.

Albright-Knox Art Gallery, Buffalo, January 19–February 20, 1972, *Abstract Expressionism: The First and Second Generations in the Albright-Knox Art Gallery*, checklist, #[18]

References

Hubert Crehan, "Adolph Gottlieb," *Art News*, vol. 59, no. 8, December, 1960, p. 12

Martin Friedman, "Adolph Gottlieb: Private Symbols in Public Statements," *Art News*, vol. 62, no. 3, May, 1963, p. 53, ill. p. 35

Philip Guston
Voyage, 1956
Inscribed lower edge center "Philip Guston '56." Inscribed on reverse u.l. "VOYAGE/1956/PHILIP GUSTON/ 72 x 76"

Exhibitions

Albright Art Gallery, Buffalo, January 5–27, 1957, *Contemporary Americans*

Albright Art Gallery, Buffalo, May 15, 1957–February 15, 1958, *Contemporary Art—Acquisitions 1954–1957*, #8, p. 5, ill. p. [22]

Sidney Janis Gallery, New York, February 24–March 22, 1958, *Exhibition of Recent Paintings by Philip Guston*

Whitney Museum of American Art, New York, March 5–April 12, 1959, *The Museum and Its Friends—Eighteen Living American Artists Selected by the Friends of the Whitney Museum*, p. 47

The Columbus (Ohio) Gallery of Fine Arts, January 14–February 18, 1960, *Contemporary American Painting*, #13, p. [4]

XXX *Biennale di Venezia*, June 18–October 16, 1960, *Four American Artists: Guston, Hofmann, Kline, Rozak*, #4, p. 48

Memorial Art Gallery of the University of Rochester, January 15–March 5, 1961, *Paintings and Sculpture from the Albright Art Gallery*

Yale University Art Gallery, New Haven, April 27–September 24, 1961, *Paintings and Sculpture from the Albright Art Gallery*, checklist, #29

The Solomon R. Guggenheim Museum, New York, May 2–July 1, 1962, *Philip Guston*, #31, p. 28, ill. p. 67; traveled to: Los Angeles County Museum, May 15–June 23, 1963

Colgate University, Hamilton, N. Y., October 6–25, 1964, *Festival of the Creative Arts*, checklist in *Poiesis*, #[12], Colgate University, 1964, p. 14

National Gallery of Art, Washington, D.C., May 19–July 21, 1968, *Paintings from the Albright-Knox Art Gallery*, ill. p. 59

Museo Nacional de Bellas Artes, Buenos Aires, October 23–November 30, 1969, *109 obras de Albright-Knox Art Gallery*, #103, p. 114, ill.

Albright-Knox Art Gallery, Buffalo, September 15–November 1, 1970, *Color and Field: 1890–1970*, #41, ill. p. 45; traveled to: Dayton (Ohio) Art Institute, November 20–January 10, 1971; The Cleveland Museum of Art, February 4–March 28

References

Dore Ashton, "Art," *Arts and Architecture*, vol. 75, no. 5, May, 1958, p. 28

Dore Ashton, *Philip Guston*, Grove Press, Inc., New York, 1960, p. 56, color ill. p. [24]

Time, vol. 98, no. 19, November 9, 1970, color ill. p. 63

David Hare
Sunrise, 1954–55
Inscribed on the stone base "Hare"

Exhibitions

Kootz Gallery, New York, March 15–April 2, 1955, *David Hare*, #1, p. [3], ill.

Whitney Museum of American Art, New York, May 11–August 7, 1955, *The New Decade/35 American Painters and Sculptors*, p. 93, ill. p. 39; traveled to: San Francisco Museum of Art, October 6–November 6; Art Galleries, University of California at Los Angeles, November 20–January 7, 1956; Colorado Springs Fine Arts Center, February 9–March 20; City Art Museum of St. Louis, April 15–May 15

Albright-Knox Art Gallery, Buffalo, May 15, 1957–February 15, 1958, *Contemporary Art—Acquisitions 1954–1957*, #41, p. 10, ill. p. [46]

Universal and International Exhibition, Brussels, April 17–October 18, 1958, *American Art/Four Exhibitions/Contemporary American Sculpture*, #164, p. 82, ill. p. 83

References

Frank O'Hara, "David Hare," *Art News*, vol. 54, no. 1, March, 1955, p. 51

Sam Feinstein, "David Hare," *Arts Digest*, vol. 29, no. 12, March 15, 1955, p. 27, ill.

Robert Goldwater, "David Hare," *Art in America*, vol. 44, no. 4, Winter 1956, ill. p. 20

Germain Bazin, *The History of World Sculpture*, New York Graphic Society, Ltd., Greenwich, Conn, 1968, p. 446, color ill.

"Letters from 31 Artists," *Gallery Notes*, The Buffalo Fine Arts Academy, vol. XXXI, no. 2, and vol. XXXII, no. 2, Spring, 1970, pp. 12–13, ill. p. 12

Grace Hartigan
New England, October, 1957
Inscribed "Hartigan 57/E.H."

Exhibitions

Albright Art Gallery, Buffalo, December 8, 1958–January 18, 1959, *Contemporary Art—Acquisitions 1957–1958*, #7, ill. p. [18]

Museum Fredericianum, Kassel, Germany, July 11–October 15, 1959, *11. Documenta, Grace Hartigan*, #1, p. 31

State University of Iowa, Department of Art, Iowa City, May 26–August 7, 1960, *Main Currents of Contemporary American Painting*, #26, p. 15, ill. p. 14

Carnegie Institute, Department of Fine Arts, Pittsburgh, January 10–February 19, 1961, *Paintings from the Albright Art Gallery*, checklist, #[16]

St. Catharines and District Arts Council, Rodman Hall Arts Centre, St. Catharines, Ontario, Canada, February 1–March 3, 1963, *Contemporary Paintings from the Permanent Collection of the Albright-Knox Gallery*

National Gallery of Art, Washington, D.C., May 19–July, 21, 1968, *Paintings from the Albright-Knox Art Gallery*, ill. p. 65

Museo Nacional de Bellas Artes, Buenos Aires October 23–November 30, 1969, *109 obras de Albright-Knox Art Gallery*, #109, p. 120, ill.

Albright-Knox Art Gallery, Buffalo, January 19–February 20, 1972, *Abstract Expressionism: The First and Second Generations in the Albright-Knox Art Gallery*, checklist, #22

Reference

"Letters from 31 Artists," *Gallery Notes*, The Buffalo Fine Arts Academy, vols. XXXI, no. 2, and XXXII, no. 2, Spring, 1970, p. 14, ill.

Auguste Herbin
Vie No. 1 (Life No. 1), **1950**
Inscribed l.r. "herbin 1950"

Exhibitions

Sidney Janis Gallery, New York, December 29, 1952–January 17, 1953, *Auguste Herbin*, checklist, #6

Albright-Knox Art Gallery, Buffalo, March 2–April 14, 1968, *Plus by Minus: Today's Half-Century*, #50

National Gallery of Art, Washington, D.C., May 19–July 21, 1968, *Paintings from the Albright-Knox Art Gallery*, color ill. p. 66

Albright-Knox Art Gallery, Buffalo, June 17–September 1, 1969, *Contemporary Art—Acquisitions 1966-1969*, #69, color ill. p. 61

Museo Nacional de Bellas Artes, Buenos Aires, October 23–November 30, 1969, *109 obras de Albright-Knox Art Gallery*, #68, p. 79, ill.

Albright-Knox Art Gallery, Buffalo, July 21–August 27, 1972, *Continental Painting and Sculpture, 1942-1972, in the Albright-Knox Art Gallery*, checklist, #52

Hans Hofmann
Exuberance, **1955**
Inscribed l.r. "Hans Hofmann/55"

Exhibitions

Kootz Gallery, New York, November 7–December 3, 1955, *Hans Hofmann/New Paintings*

Colorado Springs Fine Arts Center, June 3–August 5, 1956, *New Accessions USA*, #2, p. [4]

Albright Art Gallery, Buffalo, May 15, 1957–February 15, 1958, *Contemporary Art—Acquisitions 1954-1957*, #9, color ill., p. [17]

Whitney Museum of American Art, New York, April 24–June 16, 1957, *Hans Hofmann Retrospective Exhibition*, #46, p. 44, color ill. p. 55; traveled to: Des Moines (Iowa) Art Center, July 4–August 4; San Francisco Museum of Art, August 21–September 22; UCLA Art Galleries, University of California at Los Angeles, October 6–November 4; Seattle Art Museum, December 11–January 12, 1958; Walker Art Center, Minneapolis, February 7–March 11; Munson-Williams-Proctor Institute, Utica, N.Y., March 28–April 30; The Baltimore Museum of Art, May 16–June 17

State University of Iowa, Department of Art, Iowa City, May 26–August 7, 1960, *Main Currents of Contemporary American Painting*, #27, p. 7, ill. p. 15

Colgate University, Hamilton, N.Y., October 9–25, 1964, *Festival of the Creative Arts Exhibition*, checklist in *Poiesis*, #[15], Colgate University, 1964, p. 14

National Gallery of Art, Washington, D.C., May 19–July 21, 1968, *Paintings from the Albright-Knox Art Gallery*, ill. p. 60, and color frontispiece

Museo Nacional de Bellas Artes, Buenos Aires, October 23–November 30, 1969, *109 obras de Albright-Knox Art Gallery*, #47, p. 58, color ill.

Albright-Knox Art Gallery, Buffalo, January 19–February 20, 1972, *Abstract Expressionism: The First and Second Generations in the Albright-Knox Art Gallery*, checklist, #23

Hans Hofmann
Summer Night's Dream (Sommernachtstraum), **1957**
Inscribed l.r. "57/hans hofmann"

Exhibitions

Kootz Gallery, New York, January 7–25, 1958, *New Paintings by Hans Hofmann*, #11, p. [5]

Albright Art Gallery, Buffalo, December 8, 1958–January 18, 1959, *Contemporary Art—Acquistiions 1957-1958*, #8, ill. p. [19]

Memorial Art Gallery of the University of Rochester, January 15–March 5, 1961, *Paintings and Sculpture from the Albright Art Gallery*

Yale University Art Gallery, New Haven, April 27–September 24, 1961, *Paintings and Sculpture from the Albright Art Gallery*, checklist, #33

National Gallery of Art, Washington, D.C., May 19–July 21, 1968, *Paintings from the Albright-Knox Art Gallery*, ill. p. 60

Albright-Knox Art Gallery, Buffalo, January 19–February 20, 1972, *Abstract Expressionism: The First and Second Generations in the Albright-Knox Art Gallery*, checklist, #24

Gottfried Honegger
Permanence, **1961**
Inscribed on reverse "150 x 150 HONEGGER PERMANENCE/1961/PARIS"

Exhibitions

Albright-Knox Art Gallery, Buffalo, November 19–December 15, 1963, *Mixed Media and Pop Art*, #15, p. 6

Albright-Knox Art Gallery, Buffalo, September 30–October 30, 1966, *Contemporary Art—Acquisitions 1962-1965*, #11, p. 5

Albright-Knox Art Gallery, Buffalo, July 21–August 27, 1972, *Continental Painting and Sculpture, 1942-1972, in the Albright-Knox Art Gallery*, checklist, #57

Robert Indiana
Year of Meteors, **1961**
Inscribed on reverse l.r. "Indiana"

Exhibitions

Stable Gallery, New York, October 16–November 3, 1962, *Robert Indiana*, checklist, #13

The Art Institute of Chicago, January 11–February 10, 1963, *66th American Exhibition of Painting and Sculpture*, #34, ill. p. 46

Walker Art Center, Minneapolis, October 21–November 24, 1963, *Richard Stankiewicz and Robert Indiana*, #6, p. [16], ill. p. [13]; traveled to: Boston Institute of Contemporary Art, December 14–January 26, 1964

The Tate Gallery, London, April 22–June 28, 1964, *Painting and Sculpture of a Decade, 1954-1964*, #310, ill. p. 241

Albright-Knox Art Gallery, September 30–October 30, 1966, *Contemporary Art—Acquisitions 1962-1965*, #13, ill. p. 34

National Gallery of Art, Washington, D.C., May 19–July 21, 1968, *Paintings from the Albright-Knox Art Gallery*, ill, p. 85

Museo Nacional de Bellas Artes, Buenos Aires, October 23–November 30, 1969, *109 obras de Albright-Knox Art Gallery*, #92, p. 103, ill.

References

Lawrence Alloway, "Notes on Five New York Painters," *Gallery Notes*, The Buffalo Fine Arts Academy, vol. XXVI, no. 2, Autumn, 1963, p. 16, ill. p. 17, and color ill. cover

John McCoubrey, *Robert Indiana*, Institute of Contemporary Art, University of Pennsylvania, Philadelphia, 1968, p. 16, ill. p. 17

Robert Indiana
Star, 1962
Inscribed below wheels at right "I." Inscribed below wheels at left "1960/1962, USA"

Exhibitions

The Museum of Modern Art, New York, May 20–August 18, 1963, *Americans 1963*, p. 108, ill. p. 41

Albright-Knox Art Gallery, Buffalo, November 19–December 15, 1963, *Mixed Media and Pop Art*, #55, p. 10

Colgate University, Hamilton, New York, October 9–25, 1964, *Festival of the Creative Arts*, checklist in *Poiesis*, #[17], Colgate University, 1964, p. 14

Albright-Knox Art Gallery, September 30–October 30, 1966, *Contemporary Art—Acquisitions 1962–1965*, #55, ill. p. 58

Syracuse University, Syracuse, N.Y., November 7–December 30, 1967, *Design and Aesthetics, in Wood*, #32, p. 5

Jasper Johns
Numbers in Color, 1959
Not inscribed

Exhibitions

The Museum of Modern Art, New York, December 16, 1959–February 14, 1960, *Sixteen Americans*, p. 91, ill. p. 23

Yale University Art Gallery, New Haven, April 27–September 24, 1961, *Paintings and Sculpture from the Albright Art Gallery*, checklist, #36

The Solomon R. Guggenheim Museum, New York, March 14–June 12, 1963, *Six Painters and the Object*, #[9], p. [14]

Albright-Knox Art Gallery, Buffalo, November 19–December 15, 1963, *Mixed Media and Pop Art*, #43, p. 8

The Jewish Museum, New York, February 16–April 12, 1964, *Jasper Johns*, #33, p. 27

XXXII Biennale di Venezia, June 20–October 18, 1964, #2, p. 276

Whitechapel Gallery, London, November 25–December 31, 1964, *Jasper Johns' Paintings, Drawing and Sculpture 1954–1964*, #20, p. [27], ill.

Pasadena (Calif.) Art Museum, January 26–February 15, 1965, *Jasper Johns*

National Gallery of Art, Washington, D.C., May 19–July 21, 1968, *Paintings from the Albright-Knox Art Gallery*, ill. p. 82

References

Nicolas Calas, "ContiNuance," *Art News*, vol. 57, no. 10, February, 1959, p. 39, ill.

Lawrence Alloway, "Notes on Five New York Painters," *Gallery Notes*, The Buffalo Fine Arts Academy, vol. XXVI, no. 2, Autumn, 1963, pp. 18–19, ill. p. 18

Art and Architecture, Aldus International Library of Knowledge, London, 1968, p. 51, ill.

Max Kosloff, *Jasper Johns*, Harry N. Abrams, Inc., New York, 1968, p. 19, ill. p. [79]

Arnold Bittleman, "Visions of Technology," *Innovation*, no. 2, June, 1969, p. 31, ill. p. 30

Robert Morris, "Some Notes on the Phenomenology of Making: The Search for the Motivated," *Artforum*, vol. VIII, no. 8, April, 1970, p. 66, ill. p. 65

John Russell, "Jasper Johns," *Réalités*, no. 251, October, 1971, p. 74

Asger Jorn
Untitled, 1961
Inscribed l.r. "Jorn '61"

Exhibitions

Albright-Knox Art Gallery, Buffalo, September 30–October 30, 1966, *Contemporary Art—Acquisitions 1962–1965*, #15

National Gallery of Art, Washington, D.C., May 19–July 21, 1968, *Paintings from the Albright-Knox Art Gallery*, ill. p. 78

Museo Nacional de Bellas Artes, Buenos Aires, October 23–November 30, 1969, *109 obras de Albright-Knox Art Gallery*, #51, p. 62, ill.

Albright-Knox Art Gallery, Buffalo, July 21–August 27, 1972, *Continental Painting and Sculpture, 1942–1972, in the Albright-Knox Art Gallery*, checklist, #61

Donald Judd
Untitled, 1969
Not inscribed

Reference

John Coplans, "An Interview with Don Judd," *Artforum*, vol. IX, no. 10, June, 1971, pp. 45, 47

Ellsworth Kelly
New York, N.Y., 1957
Inscribed on the stretcher "Ellsworth Kelly 1957"

Exhibitions

Universal and International Exhibition, Brussels, April 17–October 18, 1958, *American Art/Four Exhibitions/Seventeen Contemporary American Painters*, #132, p. 69, ill. p. [67]

U.S. Information Service Library, London, October 31–November 21, 1958, *Seventeen American Artists and Eight Sculptors*, checklist, #20, ill.

World House Galleries, New York, December 15, 1958–January 17, 1959, *Brussels '58 Contemporary American Art*, checklist, #18

Carnegie Institute, Department of Fine Arts, Pittsburgh, January 10–February 19, 1961, *Paintings from the Albright Art Gallery* checklist, #[15]

The Pennsylvania State University College of Arts and Architecture, University Park, October 6–November 16, 1963, *Aspects of the Apollonian Ideal*, #9

National Gallery of Art, Washington, D.C., May 19–July 21, 1968, *Paintings from the Albright-Knox Art Gallery*, ill. p. 84

Reference

Roger Coleman, "Reinforcements," *Art News and Review*, vol. X, no. 22, November 22, 1958, p. 6, ill.

Ellsworth Kelly
Blue, Yellow and Red, 1968
Inscribed on the stretcher "Kelly 68"

Exhibitions

Sidney Janis Gallery, New York, October 7–November 2, 1968, *Ellsworth Kelly*, #19

Museo Nacional de Bellas Artes, Buenos Aires, October 23–November 30, 1969, *109 obras de Albright-Knox Art Gallery*, #94, p. 105, ill.

Albright-Knox Art Gallery, Buffalo, July 25–September 6, 1971, *¿Kid Stuff?*, checklist, #20

Lyman Kipp
Flat Rate II, 1969
Not inscribed

Exhibition

Albright-Knox Art Gallery, Buffalo, June 17–September 1, 1969, *Contemporary Art—Acquisitions 1966–1969*, #39, ill. p. 37

Ronald B. Kitaj
Walter Lippmann, 1966
Inscribed l.r. "Walter/Lippman." Inscribed on reverse top "R. B. KITAJ WALTER LIPPMANN"

Exhibitions

The Cleveland Museum of Art, March 7–April 2, 1967, *R. B. Kitaj*, #[15], p. [3]

Worth Ryder Art Gallery, University of California at Berkeley, October 7–November 12, 1967, *R. B. Kitaj*, #5, p. [11]

National Gallery of Art, Washington, D.C., May 19–July 21, 1968, *Paintings from the Albright-Knox Art Gallery*, ill. p. 94

Albright-Knox Art Gallery, Buffalo, June 17–September 1, 1969, *Contemporary Art—Acquisitions 1966–1969*, #19, ill. p. 25

Museo Nacional de Bellas Artes, Buenos Aires, October 23–November 30, 1969, *109 obras de Albright-Knox Art Gallery*, #62, p. 73, ill.

Kestner-Gesellschaft, Hanover, Germany, January 23–February 22, 1970, *R. B. Kitaj*, #18, ill. p. [40]; traveled to: Museum Boymans-van Beuningen, Rotterdam, The Netherlands, February 28–April 5, #18, ill. p. [44]; Marlborough Fine Art Limited, New London Gallery, London, April–May, p. [4], ill.

Akron (Ohio) Art Institute, September 27–November 7, 1971, *Celebrate Ohio*, p. [54], color ill. p. [49]

The National Museum of Modern Art, Tokyo, September 9–October 25, 1970, *Contemporary British Art*, ill. p. 51

References

"Letters From 31 Artists," *Gallery Notes*, The Buffalo Fine Arts Academy, vol. XXXI, no. 2, and vol. XXXII, no. 2, Spring, 1970, p. 18, ill.

Keith Roberts, "Current and Forthcoming Exhibitions: London and Leeds," *The Burlington Magazine*, vol. CXII, no. 807, June, 1970, p. 416, ill. p. 417

Yves Klein
Lecteur I.K.B. 1960 (No. 1), 1960
Inscribed underside of base "Lecteur I K B/Yves Klein 1960/Blue"
Lecteur I.K.B. 1960 (No. 2), 1960
Inscribed underside of base "Lecteur I K B/Yves Klein 1960/Blue"
Lecteur I.K.P. 1960, 1960
Inscribed underside of base: "Lecteur I K P/Yves Klein 1960/Rose"

Exhibitions

Albright-Knox Art Gallery, Buffalo, November 19–December 15, 1963, *Mixed Media and Pop Art*, #19, p. 6

The Jewish Museum, New York, January 25–March 12, 1967, *Yves Klein*, p. 63

Albright-Knox Art Gallery, Buffalo, July 21–August 27, 1972, *Continental Painting and Sculpture, 1942–1972, in the Albright-Knox Art Gallery*, checklist, #[64]

Reference

Paul Wember,: *Yves Klein*, M. DuMont Verlag, 1969, #SE 171, #SE 172, p. 93, ill.; #SE 198, p. 95, ill.

Franz Kline
New York, N.Y., 1953
Inscribed on reverse l.r. "Franz Kline/Egan Gallery/'53" Inscribed on the stretcher l.r. "79" x 51""

Exhibitions

Sidney Janis Gallery, New York, March 5–31, 1956, *Franz Kline*, #21

XXVIII *Biennale di Venezia*, June 16–October 21, 1956, *American Artists Paint the City*, p. 31, ill. p. 25

The Art Institute of Chicago, January 17–March 3, 1957, *LXII American Exhibition: Painting and Sculpture*, d.c.

Albright Art Gallery, Buffalo, May 15, 1957–February 15, 1958, *Contemporary Art—Acquisitions 1954–1957*, #12, ill. p. [24]

The Cleveland Museum of Art, October 4–November 13, 1960, *Paths of Abstract Art*, #47, p. 32, ill.

New York World's Fair, New York, April–September 1965, *The City: Places and People*, #[24]

National Gallery of Art, Washington, D.C., May 19–July 21, 1968, *Paintings from the Albright-Knox Art Gallery*, ill. p. 50

References

B. H. Friedman, "Current and Forthcoming Exhibitions," *The Burlington Magazine*, vol. XCVIII, no. 638, May, 1956, p. 177

Dorothy Seiberling, "The Varied Art of Four Pioneers—Franz Kline," *Life*, vol. 47, No. 20, November 16, 1959, p. 79, ill. pp. 78–79

Charlotte Buel Johnson, "New York," *School Arts*, vol. 61, no. 9, May, 1962, p. 32, ill.

"American Artists Paint the City," *Arts*, vol. 30, no. 9, June, 1956, p. 29

Katharine Kuh, *Break-Up: The Core of Modern Art*, New York Graphic Society, Ltd., Greenwich, Conn., 1965, pp. 100–101, ill. p. 100

Calvin Tomkins, *The World of Marcel Duchamp/1887*, Time-Life Books, Inc., New York, 1966, p. 175, color ill.

Barbara Rose, *American Painting/The 20th Century*, Skira, Lausanne, 1969, color ill. p. 82

Scott Burton, "Generation of Light 1945–1969," *Art News Annual: Light from Aten to Laser*, XXXV, 1970, p. 24, ill. p. 20

Franz Kline
Requiem, 1958
Inscribed on reverse u.r. "Franz Kline, 58"

Exhibitions

Sidney Janis Gallery, New York, May 19–June 14, 1958, *New Paintings by Franz Kline*

Museu de Arte Moderna, Buenos Aires, October 12–November 12, 1960, *First International Modern Art Exposition*, p. [232], ill.

Memorial Art Gallery of the University of Rochester, January 15–March 5, 1961, *Paintings and Sculpture from the Albright Art Gallery*

Yale University Art Gallery, New Haven, April 27–September 24, 1961, *Paintings and Sculpture from the Albright Art Gallery*, checklist, #39

The Tate Gallery, London, April 20–June 28, 1964, *Painting and Sculpture of a Decade: 1954–1964*, #146, p. 135, ill.

National Gallery of Art, Washington, D.C., May 19–July 21, 1968, *Paintings from the Albright-Knox Art Gallery*, ill. p. 50

Whitney Museum of American Art, New York, October 1–November 30, 1968, *Franz Kline/1910–1962*, #61, ill. p. 40

Museo Nacional de Bellas Artes, Buenos Aires, October 23–November 30, 1969, *109 obras de Albright-Knox Art Gallery*, #102, p. 113, ill.

Albright-Knox Art Gallery, Buffalo, January 19–February 20, 1972, *Abstract Expressionism: The First and Second Generations in the Albright-Knox Art Gallery*, checklist, #29

References

Dore Ashton, "Art," *Arts & Architecture*, vol. 75, no. 7, July 1958, p. 3

M[artica] S[awin], "In the Galleries/Franz Kline," *Arts*, vol. 32, no. 10, September, 1958, p. 58

American Painting/1900–1970, Time-Life Books, Inc, New York, 1970, p. 148, color ill. p. 149

Willem de Kooning
Gotham News, c. 1955
Inscribed u.r. "de Kooning"

Exhibitions

Sidney Janis Gallery, New York, April 2–28, 1956, *Willem de Kooning*, #3

XXVIII *Biennale di Venezia*, June 16–October 21, 1956, *American Artists Paint the City*, p. 31, ill. p. 30

The Art Institute of Chicago, January 17–March 3, 1957, *LXII American Exhibition: Painting and Sculpture*, d.c.

Albright Art Gallery, Buffalo, May 15, 1957–February 15, 1958, *Contemporary Art—Acquisitions 1954–1957*, #3, color ill. pp. [36–37]

Carnegie Institute, Department of Fine Arts, Pittsburgh, December 5, 1958–February 8, 1959, *The 1958 Pittsburgh Bicentennial International Exhibition of Contemporary Painting and Sculpture*, checklist, #247

The Cleveland Museum of Art, October 4–November 13, 1960, *Paths of Abstract Art*, #93, ill. p. 61

Memorial Art Gallery of the University of Rochester, January 15–March 5, 1961, *Paintings and Sculpture from the Albright Art Gallery*

Yale University Art Gallery, New Haven, April 27 September 24, 1961, *Paintings and Sculpture from the Albright Art Gallery*, #41

Stedelijk Museum, Amsterdam, The Netherlands, June 29–September 17, 1962, *The Dutch Contribution to the International Development of Art Since 1945*, #52a; traveled to: Montreal Museum of Fine Arts, Montreal, Canada, October 5–November 4; The National Gallery of Canada, Ottawa, November 15–December 31; Albright-Knox Art Gallery, Buffalo, January 14–February 17, 1963

The Baltimore Museum of Art, February 4–23, 1964, *February Masterpiece Celebrating the Fiftieth Anniversary of The Baltimore Museum of Art*

The Tate Gallery, London, April 22–June 28, 1964, *Painting and Sculpture of a Decade, 1954–1964*, #96, ill. p. 107

Colgate University, Hamilton, N.Y., October 6–25, 1964, *Festival of the Creative Arts Exhibition*, checklist in *Poiesis*, #[19], Colgate University, 1964, p. 14, ill. p. 18

New York World's Fair, New York, April–September, 1965, *The City: Places and People*, checklist #[26]

National Gallery of Art, Washington, D.C., May 19–July 21, 1968, *Paintings from the Albright-Knox Art Gallery*, color ill. p. 57

Stedelijk Museum, Amsterdam, The Netherlands, September 19–November 17, 1968, *Willem de Kooning*, #60, p. [16], ill. p. [54]; traveled to: The Tate Gallery, London, December 8–January 26, 1969, #69, p. 76, ill. p. 108; The Museum of Modern Art, New York, March 4–April 27, #69, p. 76, ill. p. 108

Museo Nacional de Bellas Artes, Buenos Aires, October 23–November 30, 1969, *109 obras de Albright-Knox Art Gallery*, #104, p. 115, color ill.

Albright-Knox Art Gallery, Buffalo, January 19–February 20, 1972, *Abstract Expressionism: The First and Second Generations in the Albright-Knox Art Gallery*, checklist, #[30]

References

"The Wild Ones," *Time*, vol. 67, no. 8, February 20, 1956, pp. 73, 75, color ill. pp. 72–73

"American Artists Paint the City," *Arts*, vol. 30, no. 9, June, 1956, p. 29

Milton Gendel, "The Iron Curtain in the Glass-Factory," *Art News*, vol. 55, no. 5, September, 1956, p. 26, color ill. p. 27

Hilton Kramer, "Report on the Carnegie International," *Arts*, vol. 33, no. 4, January, 1959, p. 33, ill.

Charlotte Buel Johnson, "Willem De Kooning—Innovator," *Art Education*, vol. 14, no. 4, April, 1961, p. 26, ill. p. 11

"Gotham News/Willem de Kooning," *Comment*, no. 194, J. W. Clement Co., Buffalo, 1960, color ill. pp. [9–10]

Irving Sandler, *The Triumph of American Painting*, Praeger Publishers, New York, 1970, p. 134, ill. p. 135

Nicholas Krushenick
Lotus Europa, 1969
Inscribed on reverse top "Nicholas Krushenick/Mar 1969"

Exhibitions

The Pace Gallery, New York, April 26–May 21, 1969, *Krushenick*

Albright-Knox Art Gallery, Buffalo, June 17–September 1, 1969, *Contemporary Art—Acquisitions 1966–1969*, #21, p. 6

Reference

Peter Schjeldahl, "New York Letter," *Art International*, vol. XIII, no. 6, Summer, 1969, p. 69, ill.

Fernand Léger
The Walking Flower (La Fleur qui marche), 1951
Not inscribed

Exhibitions

Galerie Louis Carré, Paris, January 16–February 28, 1953, *Sculptures polychromes de Fernand Léger*, #23

Sidney Janis Gallery, New York, November 30–December 31, 1954, *Ceramics by Léger*, checklist, #11

Albright-Knox Art Gallery, Buffalo, July 25–September 6, 1971, *¿Kid Stuff?*, checklist, #22

Albright-Knox Art Gallery, Buffalo, July 21–August 27, 1972, *Continental Painting and Sculpture, 1942–1972, in the Albright-Knox Art Gallery*, checklist, #[68]

References

"Fernand Léger: Sculptures polychromes en céramique," *Cahiers d'Art*, vol. 28, no. 1, 1953, p. 153

Otis Gage, "Fernand Léger: Ceramist," *Craft Horizons*, vol. 15, no. 1, January, 1955, p. 11, ill.

F[red] M[itchell], "Gallery Previews in New York," *Pictures on Exhibit*, vol. XVIII, no. 4, January, 1955, p. 24

Alain Jouffroy, "Ceramics and Small Sculpture by Painters," *Graphis*, vol. 13, no. 71, May, 1957, p. 236, ill.

Mark Roskill, "Reviews and Previews," *Art News*, vol. 59, No. 7, November, 1960, p. 17

Julio Le Parc
14 Series, No. 2 (Série 14 No. 2), 1970
Inscribed on reverse u.l. "Serie 14 No. 2 / Le Parc"

Exhibitions

Galerie Denise René, Paris, December 1970–January, 1971, *Le Parc couleur 1959*, color ill. p. [11], ill. p. [12]

Albright-Knox Art Gallery, Buffalo, March 4–April 9, 1972, *Movement, Optical Phenomena and Light: Kinetic and Optic Painting and Sculpture in the Albright-Knox Art Gallery*, checklist, #[27]

Alexander Liberman
Bond, 1969
Not inscribed

Exhibition

André Emmerich Gallery, New York, October 4–23, 1969, *Alexander Liberman: New Sculpture*, ill. p. [4]

Reference

James Harithas, "A Retrospective for Alexander Liberman," *Art in America*, vol. 58, no. 2, March–April, 1970, p. 106, color ill.

Roy Lichtenstein
Head—Red and Yellow, 1962
Inscribed on reverse "rf Lichtenstein/'62"

Exhibitions

Contemporary Art Association, Houston, April, 1963, *Pop Goes the Easel*, #10, p. [5]

Albright-Knox Art Gallery, Buffalo, November 19–December 15, 1963, *Mixed Media and Pop Art*, #59, p. 11, and color ill. cover

Albright-Knox Art Gallery, Buffalo, September 30–October 30, 1966, *Contemporary Art—Acquisitions 1962–1965*, #18, ill. p. 48

The Columbus Gallery of Fine Arts and Graduate School, Ohio State University, November 11–December 2, 1966, *Two Generations of American Art/1943–1965*, #17

National Gallery of Art, Washington, D.C., May 19–July 21, 1968, *Paintings from the Albright-Knox Art Gallery*, ill. p. 92

Winnipeg Art Gallery, Winnipeg, Manitoba, Canada, February 7–March 4, 1969, *O.K. America*, #2, p. [5], ill. p. [4]

Philbrook Art Center, Tulsa, Okla., March 4–30, 1969, *The American Sense of Reality*, p. 10, ill.; traveled to: Oklahoma Art Center, Oklahoma City, April 6–May 11, 1969

Museo Nacional de Bellas Artes, Buenos Aires, October 23–November 30, 1969, *109 obras de Albright-Knox Art Gallery*, #90, p. 101, ill.

Albright-Knox Art Gallery, Buffalo, July 25–September 6, 1971, *¿Kid Stuff?*, checklist, #23

Reference

Lawrence Alloway, "Notes on Five New York Painters," *Gallery Notes*, The Buffalo Fine Arts Academy, vol. XXVI, no. 2, Autumn, 1963, p. 14, ill.

Jacques Lipchitz
Sacrifice, 1948
Inscribed "J. Lipchitz"

Exhibitions

Portland (Ore.) Art Museum, October 24–December 3, 1950, *Jacques Lipchitz: An Exhibition of his Sculpture and Drawings*, #20, ill. p. [21]; traveled to: San Francisco Museum of Art, January 2–February 11, 1951; Cincinnati Art Museum, March 3–April 8

Buchholz Gallery/Curt Valentin, New York, May 1–26, 1951, *Lipchitz*, #26, ill. p. [11]

XXVI *Biennale di Venezia*, June 14–October 19, 1952, #138, p. 278

Walker Art Center, Minneapolis, October 1–December 12, 1954, *The Sculpture of Jacques Lipchitz*, p. 21, p. 92; traveled to: The Cleveland Museum of Art, January 25–March 13, 1955

Yale University Art Gallery, New Haven, April 27–September 24, 1961, *Paintings and Sculpture from the Albright Art Gallery*, checklist, #98

References

C. Ludwig Brumme, "Contemporary Sculpture: A Renaissance," *Magazine of Art*, vol. 42, no. 6, October, 1949, p. 216, ill. p. 215

Rachel Griffin, "Portland Gives U.S. First Large Lipchitz Show," *Art Digest*, vol. 25, no. 2, October 15, 1950, p. 12

Herman Reuter, "Another Phoenix," *Art Digest*, vol. 26, no. 10, February 15, 1952, p. 13, ill.

Patrick J. Kelleher, "Additions to the Permanent Collection," *Gallery Notes*, The Buffalo Fine Arts Academy, vol. XVI, nos. 2–3, May–October, 1952, pp. 2–3, ill. pp. 5–7

"Contemporary Art Augments 11 Museum Collections," *Art Digest*, vol. 27, no. 12, March 15 ,1953, p. 9, cover ill.

Albert Elsen, "The Humanism of Rodin and Lipchitz," *College Art Journal*, vol. XVII, no. 3, Spring, 1958, p. 250

Seymour Lipton
Sea King, 1956
Not inscribed

Exhibitions

The Museum of Modern Art, New York, May 29–September 9, 1956, *Twelve Americans*, p. 96, ill. p. 77

Albright Art Gallery, Buffalo, May 15, 1957–February 15, 1958, *Contemporary Art—Acquisitions 1954–1957*, #42, ill. p. [47]

Betty Parsons Gallery, New York, January 28–February 15, 1958, *Seymour Lipton—Recent Sculpture*, #2

Universal and International Exhibition, Brussels, April 17–October 18, 1958, *American Art/Four Exhibitions/Contemporary American Sculpture*, #168, p. 86, ill. p. [88]

World House Galleries, New York, December 15, 1958–January 17, 1959, *Brussels '58/Contemporary American Art*, checklist, #39

Memorial Art Gallery of the University of Rochester, January 15–September 30, 1961, *Paintings and Sculpture from the Albright Art Gallery*

The Phillips Collections, Washington, D.C., January 12–February 24, 1964, *Seymour Lipton*, #3

References

Leo Steinberg, "Month in Review, Twelve Americans," *Arts*, vol. 30, no. 10, July, 1956, p. 26, ill.

Dore Ashton, "Art," *Arts and Architecture*, vol. 73, no. 9, September, 1956, p. 13, ill.

Andrew C. Ritchie, "Seymour Lipton," *Art in America*, vol. 44, Winter, 1956–57, p. 17, ill.

Albert Elsen, "Seymour Lipton, Odyssey of the Unquiet Metaphor," *Art International*, vol. V, no. 1, February, 1961, p. 42, ill. p. 38

Albert Elsen, "Seymour Lipton's Sea King," *Gallery Notes*, The Buffalo Fine Arts Academy, vol. XXIV, no. 2, Summer, 1961, pp. 5, 7, ill. p. 6

Charlotte Buel Johnson, "Sea King," *School Arts Magazine*, vol. 61, no. 4, December, 1961, p. 15

Charlotte Buel Johnson, "Sea King—Seymour Lipton," *The Instructor*, vol. LXXVI, no. 9, May, 1967, p. 3, and color ill. cover

Erwin O. Christensen, *A Guide to Art Museums in the United States*, Dodd, Mead & Co., New York, 1968, p. 100, ill.

Robert Goldwater, *What is Modern Sculpture?*, The Museum of Modern Art, New York, 1969, p. 85, ill.

Albert Elsen, *Seymour Lipton*, Harry N. Abrams, Inc., New York, 1970, #133, pp. 47, [7], color ill., p. [159]

"Letters from 31 Artists," *Gallery Notes*, The Buffalo Fine Arts Academy, vol. XXXI, no. 2, and vol. XXXII, no. 2, Spring, 1970, p. 23, ill.

Morris Louis
Alpha, 1960
Inscribed on reverse " 'Alpha'/M. Louis 1960"

Exhibitions

Albright-Knox Art Gallery, Buffalo, September 30–October 30, 1966, *Contemporary Art—Acquisitions 1962–1965*, #20, ill. p. 43

National Gallery of Art, Washington, D.C., May 19–July 21, 1968, *Paintings from the Albright-Knox Art Gallery*, ill. p. 88

Museo Nacional de Bellas Artes, Buenos Aires, October 23–November 30, 1969, *109 obras de Albright-Knox Art Gallery*, #95, p. 106, ill.

References

Ursula Eland, "Morris Louis," *Gallery Notes*, The Buffalo Fine Arts Academy, vol. XXVII, no. 2, Spring, 1964, p. 12, ill. p. 13

Udo Kultermann, *The New Painting*, Frederick A. Praeger, Inc., New York, 1969, p. 54, #318, p. 132, ill.

Giacomo Manzù
Standing Cardinal, 1957
Inscribed (foundry mark on base r.r.) "MANZU—Fonderia MAF Milano"

Exhibitions

World House Gallery, New York, April 5–May 7, 1960, *Manzù*, #18, ill. p. [12]

The Tate Gallery, London, October 1–November 6, 1960, *Giacomo Manzù, Sculpture and Drawings*, #49, ill. p. [25]

Paul Rosenberg & Co., New York, December 6, 1965–January 29, 1966, *Exhibition of the Bronze Reliefs for the Door of St. Peter's and Sculpture, Paintings, Drawings by Giacomo Manzù*, #32, ill. p. 46

Cordier & Ekstrom, New York, April 26–May 21, 1966, *Seven Decades 1895–1965, Cross Currents in Modern Art*, #281, ill. p. 154

Paul Rosenberg Gallery, New York, March 18–April 27, 1968, *Recent Work by Giacomo Manzù*, #5, ill. p. 26

Albright-Knox Art Gallery, Buffalo, July 21–August 27, 1972, *Continental Painting and Sculpture, 1942–1972, in the Albright-Knox Art Gallery*, checklist, #[74]

Reference

"Provocative Parallels," *Art in America*, vol. 57, no. 4, July, 1969, p. 54, ill.

Conrad Marca-Relli
Odalisque, 1957
Inscribed l.l. "Marca-Relli"

Exhibitions

Stable Gallery, New York, February 3–March 1, 1958, *Marca-Relli*

Albright Art Gallery, Buffalo, December 8, 1958–January 18, 1959, *Contemporary Art—Acquisitions 1957-1958*, #9, ill. p. [20]

Yale University Art Gallery, New Haven, April 27–September 24, 1961, *Paintings and Sculpture from the Albright Art Gallery*, checklist, #46

Albright-Knox Art Gallery, Buffalo, November 19–December 15, 1963, *Mixed Media and Pop Art*, #23, p. 7

Colgate University, Hamilton, N.Y., October 9–25, 1964, *Festival of the Creative Arts Exhibition*, checklist in *Poiesis*, #[22], Colgate University, 1964, p. 14

Whitney Museum of American Art, New York, October 4–November 12, 1967, *Marca-Relli*, #21, p. 17, ill. p. 35; traveled to: Rose Art Museum, Brandeis University, Waltham, Mass., December 3, 1967–January 28, 1968

National Gallery of Art, Washington, D.C., May 19–July 21, 1968, *Paintings from the Albright-Knox Art Gallery*, ill. p. 61

Museo Nacional de Bellas Artes, Buenos Aires, October 23–November 30, 1969, *109 obras de Albright-Knox Art Gallery*, #107, p. 118, ill.

Reference

H. H. Arnason, *Marca-Relli*, Harry N. Abrams, Inc., New York, 1963, #59, ill. p. [89]

Marino Marini
Dancer, 1952
Inscribed (stamped on top of base) "M.M"

Exhibitions

Curt Valentin Gallery, New York, October 27–November 21, 1953, *Marino Marini*, #21, ill. p. [6], p. [18]

City Art Museum of St. Louis, October 13–November 14, 1955, *Contemporary Italian Art*, #79, ill. p. [21]; traveled to: The University Art Gallery, University of Minnesota, Minneapolis, December 1–23

The Columbus (Ohio) Gallery of Fine Arts, March 9–April 15, 1956, *Italian Design Today*, #178, p. [11]

Albright-Art Gallery, Buffalo, May 15, 1957–February 15, 1958, *Contemporary Art—Acquisitions 1954-1957*, #46, ill. p. [49]

The Museum of Fine Arts, Houston, April 25–June 1, 1958 *Ten Contemporary Italian Sculptors*, #14, p. [12]

Yale University Art Gallery, New Haven, April 27–September 24, 1961, *Painting and Sculpture from the Albright Art Gallery*, checklist, #100

The Baltimore Museum of Art, October 25–November 27, 1966, *Twentieth Century Italian Art*, checklist, #48

Albright-Knox Art Gallery, Buffalo, July 21–August 27, 1972, *Continental Painting and Sculpture, 1942-1972, in the Albright-Knox Art Gallery*, checklist, #[76]

References

D[orothy] G. S[eckler], "Reviews and Previews," *Art News*, vol. 52, no. 7, November, 1953, p. 42

E[lizabeth] M. S[mith], "Archaic in Modern Mood," *Gallery Notes*, The Buffalo Fine Arts Academy, vol. XX, no. 1, October, 1956, pp. 4, 6, 8, ill. p. 5

Edward Trier and H. Helmut Lederer, *The Sculpture of Marino Marini*, Frederick A. Praeger, Inc., New York, 1961, ill. pp. 100–103

Giovanni Carandente, *Mostra di Marino Marini*, Rome, Palazzo Venezia, Edizione De Luca-Toninelli, 1966, #66, p. 41

A. M. Hammacher, *Marino Marini/Sculpture/Painting/Drawing*, Harry N. Abrams, Inc., New York, 1969, #192, ill. pp. 190, 191, 193

G. di San Lazzaro, *Marino Marini, Complete Works*, Tudor Publishing Co., New York, 1970, ill. p. [148]

Marisol (Escobar)
The Generals 1961–62
Not inscribed

Exhibitions

Stable Gallery, New York, May 8–24, 1962, *Marisol*

The Museum of Modern Art, New York, May 22–August 18, 1963, *Americans 1963*, ill. p. 73

Albright-Knox Art Gallery, Buffalo, November 19–December 15, 1963, *Mixed Media and Pop Art*, #61, p. 11

The Minneapolis Institute of Arts, November 27, 1963–January 19, 1964, *Four Centuries of American Art*, p. [49], ill. p. [52]

Albright-Knox Art Gallery, Buffalo, September 30–October 30, 1966, *Contemporary Art—Acquisitions 1962-1965*, #66, ill. p. 59

Albright-Knox Art Gallery, Buffalo, July 25–September 6, 1971, *¿Kid Stuff?*, checklist, #26

References

"Marisol's Mannequins," *Horizon*, vol. 5, no. 4, March, 1963, ill. p. 102

"Marisol," *Time*, vol. 81, no. 23, June 7, 1963, p. 79

Gene Baro, "A Gathering of Americans," *Arts Magazine*, vol. 37, no. 10, September, 1963, ill. p. 33

Charlotte Buel Johnson, "The Generals," *The Instructor*, vol. LXXI, no. 1, August–September 1966, p. 9, and cover ill.

Jose Ramon Medina, *Marisol*, Ediciones Armitano, Caracas, Venezuela, 1968, pp. 161, 163, 165, ill.

Matta (Echaurren)
Poly-joueurs des cartes (Card Players), c. 1957
Inscribed on reverse l.r. "poly-joueurs/des cartes/#126/Matta"

Exhibitions

Albright-Knox Art Gallery, Buffalo, September 30–October 30, 1966, *Contemporary Art—Acquisitions 1962-1965*, #180, ill. p. 71

National Gallery of Art, Washington, D.C., May 19–July 21, 1968, *Paintings from the Albright-Knox Art Gallery*, ill. p. 56

Museo Nacional de Bellas Artes, Buenos Aires, October 23–November 30, 1969, *109 obras de Albright-Knox Art Gallery*, #63, p. 74, ill.

Albright-Knox Art Gallery, Buffalo, July 25–September 6, 1971, *¿Kid Stuff?*, #28, ill. p. [27]

Antoni Milkowski
Diamond–I of III, 1967 (first in an edition of three)
Not inscribed

Exhibitions

Albright-Knox Art Gallery, Buffalo, March 3–April 14, 1968, *Plus by Minus: Today's Half-Century*, #119, p. [53]

Albright-Knox Art Gallery, Buffalo, June 17–September 1, 1969, *Contemporary Art—Acquisitions 1966–1969*, #88, ill. p. 52

Joan Miró
Woman and Bird in the Night (Femme et oiseau dans la nuit), 1945
Inscribed on reverse u.l. "Miró/8–3–45"

Exhibitions

Sidney Janis Gallery, New York, October 24–November 26, 1955, *New Arrivals from France*

Sidney Janis Gallery, New York, May 21–June 9, 1956, *Selection of Recent Acquisitions of European Art: 1911–1950*, checklist, #20

Sidney Janis Gallery, New York, April 22–May 11, 1957, *Selection of Modern Art: Brancusi to Giacometti*, checklist, #24

Sidney Janis Gallery, New York, September 29–November 1, 1958, *X Years of Janis*, #48

Albright Art Gallery, Buffalo, December 8, 1958–January 18, 1959, *Contemporary Art—Acquisitions 1957–1958*, #41, ill. frontispiece

The Museum of Modern Art, New York, March 16–May 10, 1959, *Joan Miró*, #83

The Museum of Fine Arts, Houston, October 20–December 11, 1960, *From Gauguin to Gorky*, #42, ill. p. [31]

Carnegie Institute, Department of Fine Arts, Pittsburgh, January 10–February 19, 1961, *Paintings from the Albright Art Gallery*

National Gallery of Art, Washington, D.C., May 19–July 21, 1968, *Paintings from the Albright-Knox Art Gallery*, ill. p. 48

Sidney Janis Gallery, New York, January 8–February 1, 1969, *Selected Works by XXth Century European Artists*, #32, ill.

Museo Nacional de Bellas Artes, Buenos Aires, October 23–November 30, 1969, *109 obras de Albright-Knox Art Gallery*, #18, p. 29, ill.

Albright-Knox Art Gallery, Buffalo, July 21–August 27, 1972, *Continental Painting and Sculpture, 1942–1972, in the Albright-Knox Art Gallery*, checklist, #[80]

References

James Thrall Soby, *Joan Miró*, The Museum of Modern Art, New York, 1959, p. 118, ill. p. 114

Charlotte Buel Johnson, "Gallery for Young People/Joan Miró," *School Arts*, vol. 64, no. 6, February, 1965, p. 47, ill. p. 46

Charlotte Buel Johnson, *Color and Shape*, The Buffalo Fine Arts Academy, Buffalo, 1971, p. 2, color ill.

Joan Mitchell
George Went Swimming at Barnes Hole, but It Got Too Cold, 1957
Inscribed l.r. "J. Mitchell"

Exhibitions

Stable Gallery, New York, March 4–23, 1957, *Joan Mitchell*

Whitney Museum of American Art, New York, November 20, 1957–January 12, 1958, *Annual Exhibition/Sculpture, Paintings, Watercolors*, #126, p. [14]

Albright Art Gallery, Buffalo, December 8–January 18, 1959, *Contemporary Art—Acquisitions 1957–1958*, #11, ill. p. [22]

William Rockhill Nelson Gallery of Art, Kansas City, Mo., January 19–February 26, 1961, *The Logic of Modern Art*, #51, ill. p. 36

The National Museum of Modern Art, Tokyo, October 15–November 27, 1966, *Two Decades of American Painting* (organized by The Museum of Modern Art, New York), #[57], p. 68; traveled to: National Museum of Modern Art, Kyoto, Japan, December 10–January 22, 1967; Lalit Kala Gallery, Rabindra Bhavan, New Delhi, #53, ill. p. 20; National Gallery of Victoria, Melbourne, Australia, June 6–July 9, #53, p. [47], ill. p. [46]; Art Gallery of New South Wales, Sydney, Australia, July 26–August 20

National Gallery of Art, Washington, D.C., May 19–July 21, 1968, *Paintings from the Albright-Knox Art Gallery*, ill. p. 64

Albright-Knox Art Gallery, Buffalo, January 19–February 20, 1972, *Abstract Expressionism: The First and Second Generations in the Albright-Knox Art Gallery*, checklist, #[33]

References

Irving Sandler, "Mitchell Paints a Picture," *Art News*, vol. 56, no. 6, October, 1957, p. 70, color ill. pp. 46, 47

Allen S. Weller and Lee Nordness, *Art USA Now*, vol. II, The Viking Press, New York, 1963, p. 434, ill.

Joan Mitchell
Blue Territory, 1972
Inscribed l.r. "J. Mitchell." Inscribed on reverse "Blue Territory/2:60 × 1:80"

Exhibition

Everson Museum of Art, Syracuse, N.Y., *Joan Mitchell, My Five Years in the Country*, March 25–April 21, 1972, ill. p. 21; traveled to: Martha Jackson Gallery, New York, April 26–June 3

Piet Mondrian
Composition London, 1940–42
Inscribed l.l. "P.M." Inscribed l.r. "40/42"

Exhibitions

Valentine Gallery, New York, January–February, 1942

The Museum of Modern Art, New York, March 20–May 13, 1945, *Piet Mondrian*, checklist, #46

Albright-Knox Art Gallery, Buffalo, November 19–December 15, 1963, *Mixed Media and Pop Art*, #28, p. 7

The White House, Washington, D.C., June 14, 1965, *The White House Festival of the Arts*, #19, p. 27

Albright-Knox Art Gallery, Buffalo, September 30–October 30, 1966, *Contemporary Art—Acquisitions 1962–1965*, #67, ill. p. 44

References

Dore Ashton, "Art," *Arts and Architecture*, vol. 78, no. 6, June, 1961, p. 4, ill.

Lil Picard, "Tausend und einige Hölzer Besuch bei Louise Nevelson," *Kunstwerk*, vol. XV, no. 3, September, 1961, pp. 15–24, p. 24 ill.

"All That Glitters," *Time*, vol. LXXX, no. 9, August 31, 1962, p. 40, ill.

Ben Nicholson
Tableform, 1952
Inscribed on reverse "June 4–52 Ben Nicholson"

Exhibitions

The Tate Gallery, London, June–July, 1955, *Ben Nicholson/A Retrospective Exhibition*, #48, p. [18], ill. p. [5]

Albright Art Gallery, Buffalo, May 15, 1957–February 15, 1958, *Contemporary Art—Acquisitions 1954–1957*, #21, ill. p. [30]

Memorial Art Gallery of the University of Rochester, January 15–March 5, 1961, *Painting and Sculpture from the Albright Art Gallery*

Yale University Art Gallery, New Haven, April 27–September 24, 1961, *Paintings and Sculpture from the Albright Art Gallery*, checklist, #54

National Gallery of Art, Washington, D.C., May 19–July 21, 1968, *Paintings from the Albright-Knox Art Gallery*, ill. p. 69

Museo Nacional de Bellas Artes, Buenos Aires, October 23–November 30, 1969, *109 obras de Albright-Knox Art Gallery*, #66, p. 77, ill.

Albright-Knox Art Gallery, Buffalo, June 13–July 16, 1972, *English Painting and Sculpture, 1942–1972, in the Albright-Knox Art Gallery*, #[40]

Isamu Noguchi
The Cry, 1962 (third in an edition of six)
Inscribed on lower part of sculpture "I Noguchi 3/6"

Exhibitions

The White House, Washington, D.C., June 14, 1965, *The White House Festival of the Arts*, #20, p. 28

Albright-Knox Art Gallery, Buffalo, September 30–October 30, 1966, *Contemporary Art—Acquisitions 1962–1965*, #187, ill. p. 76

Expo '67, Montreal, Canada, April 28–October 27, 1967, *International Exhibition of Contemporary Sculpture*, pp. 40, 120, ill. p. 101

References

Charlotte Buel Johnson, "Isamu Noguchi," *School Arts*, vol. LXIV, no. 5, January, 1965, p. 44, ill. p. 45

Jack Burnham, *Beyond Modern Sculpture*, George Braziller, Inc., New York, 1968, p. 157, ill. p. 158

Kenneth Noland
Yellow Half, 1963
Inscribed on reverse "Kenneth Noland/1963 Feb."

Exhibitions

André Emmerich Gallery, New York, April 23–May 11, 1963, *Kenneth Noland Paintings*, ill. p. 2

Albright-Knox Art Gallery, Buffalo, September 30–October 30, 1966, *Contemporary Art—Acquisitions 1962–1965*, #23, p. 47, ill.

National Gallery of Art, Washington, D.C., May 19–July 21, 1968, *Paintings from the Albright-Knox Art Gallery*, ill. p. 89

Museo Nacional de Bellas Artes, Buenos Aires, October 23–November 30, 1969, *109 obras de Albright-Knox Art Gallery*, #96, p. 107, ill.

References

Michael Fried, "New York Letter," *Art International*, vol. VII, no. 5, May 25, 1963, p. 70, ill. p. 71

Charlotte Buel Johnson, "Trends and Traditions: Recent Acquisitions," *Gallery Notes*, The Buffalo Fine Arts Academy, vol. XXVII, no. 2, Spring, 1964, pp. 3–4, ill. p. 4

Kenneth Noland
Wild Indigo, 1967
Inscribed on reverse "Kenneth Noland, *Wild Indigo*, 1967"

Kenzo Okada
White and Gold, 1961
Inscribed l.r. "Kenzo Okada"

Exhibitions

Carnegie Institute, Department of Fine Arts, Pittsburgh, October 27, 1961–January 7, 1962, *The 1961 Pittsburgh International Exhibition of Contemporary Painting and Sculpture*, #295

Albright-Knox Art Gallery, Buffalo, October 20–November 28, 1965, *Kenzo Okada/Paintings 1931–1965*, #43

National Gallery of Art, Washington, D.C., May 19–July 21, 1968, *Paintings from the Albright-Knox Art Gallery*, ill. p. 69

Museo Nacional de Bellas Artes, Buenos Aires, October 23–November 30, 1969, *109 obras de Albright-Knox Art Gallery*, #74, p. 85, ill.

Albright-Knox Art Gallery, Buffalo, January 19–February 20, 1972, *Abstract Expressionism: The First and Second Generations in the Albright-Knox Art Gallery*, checklist, #[36]

Georgia O'Keeffe
Green Patio Door, 1955, 1955
Not inscribed

Exhibitions

The Downtown Gallery, New York, December 30, 1957–January 25, 1958, *32nd Annual Exhibition*

Albright Art Gallery, Buffalo, December 8, 1958–January 18, 1959, *Contemporary Art—Acquisitions 1957–1958*, #14, ill. p. [16]

Pennsylvania State University College of Arts and Architecture, University Park, October 6–November 16, 1963, *Aspects of the Apollonian Ideal*, #8

The Kitchener-Waterloo Art Gallery Kitchener, Ontario, Canada, February 19–March 28, 1965, *Contemporary American Painters*

Amon Carter Museum of Western Art, Fort Worth, March 17–May 8, 1966, *Georgia O'Keeffe*, p. 30; traveled to: The Museum of Fine Arts, Houston, May 17–July 3

Whitney Museum of American Art, New York, October 8–November 29, 1970, *Georgia O'Keeffe*, #108, p. 35; traveled to: The Art Institute of Chicago, January 6–February 7, 1971; San Francisco Museum of Art, March 15–April 30

Reference

"Letters from 31 Artists," *Gallery Notes*, The Buffalo Fine Arts Academy, vol. XXXI, no. 2, and vol. XXXII, no. 2, Spring, 1970, p. 28, ill.

Claes Oldenburg
Soft Manhattan #1 (Postal Zones), 1966
Inscribed on reverse "Soft Manhattan #1 (Postal Zones) Claes Oldenburg 1966"

Exhibitions

Sidney Janis Gallery, New York, March 9–April 2, 1966, *New Work by Oldenburg*, #25, p. [16], ill.

The Art Gallery of Ontario, Toronto, Canada, January 13–February 12, 1967, *Dine, Oldenburg, Segal, Painting/Sculpture*, #39, p. 39, ill. p. 53; traveled to: Albright-Knox Art Gallery, Buffalo, February 23–April 2

Ithaca (N.Y.) College Museum of Art, April 3–May 27, 1967, *Selected N.Y.C. Artists*, 1967, p. [9], ill. p. [5]

New York State Fair, Syracuse, N.Y., August 29–September 4, 1967, *Art Today*

The Cleveland Museum of Art, July 2–September 15, 1968, *Pop Images and Sensibility*, p. [13], ill. p. [8]

Albright-Knox Art Gallery, Buffalo, June 17–September 1, 1969, *Contemporary Art—Acquisitions 1966–1969*, #49, ill. p. 45

The Museum of Modern Art, New York, September 25–November 23, 1969, *Claes Oldenburg*, #98, pp. 147–48, ill. p. 10; traveled to: Stedelijk Museum, Amsterdam, The Netherlands, January 16–March 15, 1970, *Claes Oldenburg*, #91 p. 60, ill.; Städtische Kunsthalle, Düsseldorf, Germany, April 15–May 24, *Claes Oldenburg*, #87, p. 57, ill.; The Tate Gallery, London, June 24–August 16, *Claes Oldenburg*, #92, p. 64, ill.

References

Brydon Smith, "Claes Oldenburg," *Gallery Notes*, The Buffalo Fine Arts Academy, vol. XXIX, no. 2, Autumn, 1966, p. 20, ill. p. 21

Barbara Rose, *Claes Oldenburg*, The Museum of Modern Art, New York, 1970, pp. 147–48, ill. p. 10

Jules Olitski
Second Tremor, 1969
Not inscribed

Exhibition

Lawrence Rubin Gallery, New York, February 10–21, 1970

Eduardo Paolozzi
Japanese War God, 1958
Inscribed on base "Eduardo/London/Paolozzi/58"

Exhibitions

The Hanover Gallery, London, November 11–December 31, 1958, *Paolozzi Sculpture*, #1, ill. p. [2]

Yale University Art Gallery, New Haven, April 27–September 24, 1961, *Paintings and Sculpture from the Albright Art Gallery*, checklist, #104

Albright-Knox Art Gallery, Buffalo, October 27–November 29, 1964, *Contemporary British Paintings and Sculpture*, #40, ill. p. 21

Albright-Knox Art Gallery, Buffalo, June 13–July 16, 1972, *English Painting and Sculpture, 1942–1972, in the Albright-Knox Art Gallery*, checklist, #[41]

References

Francine-Claire Legrand, "La Peinture et la sculpture au defi," *Quadrum*, no. 7, 1959, ill. p. 49

Robert Melville, "Eduardo Paolozzi," *Motif*, no. 2, February, 1959, p. 62, ill. p. 61

H[ubert] C[rehan], "Eduardo Paolozzi," *Art News*, vol. 59, no. 2, April, 1960, p. 46, ill.

J. J. Kelly, *The Sculptural Idea*, Burgess, Minneapolis, 1970, pp. 15–16, ill. p. 15

Carl-Henning Pedersen
Flying Bird, 1951
Inscribed on reverse: at top "chp 1951"; in center "Den svaevende fogl"; at bottom "Carl-Hennnig Pedersen"

Exhibitions

Lefebre Gallery, New York, February 18–March 21, 1964, *Salute to Denmark*, ill. p. [5]

Albright-Knox Art Gallery, Buffalo, September 30–October 30, 1966, *Contemporary Art—Acquisitions 1962–1965*, #27, ill. p. 42

National Gallery of Art, Washington, D.C., May 19–July 21, 1968, *Paintings from the Albright-Knox Art Gallery*, ill. p. 78

Albright-Knox Art Gallery, Buffalo, July 21–August 27, 1972, *Continental Painting and Sculpture, 1942–1972, in the Albright-Knox Art Gallery*, checklist, #[88]

Reference

Virtus Schade, *Carl-Henning Pedersen*, Stig Vendelkaers Forlag, Copenhagen, 1966, p. 87, ill.

Beverly Pepper
Zig-Zag, 1967
Not inscribed

Exhibitions

Marlborough Galleria d'Arte, Rome, February 1968, *Beverly Pepper*, #7, ill. inside front cover, and title page

Albright-Knox Art Gallery, Buffalo, March 3–April 14, 1968, *Plus by Minus: Today's Half-Century*, #139, p. 54

Albright-Knox Art Gallery, Buffalo, June 17–September 1, 1969, *Contemporary Art—Acquisitions 1966–1969*, #50, ill. p. 46

Albright-Knox Art Gallery, Buffalo, September 30–November 2, 1969, *Beverly Pepper*, checklist, #22

Reference

"Letters from 31 Artists," *Gallery Notes*, The Buffalo Fine Arts Academy, vol. XXXI, no. 2, and vol. XXXII, no. 2, Spring, 1970, p. 32, ill.

Antoine Pevsner
Construction in the Egg (Construction dans l'oeuf), **1948**
Inscribed lower edge center "A.P." Inscribed top edge center "48"

Exhibitions

Staempfli Gallery, New York, December 8, 1964–January 9, 1965, *The Sculptor and the Architect*, #11

Dallas Museum of Fine Arts, May 12–June 13, 1965, *Sculpture/Twentieth Century*, #63, p. 37, ill. p. 28

The Cleveland Museum of Art, June 14–July 31, 1966, *Fifty Years of Modern Art/1916–1966*, #104, p. [205], color ill. p. [131]

Albright-Knox Art Gallery, Buffalo, September 30–October 30, 1966, *Contemporary Art—Acquisitions 1962–1965*, #148, ill. p. 69

Albright-Knox Art Gallery, Buffalo, March 3–April 14, 1968, *Plus by Minus: Today's Half-Century*, #149, p. [55]

Albright-Knox Art Gallery, Buffalo, July 21–August 27, 1972, *Continental Painting and Sculpture, 1942–1972, in the Albright-Knox Art Gallery*, checklist, #[90]

References

Michel Seuphor, *The Sculpture of This Century*, George Braziller, Inc., New York, 1960, p. 67, ill.

Carola Giedion-Welcker, *Antoine Pevsner*, Editions du Griffon, Neuchatel, 1961, p. 9, ill. pp. [198–201] (pl. #105)

Pablo Picasso
Female Bather Playing (Baigneuse jouant), **1958**
(second in an edition of two)
Inscribed (foundry mark on base r.r.) "CIRE/C. VALSUANI/PERDUE"

Exhibitions

Worcester (Mass.) Art Museum, January 25–February 25, 1962, *Picasso/His Later Works, 1938–1961*, #91, p. 53, ill.

Albright-Knox Art Gallery, Buffalo, September 30–October 30, 1966, *Contemporary Art—Acquisitions 1962–1965*, #149, ill. p. 67

Albright-Knox Art Gallery, Buffalo, July 21–August 27, 1972, *Continental Painting and Sculpture, 1942–1972, in the Albright-Knox Art Gallery*, checklist, #[91]

Reference

Pierre Dufour, *Picasso 1950–1968*, Skira, Geneva, 1969, p. 51

Pablo Picasso
The Artist and His Model, **1964**
Inscribed l.l. "Picasso." Inscribed on reverse u.r. "11.11.64"

Exhibitions

Kootz Gallery, New York, October 5–23, 1965, *Picasso*

Albright-Knox Art Gallery, Buffalo, September 30–October 30, 1966, *Contemporary Art—Acquisitions 1962–1965*, #108, color ill. cover

National Gallery of Art, Washington, D.C., May 19–July 21, 1968, *Paintings from the Albright-Knox Art Gallery*, ill. p. 45

Museo Nacional de Bellas Artes, Buenos Aires, October 23–November 30, 1969, *109 obras de Albright-Knox Art Gallery*, #28, p. 39, color ill.

Albright-Knox Art Gallery, Buffalo, July 21–August 27, 1972, *Continental Painting and Sculpture, 1942–1972, in the Albright-Knox Art Gallery*, checklist, #[92]

Otto Piene
Any Fire Flower, **1964**
Inscribed on reverse "Piene/Philadelphia/64"

Exhibitions

Howard Wise Gallery, New York, November 12–December 5, 1964, *Zero: Mack, Piene, Uecker*, #4, p. 12

Albright-Knox Art Gallery, Buffalo, February 27–April 11, 1965, *Art Today: Kinetic and Optic*, #47, p. [11]

Albright-Knox Art Gallery, Buffalo, September 30–October 30, 1966, *Contemporary Art—Acquisitions 1962–1965*, #29

Albright-Knox Art Gallery, Buffalo, March 4–April 9, 1972, *Movement, Optical Phenomena and Light: Kinetic and Optic Painting and Sculpture in the Albright-Knox Art Gallery*, checklist, #[39]

Albright-Knox Art Gallery, Buffalo, July 21–August 27, 1972, *Continental Painting and Sculpture, 1942–1972, in the Albright-Knox Art Gallery*, checklist, #[93]

Reference

"Letters from 31 Artists," *Gallery Notes*, The Buffalo Fine Arts Academy, vol. XXXI, no. 2, and vol. XXXII, no. 2, Spring, 1970, p. 33, ill.

Michelangelo Pistoletto
Sacra Conversazione, (Sacred Conversation), **1963**
Inscribed on reverse u.r. "Pistoletto 63"

Exhibitions

Walker Art Center, Minneapolis, April 4–May 8, 1966, *Michelangelo Pistoletto: A Reflected World*, checklist, #2

National Gallery of Art, Washington, D.C., May 19–July 21, 1968, *Paintings from the Albright-Knox Art Gallery*, ill. p. 94

Albright-Knox Art Gallery, Buffalo, May 13–June 15, 1969, *Ceroli/Pistoletto*, #2, ill. p. [2]

Museo Nacional de Bellas Artes, Buenos Aires, October 23–November 30, 1969, *109 obras de Albright-Knox Art Gallery*, #61, p. 72, ill.

Albright-Knox Art Gallery, Buffalo, July 21–August 27, 1972, *Continental Painting and Sculpture, 1942–1972, in the Albright-Knox Art Gallery*, checklist, #[94]

Reference

Barry Lord, "b + w =3," *Artscanada*, vol. XXVI, no. 4, August, 1969, p. 2, ill. p. 5

Rogelio Polesello
Painting (Pintura), 1969
Inscribed u.r. "Polesello 1969"

Exhibitions

Instituto Torcuato di Tella, Buenos Aires, September–October, 1969, *Rogelio Polesello*

Albright-Knox Art Gallery, Buffalo, March 4–April 9, 1972, *Movement, Optical Phenomena and Light: Kinetic and Optic Painting and Sculpture in the Albright-Knox Art Gallery*, checklist, #[40]

Serge Poliakoff
Composition, 1953
Inscribed l.l. "Serge Poliakoff/53   8"

Exhibitions

The Hanover Gallery, London, May–June, 1959, *Poliakoff Exhibition of Paintings and Gouaches*, #5

National Gallery of Art, Washington, D.C., May 19–July 21, 1968, *Paintings from the Albright-Knox Art Gallery*, ill. p. 73

Museo Nacional de Bellas Artes, Buenos Aires, October 23–November 30, 1969, *109 obras de Albright-Knox Art Gallery*, #56, p. 67, ill.

Albright-Knox Art Gallery, Buffalo, July 21–August 27, 1972, *Continental Painting and Sculpture, 1942–1972, in the Albright-Knox Art Gallery*, checklist, #[96]

Jackson Pollock
Convergence (Number 10, 1952), 1952
Not inscribed

Exhibitions

Sidney Janis Gallery, New York, November 10–29, 1952, *Jackson Pollock*, checklist, #10

Musée National d'Art Moderne, Paris, April 24–June 8, 1953, *12 Peintres et sculpteurs Américains contemporains*, #49, p. [18]; traveled to: Kunsthaus, Zurich, Switzerland, July 25–August 30; Kunstsammlungen der Stadt Düsseldorf, Düsseldorf, Germany, September 20–October 25; Liljevalchs Konsthall, Stockholm, November 25–December 23; Taidehalli, Helsinki, January 8–24, 1954; Kunstnernes Hus, Oslo, February 17–March 7

Sidney Janis Gallery, New York, November 28–December 31, 1955, *15 Years of Jackson Pollock*, checklist #13

The Pennsylvania Academy of the Fine Arts, Philadelphia, January 22–February 26, 1956, *One Hundred and Fifty-first Annual Exhibition of Painting and Sculpture*, #76

XXVIII *Biennale di Venezia*, June 16–September 21, 1956, *American Artists Paint the City*, #6, p. 9, ill. p. 12

Albright Art Gallery, Buffalo, May 15, 1957–February 15, 1958, *Contemporary Art—Acquisitions 1954–1957*, #15, ill. p. [27]

The Museum of Modern Art, New York, April 3–June 4, 1967, *Jackson Pollock*, #71, pp. 45, 66, 69, 72, 74, ill. p. 121; traveled to: Los Angeles County Museum, July 15–September 15

National Gallery of Art, Washington, D.C., May 19–July 21, 1968, *Paintings from the Albright-Knox Art Gallery*, p. 55, ill., and color ill. cover

Museo Nacional de Bellas Artes, Buenos Aires, October 23–November 30, 1969, *109 obras de Albright-Knox Art Gallery*, #101, p. 112, ill.

Albright-Knox Art Gallery, Buffalo, January 19–February 20, 1972, *Abstract Expressionism: The First and Second Generations in the Albright-Knox Art Gallery*, checklist, #[38]

References

J[ames] F[itzsimmons], "57th Street in Review," *Art Digest*, vol. 27, no. 4, November 15, 1952, p. 17

"American Artists Paint the City," *Arts*, vol. 30, no. 9, June, 1956, p. 29

J. P. Hodin, "The Venice Biennale," *Arts*, vol. 30, no. 11, August, 1956, p. 16

Milton Gendel, "The Iron Curtain in the Glass-Factory," *Art News*, vol. 55, no. 5, September, 1956, p. 59, ill. p. 26

Gordon M. Smith, "The Brave Buffalo," *Art News*, vol. 56, no. 3, May, 1957, p. 70

Frank O'Hara, *Jackson Pollock*, George Braziller, Inc., New York, 1959, #7, p. 26, color ill. p. [97]

Bryan Robertson, *Jackson Pollock*, Harry N. Abrams, Inc., New York, 1960, #158, ill. p. [183]

Lawrence Alloway, *Jackson Pollock*, Marlborough, London, 1961, p. 52

Yoshiaki Tono, "Jackson Pollock, or the New Rite of Hate-Love for Image," *Mizue*, no. 672, April, 1961, pp. 1–27, color ill. p. 12[a]

Art and Mankind, Larousse Encyclopedia of Modern Art, Paul Hamlyn, Ltd, London, 1966, p. 418, color ill. p. 368

The United States, Life World Library, *Time*, Inc., New York, 1965, p. 111, color ill.

M[el] B[ochner], "Jackson Pollock," *Arts Magazine*, vol. 41, no. 7, May, 1967, p. 54

Matthew Baigell, "American Painting: On Space and Time in the Early 1960's," *Art Journal*, vol. XXVIII, no. 4, Summer, 1969, p. 368, ill. p. 369

Irving Sandler, *The Triumph of American Painting*, Praeger Publishers, New York, 1970, p. 115, ill. p. 112

Larry Poons
Orange Crush, 1963
Not inscribed

Exhibitions

Sheldon Memorial Art Gallery, University of Nebraska, Lincoln, April 5–May 3, 1964, *Nebraska Art Association 73rd Annual Exhibition*, #83, p. [8]

Albright-Knox Art Gallery, Buffalo, February 27–April 11, 1965, *Art Today: Kinetic and Optic*, #49, p. [12]

Allen Memorial Art Museum, Oberlin, Ohio, May 5–30, 1965, *Three Young Americans: Poons, Hinman, Williams*

Museu de Arte Moderna, São Paulo, Brazil, September 4–November 28, 1965, *VIII Bienal Estados Unidos da America*, #36; traveled to: National Collection of Fine Arts, Washington, D.C., January 27–March 6, 1966

Albright-Knox Art Gallery, Buffalo, September 30–October 30, 1966, *Contemporary Art—Acquisitions 1962–1965*, #30, ill. p. 80

National Gallery of Art, Washington, D.C., May 19–
July 21, 1968, *Paintings from the Albright-Knox Art
Gallery*, ill. p. 90

Honolulu Academy of Arts, October 5–November 10,
1968, *Signals in the Sixties*, ill. p. [31]

Museo Nacional de Bellas Artes, Buenos Aires, October
23–November 30, 1969, *109 obras de Albright-Knox Art
Gallery*, #93, p. 104, ill.

Albright-Knox Art Gallery, Buffalo, July 25–September
6, 1971, *¿Kid Stuff?*, checklist, #35

Albright-Knox Art Gallery, Buffalo, October 5–November
14, 1971, *Six Painters*, #25, p. 13, color ill. p. 64;
traveled to: The Baltimore Museum of Art, December 11,
1971–January 23, 1972; Milwaukee Art Center, February
12–March 26

Reference

Charlotte Buel Johnson, "Trends and Traditions: Recent
Acquisitions—The Optical Illusion," *Gallery Notes*, The
Buffalo Fine Arts Academy, vol. XXVII, no. 2, Spring,
1964, p. 5, ill.

Richard Pousette-Dart
In the Forest, 1957
Not inscribed

Exhibitions

Betty Parsons Gallery, New York, February 17–March 8,
1958, *Pousette-Dart*

Albright Art Gallery, Buffalo, December 8, 1958–January
18, 1959, *Contemporary Art—Acquisitions 1957–1958*,
#16, ill. p. [24]

Yale University Art Gallery, New Haven, April 26–September 24, 1961, *Paintings and Sculpture from the
Albright Art Gallery*, checklist, #60

National Gallery of Art, Washington, D.C., May 19–July
21, 1968, *Paintings from the Albright-Knox Art Gallery*,
ill. p. 61

Albright-Knox Art Gallery, Buffalo, January 19–February
20, 1972, *Abstract Expressionism: The First and Second
Generations in the Albright-Knox Art Gallery*, checklist,
#[39]

Robert Rauschenberg
Painting with Red Letter S, 1957
Not inscribed

Exhibitions

Museu de Arte Moderno, São Paulo, September 21–December 31, 1959, *V São Paulo Bienal Estados Unidos da
America*, #87, p. 25

William Rockhill Nelson Gallery of Art, Kansas City,
January 19–February 28, 1961, *The Logic of Modern Art*

Albright-Knox Art Gallery, Buffalo, November 19–December 15, 1963, *Mixed Media and Pop Art*, #45, p. 8

Colgate University, Hamilton, N. Y., October 9–25, 1964,
Festival of the Creative Arts

Walker Art Center, Minneapolis, May 3–June 31, 1965,
Robert Rauschenberg Paintings 1953–1964, #4, p. [21]

Albright-Knox Art Gallery, Buffalo, January 19–February
20, 1972, *Abstract Expressionism: The First and Second
Generations in the Albright-Knox Art Gallery*, checklist,
#40

Reference

Andrew Forge, *Rauschenberg*, Harry N. Abrams, Inc.,
New York, ill. p. 52

Robert Rauschenberg
Ace, 1962
Inscribed l.l. and l.r. "Rauschenberg"

Exhibitions

Leo Castelli Gallery, New York, April 7–21, 1962, *Ace*

The Jewish Museum, New York, March 31–May 12,
1963, *Robert Rauschenberg*, #44, ill. p. [50]

Whitechapel Gallery, London, February–March 1964,
Robert Rauschenberg: Paintings/Drawings/Combines,
#28, ill. p. [47]

XXXII Biennale di Venezia, June 20–October 18, 1964,
#13, p. 279

Albright-Knox Art Gallery, Buffalo, September 30–October
30, 1966, *Contemporary Art—Acquisitions 1962–1965*,
#32, color ill. p. [2]

National Gallery of Art, Washington, D.C., May 19–
July 21, 1968, *Paintings from the Albright-Knox Art
Gallery*, color ill. p. 83

Museo Nacional de Bellas Artes, Buenos Aires, October
23–November 30, 1969, *109 obras de Albright-Knox Art
Gallery*, #82, p. 93, color ill.

References

G. R. Swenson, "Rauschenberg Paints a Picture," *Art
News*, vol. 62, no. 2, April, 1963, p. 45, ill.

Robert Doty, "Robert Rauschenberg," *Gallery Notes*,
The Buffalo Fine Arts Academy, vol. XXVII, no. 2,
Spring, 1964, pp. 10–11, ill. p. 11

Andrew Forge, *Rauschenberg*, Harry N. Abrams, Inc.,
New York, 1969, color ill. p. 199

Ad Reinhardt
No. 15, 1952, 1952
Inscribed on the stretcher "Ad Reinhardt, 1952"

Exhibitions

Albright-Knox Art Gallery, Buffalo, December 8, 1958–
January 18, 1959, *Contemporary Art—Acquisitions 1957–
1958*, #17, ill. p. [26]

Yale University Art Gallery, New Haven, April 27–September 24, 1961, *Paintings and Sculpture from the
Albright Art Gallery*, checklist, #62

Albright-Knox Art Gallery, Buffalo, March 3–April 14,
1968, *Plus by Minus: Today's Half-Century*, #165,
p. [57]

National Gallery of Art, Washington, D.C., May 19–
July 21, 1968, *Paintings from the Albright-Knox Art
Gallery*, ill. p. 51

Museo Nacional de Bellas Artes, Buenos Aires, October
23–November 30, 1969, *109 obras de Albright-Knox Art
Gallery*, #84, p. 95, ill.

References

Martin James, "Reinhardt," *Portfolio and Art News
Annual*, no. 3, 1960, p. 53, color ill.

Irving Sandler, *The Triumph of American Painting*,
Praeger Publishers, New York, 1970, p. 230, ill. p. 231

George Rickey
Peristyle: Five Lines, 1963–64
Not inscribed

Exhibitions

Staempfli Gallery, New York, October 20–November 7, 1964, *George Rickey/Kinetic Sculpture,* checklist, #11, p. [4]

The Corcoran Gallery of Art, Washington, D.C., September 30–November 20, 1966, *George Rickey, Sixteen Years of Kinetic Sculpture,* checklist, #25, p. [21]

Albright-Knox Art Gallery, Buffalo, February 27–April 11, 1965, *Art Today: Kinetic and Optic,* checklist, #50, p. [12]

Albright-Knox Art Gallery, Buffalo, March 4–April 9, 1972, *Movement, Optical Phenomena and Light: Kinetic and Optic Painting and Sculpture in the Albright-Knox Art Gallery,* checklist, #[42]

References

Tom L. Freudenheim, "Kinetic Art," *Gallery Notes,* The Buffalo Fine Arts Academy, vol. XXIX, no. 2, Autumn, 1966, p. 7, ill. p. 6

"Letters from 31 Artists," *Gallery Notes,* The Buffalo Fine Arts Academy, vol. XXXI, no. 2, and vol. XXXII, no. 2, Spring, 1970, pp. 34–35, ill. p. 35

Bridget Riley
Drift No. 2, 1966
Inscribed on reverse center "Riley '66/Drift 2/Emulsion on canvas/91½ x 89½"

Exhibitions

Richard Feigen Gallery, New York, April 9–May 11, 1967, *Bridget Riley Exhibition,* #2

National Gallery of Art, Washington, D.C., May 19–July 21, 1968, *Paintings from the Albright-Knox Art Gallery,* ill. p. 91

Albright-Knox Art Gallery, Buffalo, June 17–September 1, 1969, *Contemporary Art—Acquisitions 1966-1969,* #26, ill. p. 34

Museo Nacional de Bellas Artes, Buenos Aires, October 23–November 30, 1969, *109 obras de Albright-Knox Art Gallery,* #83, p. 94, ill.

Kunstverein Hannover, Hanover, Germany, November 14–December 20, 1970, *Bridget Riley,* #43, p. 97, ill. p. [61]; traveled to: Kunsthalle, Berne, January 16–February 21, 1971; Städtische Kunsthalle, Düsseldorf, Germany, March 12–April 11; Museo Civico di Torino, Turin, Italy, May 27–June 20; The Hayward Gallery, London, July 21–September 5, #44, English catalogue text p. 16, ill. p. 66

Národni Galerie, Prague, October 12–November 21, 1971, *Bridget Riley: obrazy z let 1951–1971,* #27, p. 22, ill.

Albright-Knox Art Gallery, Buffalo, June 13–July 16, 1972, *English Painting and Sculpture, 1942–1972 in the Albright-Knox Art Gallery,* checklist, #[46]

Reference

H. H. Arnason, *History of Modern Art—Painting, Sculpture, Architecture,* Harry N. Abrams, Inc., New York, 1968, p. 617, ill.

Jean-Paul Riopelle
Preo, 1964
Inscribed lower center "Riopelle"

Exhibitions

National Gallery of Art, Washington, D.C., May 19–July 21, 1968, *Paintings from the Albright-Knox Art Gallery,* ill. p. 75

Albright-Knox Art Gallery, Buffalo, June 17–September 1, 1969, *Contemporary Art—Acquisitions 1966–1969,* #74, ill. p. 62

Museo Nacional de Bellas Artes, Buenos Aires, October 23–November 30, 1969, *109 obras de Albright-Knox Art Gallery,* #57, p. 68, ill.

Albright-Knox Art Gallery, Buffalo, January 19–February 20, 1972, *Abstract Expressionism: The First and Second Generations in the Albright-Knox Art Gallery,* checklist, #[41]

Larry Rivers
The Final Veteran, 1960
Inscribed on reverse u.r. " "Final Veteran"/Rivers 60"

Exhibitions

Heckscher Museum, Huntington, N.Y., May 23–August 23, 1964, *The Face of America,* #46, p. 16, ill.

Colgate University, Hamilton, N.Y., October 6–25, 1964, *Festival of the Creative Arts Exhibition,* checklist in *Poiesis,* #[28], Colgate University, 1964, p. 14

The White House, Washington, D.C., June 14, 1965, *White House Festival of the Arts,* #31, p. 13

National Gallery of Art, Washington, D.C., May 19–July 21, 1968, *Paintings from the Albright-Knox Art Gallery,* ill. p. 63

Museo Nacional de Bellas Artes, Buenos Aires, October 23–November 30, 1969, *109 obras de Albright-Knox Art Gallery,* #59, p. 70, ill.

James Rosati
Big Red, 1970–71
Not inscribed

James Rosenquist
Nomad, 1963
Not inscribed

Exhibitions

Albright-Knox Art Gallery, Buffalo, November 19–December 15, 1963, *Mixed Media and Pop Art,* #66

Green Gallery, New York, January 15–February 8, 1964, *James Rosenquist*

The National Gallery of Canada, Ottawa, January 24–February 25, 1968, *James Rosenquist,* #18, p. 48, ill. pp. 48–49

National Gallery of Art, Washington, D.C., May 19–July 21, 1968, *Paintings from the Albright-Knox Art Gallery,* ill. p. 93

The Metropolitan Museum of Art, New York, October 18, 1969–February 1, 1970, *New York Painting and Sculpture 1940–1970,* #341, p. 58, ill. p. 293

Albright-Knox Art Gallery, Buffalo, July 25–September 6, 1971, *¿Kid Stuff?,* #36, p. [12], ill.

Whitney Museum of American Art, New York, April 10–May 29, 1972, *James Rosenquist*, #42, p. 17

References

Robert Doty, "Pop Art," *Gallery Notes*, The Buffalo Fine Arts Academy, vol. XXVII, no. 2, Spring, 1964, p. 9, ill.

John Russell, "Pop Reappraised," *Art in America*, vol. 57, no. 4, July-August, 1969, p. 79, ill.

American Painting/1900–1970, Time-Life Books, New York, 1970, p. 176, ill. pp. 176–77

Mark Rothko
Orange and Yellow, 1956
Inscribed on reverse "Mark Rothko 1956"

Exhibitions

Albright Art Gallery, Buffalo, May 15, 1957–February 15, 1958, *Contemporary Art—Acquisitions 1954–1957*, #16

The Cleveland Museum of Art, October 4–November 13, 1960, *Paths of Abstract Art*, #77, pp. 50–51, ill.

The Museum of Modern Art, New York, January 18–March 12, 1961, *Mark Rothko*, #[30], p. 43

Yale University Art Gallery, New Haven, April 27–September 24, 1961, *Paintings and Sculpture from the Albright Art Gallery*, checklist, #67

National Gallery of Art, Washington, D.C., May 19–July 21, 1968, *Paintings from the Albright-Knox Art Gallery*, ill. p. 53

Museo Nacional de Bellas Artes, Buenos Aires, October 23–November 30, 1969, *109 obras de Albright-Knox Art Gallery*, #80, p. 91, ill.

Albright-Knox Art Gallery, Buffalo, September 15–November 1, 1970, *Color and Field*, #42, p. 45, ill.; traveled to: Dayton (Ohio) Art Institute, November 20, 1970–January 10, 1971; The Cleveland Museum of Art, February 4–March 28, 1971

Yale University Art Gallery, New Haven, May 6–June 20, 1971, *Salute to Mark Rothko*, #11, p. [3]

Albright-Knox Art Gallery, Buffalo, January 19–February 20, 1972, *Abstract Expressionism: The First and Second Generations in the Albright-Knox Art Gallery*, checklist, #[44]

References

David Robb and J. J. Garrison, *Art in the Western World*, Harper & Row, New York, 1963, p. 637, ill. p. 638

H. H. Arnason, *History of Modern Art—Painting, Sculpture, Architecture*, Harry N. Abrams, Inc., New York, 1968, p. 509, color ill. p. 495

Irving Sandler, *The Triumph of American Painting*, Praeger Publishers, New York, 1970, p. 179, color ill. p. 169

Lucas Samaras
Mirrored Room (formerly *Room No. 2*), 1966
Not inscribed

Exhibitions

The Pace Gallery, New York, October 8–November 5, 1966, *Lucas Samaras*

The Art Institute of Chicago, June 23–August 27, 1967, *Sculpture: A Generation of Innovation*, checklist, p. 44, ill. p. 45; traveled to: City Art Museum of St. Louis, September 28–November 19

Albright-Knox Art Gallery, Buffalo, June 17–September 1, 1969, *Contemporary Art—Acquisitions 1966–1969*, #53, color ill. p. [4]

Albright-Knox Art Gallery, Buffalo, March 4–April 9, 1972, *Movement, Optical Phenomena and Light: Kinetic and Optic Painting and Sculpture in the Albright-Knox Art Gallery*, checklist, #[44]

References

Dore Ashton, "Art—with irony," *Studio International*, vol. 173, no. 885, January, 1967, p. 41, ill.

Colette Roberts, "Les Expositions/New York," *Aujourd'hui*, vol. 10, no. 55–56, January, 1967, p. 181, ill. p. 180

Benjamin Townsend, "Albright-Knox—Buffalo: Work in Progress," *Art News*, vol. 65, no. 9, January, 1967, pp. 32–34, ill. p. 30

Ricki Washton, "20th Century Period Pieces," *Arts Magazine*, vol. 41, no. 4, February, 1967, p. 52, ill.

Mahonri Sharp Young, "Letter from U.S.A.," *Apollo*, vol. LXXXV, no. 62, April, 1967, p. 299

H. H. Arnason, *History of Modern Art—Painting, Sculpture, Architecture*, Harry N. Abrams, Inc., New York, 1968, p. 600, ill.

"Art/Exhibitions/On All Sides," *Time*, vol. 91, no. 18, May 3, 1968, p. 56, color ill. p. 58

Udo Kultermann, *The New Sculpture/Environments and Assemblages*, Frederick A. Praeger, Inc., New York, 1968, pp. 203–4, ill. pp. 211–12

"Letters from 31 Artists," *Gallery Notes*, The Buffalo Fine Arts Academy, vol. XXXI, no. 2, and vol. XXXII, no. 2, Spring, 1970, p. 37, ill. pp. 36, 40

Ludwig Sander
Untitled, 1963
Inscribed on reverse "Sander, Fall 1963"

Exhibitions

Kootz Gallery, New York, January 7–25, 1964, *Ludwig Sander*

Albright-Knox Art Gallery, Buffalo, March 3–April 14, 1968, *Plus by Minus: Today's Half-Century*, p. [58]

National Gallery of Art, Washington, D.C., May 19–July 21, 1968, *Paintings from the Albright-Knox Art Gallery*, ill. p. 87

Nicolas Schöffer
Spatiodynamique 22, 1954
Not inscribed

Exhibitions

Albright-Knox Art Gallery, Buffalo, February 27–April 11, 1965, *Art Today: Kinetic and Optic*, checklist, #59

The Jewish Museum, New York, November 23, 1965–January 2, 1966, *Two Kinetic Sculptors: Schöffer and Tinguely*, #6, ill. p. 34; traveled to: The Washington (D.C.) Gallery of Modern Art, January 14–February 20; Walker Art Center, Minneapolis, March 7–April 10; Museum of Art, Carnegie Institute, Pittsburgh, April 28–May 29

Albright-Knox Art Gallery, Buffalo, March 4–April 9, 1972, *Movement, Optical Phenomena and Light: Kinetic and Optic Painting and Sculpture in the Albright-Knox Art Gallery*, checklist, #[45]

Kurt Schwitters
Difficult, 1942–43
Not inscribed

Exhibitions

Marlborough Fine Art Ltd., London, March–April, 1963, *Schwitters*, #236, p. 32, ill. p. 95

Wallraf-Richartz-Museum, Cologne, Germany, October 9–November 24, 1963, *Kurt Schwitters*, #241, p. 28, ill. p. 89

Toninelli-Arte Moderna, Milan, Italy, April–May, 1964, *Schwitters*, #98, p. 27, ill. p. 61

UCLA Art Galleries, Los Angeles, March 22–April 25, 1965, *Kurt Schwitters*, #153, p. 26, color ill. p. 13; traveled to: Marlborough-Gerson Gallery, New York, May-June

National Gallery of Art, Washington, D.C., May 19–July 21, 1968, *Paintings from the Albright-Knox Art Gallery*, ill. p. 42

Museo Nacional de Bellas Artes, Buenos Aires, October 23–November 30, 1969, *109 obras de Albright-Knox Art Gallery*, #22, p. 33, ill.

Städtische Kunsthalle, Düsseldorf, Germany, January 15–March 3, 1971, *Schwitters Retrospective*, #235; traveled to: Akademie der Künste, Berlin, March 12–April 18; Staatsgalerie, Stuttgart, Germany, May 14–July 18; Kunsthalle, Basel, Switzerland, July 31–September 5; Kunstverein, Hamburg, Germany, September 25–November 21

References

Keith Roberts, "Current and Forthcoming Exhibitions/London," *The Burlington Magazine*, vol. CV, no. 721, April, 1963, p. 179

Jasia Reichardt, "The London Exhibitions," *Arts Magazine*, vol. 37, no. 9, May–June, 1963, p. 30

William Scott
Blue Painting, 1960
Inscribed l.l. "W. Scott"

Exhibitions

Kestner-Gesellschaft, Hanover, Germany, June 2–July 17, 1960, *William Scott*, #64, p. 34

Albright-Knox Art Gallery, Buffalo, October 27–November 29, 1964, *Contemporary British Painting and Sculpture*, #42; traveled to: Addison Gallery of American Art, Andover, Mass., January 5–February 15, 1965

National Gallery of Art, Washington, D.C., May 19–July 21, 1968, *Paintings from the Albright-Knox Art Gallery*, ill. p. 64

Albright-Knox Art Gallery, Buffalo, June 13–July 16, 1972, *English Painting and Sculpture, 1942–1972, in the Albright-Knox Art Gallery*, checklist, #[47]

Reference

Ronald Alley, *William Scott*, Methuen & Co., London, 1963, p. [45], color ill. p. [5]

George Segal
Cinema, 1963
Not inscribed

Exhibitions

Sidney Janis Gallery, New York, January, 1964, *Four Environments*

Albright-Knox Art Gallery, Buffalo, September 30–October 30, 1966, *Contemporary Art—Acquisitions 1962–1965*, #89, ill. p. 45

The Art Gallery of Ontario, Toronto, Canada, January 14–February 12, 1967, *Dine, Oldenburg, Segal, Painting/Sculpture*, #49, p. 62, ill.; traveled to: Albright-Knox Art Gallery, Buffalo, February 24–March 26

Museum of Contemporary Art, Chicago, April 12–May 26, 1968, *George Segal—12 Human Situations*, #13, p. [11], ill.

The Hayward Gallery, London, July 9–September 3, 1969, *Pop Art*, #131, p. [7]

Albright-Knox Art Gallery, Buffalo, July 25–September 6, 1971, *¿Kid Stuff?*, checklist, #39

References

Ursula N. Eland, "George Segal," *Gallery Notes*, The Buffalo Fine Arts Academy, vol. XXVII, no. 2, Spring, 1964, p. 12, color ill. cover

Ellen H. Johnson, "The Sculpture of George Segal," *Art International*, vol VIII, no. 2, March, 1964, p. 49, ill.

Phyllis Tuchman, "George Segal," *Art International*, vol. XII, no. 7, September, 1968, p. 52, ill.

John Russell, "Pop Reappraised," *Art in America*, vol. 57, no. 4, July–August, 1969, p. 88, color ill.

David Smith
Tank Totem IV, 1953
Inscribed "David Smith/11-25-1953/ TK IV"

Exhibitions

The Art Institute of Chicago, January 17–March 3, 1957, *LXII American Exhibition: Painting and Sculpture*, #111, p. 27, ill.

The Museum of Modern Art, New York, September 10–October 20, 1957, *David Smith*, #19, ill. p. 29

XXIX Biennale di Venezia, June 14–October 19, 1958, #26, p. 343

Albright Art Gallery, Buffalo, December 8, 1958–January 18, 1959, *Contemporary Art—Acquisitions 1957–1958*, #45

Memorial Art Gallery of the University of Rochester, January 15–March 5, 1961, *Paintings and Sculpture from the Albright Art Gallery*

Yale University Art Gallery, New Haven, April 27–September 24, 1961, *Paintings and Sculpture from the Albright Art Gallery*, #106, ill. cover

References

Sam Hunter, "David Smith," *The Museum of Modern Art Bulletin*, vol. 25, no. 1, 1957, p. 10, ill. p. 29

Katharine Kuh, *The Artist's Voice*, Harper & Row, New York, 1960, p. 224, ill. p. 226

Charlotte Buel Johnson, "Tank Totem IV," *School Arts*, vol. 61, no. 2, October, 1961, p. 31, ill.

David Smith
Cubi XVI, 1963
Inscribed on base "David Smith 11–4–63 CUBI XVI"

Exhibition

Albright-Knox Art Gallery, Buffalo, June 17–September 1, 1969, *Contemporary Art—Acquisitions 1966–1969*, #94, p. 12, ill. p. 60

Tony Smith
Cigarette, 1961–68 (first in an edition of three)
Not inscribed

Exhibitions

Wadsworth Atheneum, Hartford, Conn., November 8–December 31, 1966, *Tony Smith, Two Exhibitions of Sculpture*, p. [24], ill. p. [25]; traveled to: Institute of Contemporary Art, University of Pennsylvania, Philadelphia, November 22, 1966–January 6, 1967

Los Angeles County Museum of Art, Los Angeles, April 28–June 25, 1967, *American Sculpture of the Sixties*, #129, p. 58, ill. p. 194; traveled to: Philadelphia Museum of Art, September 15–October 29

Albright-Knox Art Gallery, Buffalo, June 17–September 1, 1969, *Contemporary Art—Acquisitions 1966–1969*, #95, ill. p. 53

References

Judith Wechsler, "Why Scale?" *Art News*, vol. 66, no. 4, Summer, 1967, p. 32, ill. p. 33

Fidel A. Danieli, "Los Angeles/American Sculpture of the Sixties at Los Angeles County Museum," *Studio International*, vol. 173, no. 890, June, 1967, p. 321, ill.

H. H. Arnason, *History of Modern Art—Painting, Sculpture, Architecture*, Harry N. Abrams, Inc., New York, 1968, p. 607

Jesús Raphael Soto

Wood—Iron Rods (Bois—tiges de fer), 1964
Not inscribed

Exhibitions

Albright-Knox Art Gallery, Buffalo, February 27–April 11, 1965, *Art Today*, #63

Albright-Knox Art Gallery, Buffalo, September 30–October 30, 1966, *Contemporary Art—Acquisitions 1962–1965*, #70, ill. p. 34

Albright-Knox Art Gallery, Buffalo, March 4–April 9, 1972, *Movement, Optical Phenomena and Light: Kinetic and Optic Painting and Sculpture in the Albright-Knox Art Gallery*, checklist, #48

Reference

Tom L. Freudenheim, "Kinetic Art—Rickey, Gerstern, Soto, Mack, Tinguely, Kramer, Bury, Lye," The Buffalo Fine Arts Academy, *Gallery Notes*, vol. XXIX, no. 2, Autumn, 1966, p. 7, ill. p. 10

Pierre Soulages
4 July 1956, 1956
Inscribed l.r. "Soulages 56." Inscribed on reverse u.r. "Soulages 4-7-56"

Exhibitions

Kootz Gallery, New York, September 10–29, 1956, *Pierre Soulages*

Albright Art Gallery, Buffalo, May 15, 1957–February 15, 1958, *Contemporary Art—Acquisitions 1954–1957*, #24, ill. p. [33]

Colorado Springs Fine Arts Center, June 18–August 31, 1958, *New Accessions U.S.A.*, #2, ill. p. [16]

Walker Art Center, Minneapolis, April 5–May 17, 1959, *School of Paris 1959—The Internationals*, #61, p. 51

Yale University Art Gallery, New Haven, April 27–September 24, 1961, *Paintings and Sculpture from the Albright-Knox Art Gallery*, checklist

National Gallery of Art, Washington, D.C., May 19–July 21, 1968, *Paintings from the Albright-Knox Art Gallery*, ill. p. 73

Museo Nacional de Bellas Artes, Buenos Aires, October 23–November 30, 1969, *109 obras de Albright-Knox Art Gallery*, #55, p. 66, ill.

Albright-Knox Art Gallery, Buffalo, July 21–August 27, 1972, *Continental Painting and Sculpture, 1942–1972, in the Albright-Knox Art Gallery*, checklist, #[109]

Reference

Charlotte Buel Johnson, "Two Contemporary French Abstract Expressionists," *Gallery Notes*, The Buffalo Fine Arts Academy, vol. XXI, no. 2, Summer, 1958, pp. 16, 18, ill. p. 17

Nicolas de Staël
Landscape in Vaucluse No. 2, 1953
Inscribed l.l. "Staël." Inscribed on reverse "Paysage/Vaucluse/Staël 1953"

Exhibitions

Paul Rosenberg & Co., New York, February 8–March 6, 1954, *Recent Paintings by Nicolas de Staël*, #18

Albright Art Gallery, Buffalo, April 16–May 30, 1954, *Painters' Painters*, #45, ill. p. 57

Paul Rosenberg & Co., New York, October 31–November 26, 1955, *Nicolas de Staël*, #11

The Cleveland Museum of Art, October 4–November 13, 1960, *Paths of Abstract Art*, #81, p. 55, ill.

Paul Rosenberg & Co., New York, November 5–30, 1963, *Nicolas de Staël*, #15, ill. p. 6

National Gallery of Art, Washington, D.C., May 19–July 21, 1968, *Paintings from the Albright-Knox Art Gallery*, ill. p. 72

Albright-Knox Art Gallery, Buffalo, June 17–September 1, 1969, *Contemporary Art—Acquisitions 1966–1969*, #78, ill. p. 59

Museo Nacional de Bellas Artes, Buenos Aires, October 23–November 30, 1969, *109 obras de Albright-Knox Art Gallery*, #54, p. 65, ill.

Albright-Knox Art Gallery, Buffalo, July 21–August 27, 1972, *Continental Painting and Sculpture, 1942–1972, in the Albright-Knox Art Gallery*, checklist, #[110]

Theodoros Stamos
Levant for E.W.R., 1958
Inscribed l.l. "Stamos"

Exhibitions

André Emmerich Gallery, New York, April 1–30, 1958, *Theodoros Stamos/New Painting*, #[9]

Albright-Knox Art Gallery, Buffalo, December 8, 1958–January 18, 1959, *Contemporary Art—Acquisitions 1957–1958*, #22, ill. p. [30]

National Gallery of Art, Washington, D.C., May 19–July 21, 1968, *Paintings from the Albright-Knox Art Gallery*, ill. p. 62

Museo Nacional de Bellas Artes, Buenos Aires, October 23–November 30, 1969, *109 obras de Albright-Knox Art Gallery*, #46, p. 57, ill.

Albright-Knox Art Gallery, Buffalo, January 19–February 20, 1972, *Abstract Expressionism: The First and Second Generations in the Albright-Knox Art Gallery*, checklist, #[48]

Richard Stankiewicz
Our Lady of All Protections, 1958
Not inscribed

Exhibitions

Stable Gallery, New York, January 5–31, 1959, *Stankiewicz*

Albright-Knox Art Gallery, Buffalo, November 19–December 15, 1963, *Mixed Media and Pop Art*, #33

References

Samuel M. Green, *American Art: A Historical Survey*, The Ronald Press, New York, 1966, p. 643, ill. p. 642

"Letters from 31 Artists," *Gallery Notes*, The Buffalo Fine Arts Academy, vol. XXXI, no. 2, and vol. XXXII, no. 2, Spring, 1970, p. 41, ill.

Frank Stella
Jill, 1959
Inscribed on reverse u.l. "F.P. STELLA/366 W. B'WAY/1959/'JILL'/7½ x 6½"

Exhibitions

National Arts Club, New York, December 9, 1959–January 7, 1960, *The Metropolitan Young Artists Show*

Morgan State College, Fine Arts Building Auditorium, Baltimore, April–June 1960

References

Udo Kultermann, *The New Painting*, Frederick A. Praeger, Inc., New York, 1969, p. 46, ill. p. 120

William S. Rubin, *Frank Stella*, The Museum of Modern Art, New York, 1970, p. 34, ill. p. 33

Frank Stella
Fez, 1964
Not inscribed

Exhibitions

Albright-Knox Art Gallery, Buffalo, September 30–October 30, 1966, *Contemporary Art—Acquisitions 1962–1965*, #39

National Gallery of Art, Washington, D.C., May 19–July 21, 1968, *Paintings from the Albright-Knox Art Gallery*, color ill. p. 86

Museo Nacional de Bellas Artes, Buenos Aires, October 23–November 30, 1969, *109 obras de Albright-Knox Art Gallery*, #89, p. 100 ill.

The Museum of Modern Art, New York, March 26–May 31, 1970, *Frank Stella*, p. 104, ill. p. 109; traveled to: The Hayward Gallery, London, July 25–August 31, #22, ill. p. [21]; Stedelijk Museum, Amsterdam, The Netherlands, October 2–November 22, #23, p. 38, ill.; Pasadena (Calif.) Art Museum, January 19–February 28, 1971, #23; The Art Gallery of Ontario, Toronto, Canada, April 9–May 9, #22

Reference

J. Patrice Marandel, "Lettre de New York," *Art International*, vol. XIV, no. 5, May, 1970, p. 73

Frank Stella
Lac Laronge III, 1969
Inscribed on the stretcher "FOR L. RUBIN LAC LARONGE III 9' x 13½'." Inscribed on reverse right "F Stella '69"

Exhibition

Lawrence Rubin Gallery, New York, January 10–February 7, 1970, *Frank Stella*, checklist, #1

Reference

Terry Fenton, "The David Mirvish/Opening Show—Toronto," *Artscanada*, vol. XXVII, no. 6, December, 1970/January, 1971, p. 58

Clyfford Still
April 1962, 1962
Not inscribed

Exhibition

Albright-Knox Art Gallery, Buffalo, September 30–October 30, 1966, *Contemporary Art—Acquisitions 1962–1965*, #138, p. 16

Reference

Still/Paintings in the Albright-Knox Art Gallery, Buffalo, The Buffalo Fine Arts Academy, 1966, #32, p. 87, color ill. p. [81]

Graham Sutherland
Thorn Trees, 1945
Inscribed u.r. "Sutherland 45"

Exhibitions

Buchholz Gallery, New York, February 26–March 23, 1946, *Graham Sutherland*, #1, p. [8]

San Francisco Museum of Art, July 7–August 6, 1946, *Graham Sutherland*

Albright Art Gallery, Buffalo, November 1–December 15, 1946, *British Contemporary Painters*, #53, ill. p. 89; traveled to: Worcester (Mass.) Art Museum, February 12–March 16, 1947; The Art Gallery of Toronto, Ontario, Canada, April 3–April 30; City Art Museum of St. Louis, May 15–June 20; California Palace of the Legion of Honor, San Francisco, July 4–August 6; The Metropolitan Museum of Art, New York, September 15–October

The University of Michigan Museum of Art, Ann Arbor, November 4–November 24, 1948, *Contemporary Paintings from the Albright Art Gallery*, checklist, #37

The Institute of Contemporary Art, Boston, April 1–26, 1953

Curt Valentin Gallery, New York, October 5–30, 1954, *In Memory of Curt Valentin 1902–1954*, #30, ill. p. [18]

The Museum of Modern Art, New York, October 2–December 2, 1956, *Masters of British Painting 1800–1950*, #103, p. 136, ill. p. 141; traveled to: City Art Museum of St. Louis, January 10–March 2, 1957; California Palace of the Legion of Honor, San Francisco, March 28–May 12

Memorial Art Gallery of the University of Rochester, January 15–March 5, 1961, *Paintings and Sculpture from the Albright Art Gallery*

Yale University Art Gallery, New Haven, April 27–September 3, 1961, *Paintings and Sculpture from the Albright Art Gallery*, checklist, #78

Museum of Art, Carnegie Institute, Pittsburgh, September 18–November 17, 1963, *The Artist and the Tree*, checklist, #19

Albright-Knox Art Gallery, Buffalo, October 27–November 29, 1964, *Contemporary British Painting and Sculpture from the Collection of the Albright-Knox Art Gallery*, #45, ill. p. [24]; traveled to: Addison Gallery of American Art, Phillips Academy, Andover, Mass., January 5–February 15, 1965

Haus der Kunst, Munich, Germany, March 11–May 7, 1967, *Graham Sutherland*, #12, ill. p. [51]; traveled to: Gemeentemuseum, The Hague, The Netherlands, June 2–July 30; Haus am Waldsee, Berlin, August 11–September 24; Wallraf-Richartz-Museum, Cologne, Germany, October 7–November 20, 1967

Oscar Wells Memorial Building, Birmingham (Ala.) Museum of Art, February 20–March 9, 1970, *Contemporary British Art*

Albright-Knox Art Gallery, Buffalo, June 13–July 16, 1972, *English Painting and Sculpture, 1942–1972, in the Albright-Knox Art Gallery*, checklist, #51

References

"Additions to the Room of Contemporary Art, Graham Sutherland's *Thorn Trees*," *Gallery Notes*, The Buffalo Fine Arts Academy, vol. XI, no. 1, July, 1946, pp. 25–26, ill. p. [20]

Andrew C. Ritchie, *Contemporary Paintings and Sculpture*, The Buffalo Fine Arts Academy, 1949, p. 64, ill. p. 65

Robert Melville, *Graham Sutherland*, Ambassador Publishing Co. Ltd., London, 1950, ill. no. 10

Douglas Cooper, *The Work of Graham Sutherland*, Lund Humphries, London, 1961, #79, p. 76, pp. 32–33

Capolavori Nei Secoli, Fratelli Fabbri Editori, Milan, vol. XII, no. 138, 1964, color ill. p. 33 and cover

"Letters from 31 Artists," *Gallery Notes*, The Buffalo Fine Arts Academy, vol. XXXI, no. 2, and vol. XXXII, no. 2, Spring, 1970, p. 42, ill.

Edmund Burke Feldman, *Varieties of Visual Experience: Art as Image and Idea*, Harry N. Abrams, New York, 1972, color ill. p. 252, ill. p. 296

Tadasky (Kuwayama)
Untitled B 133, 1964
Not inscribed

Exhibitions

Kootz Gallery, New York, January 5–23, 1965, *Tadasky*

Albright-Knox Art Gallery, Buffalo, February 27–April 11, 1965, *Art Today: Kinetic and Optic*, #70, p. [13]

Albright-Knox Art Gallery, Buffalo, September 30–October 30, 1966, *Contemporary Art—Acquisitions 1962–1965*, #40, ill. p. 50

African Cultural Center, Buffalo, December 19, 1971–January 19, 1972

Albright-Knox Art Gallery, Buffalo, March 4–April 9, 1972, *Movement, Optical Phenomena and Light: Kinetic and Optic Painting and Sculpture in the Albright-Knox Art Gallery*, checklist, #[51]

Reference

George Rickey, "Scandale de succés," *Art International*, vol. IX, no. 4, May, 1965, p. 20, ill.

Yves Tanguy
Indefinite Divisibility (Divisibilité indéfinie), 1942
Inscribed l.r. "Yves Tanguy 42"

Exhibitions

Pierre Matisse Gallery, New York, May 8–June 2, 1945, *Yves Tanguy*, checklist, #2

The Art Gallery of Toronto, Ontario, Canada, November 4–December 25, 1949, *Contemporary Paintings from Great Britain, the United States and France with Sculpture from the United States*, #131

Museu de Arts Moderna, São Paulo, Brazil, October–December, 1951, *I Bienal do Museu de Arte Moderna de São Paulo*, #67, p. 118

Wadsworth Atheneum, Hartford, August 10–September 28, 1954, *Yves Tanguy and Kay Sage*, #18, p. [9]

The Museum of Modern Art, New York, September 6–October 13, 1955, *Yves Tanguy*, p. 18, color ill. p. 47

Roberson Memorial Center, Binghamton, N.Y., November 6–27, 1960, *Surrealism*

Memorial Art Gallery of the University of Rochester, January 15–March 5, 1961, *Paintings and Sculpture from the Albright Art Gallery*

Yale University Art Gallery, New Haven, April 27–September 24, 1961, *Paintings and Sculpture from the Albright Art Gallery*, checklist, #79

Fogg Art Museum, Harvard University, Cambridge, Mass., April 30–May 31, 1963, *Surrealisn*, #38

The Museum of Modern Art, New York, March 27–May 8, 1968, *Dada, Surrealism and Their Heritage*, #140, p. 102, ill. p. 103

National Gallery of Art, Washington, D.C., May 19–July 21, 1968, *Paintings from the Albright-Knox Art Gallery*, ill. p. 46

The Art Institute of Chicago, October 19–December 8, 1968, *Dada, Surrealism and Their Heritage*, #140, p. 102, ill. p. 103

Museo Nacional de Bellas Artes, Buenos Aires, October 23–November 30, 1969, *109 obras de Albright-Knox Art Gallery*, #16, p. 27, ill.

References

Margaret Breuning, "Surrealist Disillusion of Yves Tanguy," *Art Digest*, vol. 19, no. 16, May 15, 1945, p. 9, ill.

"Additions to Room of Contemporary Art/Tanguy's 'Super-Realism,'" *Gallery Notes*, The Buffalo Fine Arts Academy, vol. XI, no. 1, July, 1946, pp. 23–24, ill. p. [18]

James Thrall Soby, "Inland in the Subconscious: Yves Tanguy," *Magazine of Art*, vol. 42, no. 1, January, 1949, p. 6, ill.

Andrew C. Ritchie, *Contemporary Paintings and Sculpture*, The Buffalo Fine Arts Academy, 1949, p. 142, ill. p. 143

Marcel Jean, with the collaboration of Arpad Mezei, *Histoire de la peinture surréaliste*, Editions du Seuil, Paris, 1959, color ill. p. 316

Complete Collection of World Fine Art—Contemporary Occidental, Kodokawa Shoten, Fujimi-cho, Chiyoda-ku, Tokyo, vol. 37, no. 63, 1961, ill. p. [95]

Pierre Matisse, *Yves Tanguy—A Summary of his Works*, Pierre Matisse, New York, 1963, #297, p. 138, ill.

Martin Esslin, "Now All Artists Are Surrealists," *New York Times Magazine*, May 22, 1966, ill. p. 36

René Passeron, *Histoire de la peinture surréaliste*, Le Livre de Poche, Paris, 1968, #60, p. 129, ill. p. 124

William S. Rubin, *Dada and Surrealist Art*, Harry N. Abrams, Inc., New York, 1968, p. 374, ill. p. 385

Sarane Alexandrian, *L'Art surréaliste*, Fernand Hazan, Paris, 1969, #80, p. 85, color ill.

Donald W. Graham, *Composing Pictures*, Van Nostrand Reinhold Co., New York, 1970, p. 175, ill.

Jean Tinguely
Cocktail au cheval, (*Cocktail on Horseback*), 1966
Not inscribed

Exhibition

Albright-Knox Art Gallery, Buffalo, March 4–April 9, 1972, *Movement, Optical Phenomena and Light: Kinetic and Optic Painting and Sculpture in the Albright-Knox Art Gallery*, checklist, #[54]

Mark Tobey
Coming and Going, 1970
Inscribed l.l. "Tobey 70"

Exhibitions

Galerie Beyeler, Basel, Switzerland, December, 1970–February, 1971, *Tobey*, #83, color ill. p. [8]

Reference

John Russell, "Tobey at 80," *Art News*, vol. 69, no. 8, December, 1970, color ill. p. 45

Mark Tobey
Red Man—White Man—Black Man, 1945
Inscribed l.r. "Tobey/45"

Exhibitions

Willard Gallery, New York, November 13–December 8, 1945, *Mark Tobey*, checklist, #13

Arts Club of Chicago, February 7–27, 1946, *Mark Tobey*, checklist, #6

Munson-Williams-Proctor Institute, Utica, N.Y., October 5–26, 1947, *Ten Painters of the Pacific Northwest*, #45; traveled to: Albany Institute of History and Art, November 5–30; Albright Art Gallery, Buffalo, December 5–28; The Baltimore Museum of Art, January 9–February 4, 1948; Addison Gallery of American Art, Phillips Academy, Andover, Mass., February 27–March 29

University of Michigan, Ann Arbor, November 4–24, 1948, *Contemporary Paintings from the Albright Art Gallery*, #38

Willard Straight Hall, Cornell University, Ithaca, N.Y., November 12–December 10, 1950

California Palace of the Legion of Honor, San Francisco, March 31–May 6, 1951, *Retrospective Exhibition of Paintings by Mark Tobey*, p. [15]; traveled to: Henry Gallery, Seattle, May 20–June 27, checklist, #83; Santa Barbara (Calif.) Museum of Art, August–September; Whitney Museum of American Art, New York, October 4–November 4, #46, p. [19]

State University of Iowa, Department of Art, Iowa City, May 26–August 7, 1960, *Main Currents of Contemporary American Painting*, #56, ill. p. 23

Memorial Art Gallery of the University of Rochester, January 15–March 5, 1961, *Paintings and Sculpture from the Albright Art Gallery*

Yale University Art Gallery, New Haven, April 27–September 24, 1961, *Paintings and Sculpture from the Albright Art Gallery*, checklist, #81

Milwaukee Art Center, September 21–November 5, 1961, *Ten Americans*, #49, p. [21]

The Museum of Modern Art, New York, September 12–November 4, 1962, *Mark Tobey* #40, traveled to: The Cleveland Museum of Art, December 11, 1962–January 13, 1963; The Art Institute of Chicago, February 22–March 24, 1963

Stedelijk Museum, Amsterdam, The Netherlands, March 19–May 8, 1966, *Mark Tobey Retrospective*, #19, ill. p. [25]; traveled to: Kestner Gesellschaft, Hanover, Germany, May 19–June 26, #19; Kunsthalle, Berne, July 9–September 4, #19; Kunsthalle, Düsseldorf, Germany, September 16–October 23, #20

Dallas Museum of Fine Arts, March 20–April 21, 1968, *Mark Tobey Retrospective*, #35, ill. p. [22]

References

Joe Gibbs, "Tobey the Mystic," *Art Digest*, vol. 20, no. 4, November 15, 1945, p. 39

"Three Additions to the Room of Contemporary Art/Mark Tobey's Red Man—White Man—Black Man," *Gallery Notes*, The Buffalo Fine Arts Academy, vol XI, no. 3, June, 1947, pp. 25–29, ill. p. 26

Andrew C. Ritchie, *Contemporary Paintings and Sculpture*, The Buffalo Fine Arts Academy, 1949, p. 122, ill. p. 123

Bradley Walker Tomlin
No. 12–1952, 1952
Inscribed upper center "b. Tomlin/'52"

Exhibitions

Betty Parsons Gallery, New York, March 30–April 18, 1953, *Bradley Walker Tomlin*

Los Angeles County Museum of Art, Los Angeles, July 16–August 1, 1965, *New York School/The First Generation/Paintings of the 1940's and 1950's*, #120, p. 199, ill. p. 205

Albright-Knox Art Gallery, Buffalo, September 30–October 30, 1966, *Contemporary Art—Acquisitions 1962–1965*, #181, ill. p. 72

National Gallery of Art, Washington, D.C., May 19–
July 21, 1968, *Paintings from the Albright-Knox Art
Gallery*, ill. p. 47

Museo Nacional de Bellas Artes, Buenos Aires, October
23–November 30, 1969, *109 obras de Albright-Knox Art
Gallery*, #99, p. 110, color ill.

Albright-Knox Art Gallery, Buffalo, January 19–February
20, 1972, *Abstract Expressionism: The First and Second
Generations in the Albright-Knox Art Gallery*, checklist,
#[53]

References

Robert Doty, "Bradley Walker Tomlin," *Gallery Notes*,
The Buffalo Fine Arts Academy, vol. XXVII, no. 2,
Spring, 1964, p. 16. ill.

Irving Sandler, *The Triumph of American Painting/A
History of Abstract Expressionism*, Praeger Publishers,
New York, 1970, p. 244

Jack Tworkov
East Barrier, 1960
Inscribed l.r. "Tworkov '60." Inscribed on reverse u.r.
"Tworkov/60"; u.l. EAST BARRIER/92 x 81"

Exhibitions

Leo Castelli Gallery, New York, February 28–March 18,
1961, *Jack Tworkov*

St. Catherines and District Arts Council, Rodman Hall
Arts Centre, St. Catharines, Ontario, Canada, February
1–March 3, 1963, *Contemporary Painting from the
Permanent Collection of the Albright-Knox Art Gallery*

Whitney Museum of American Art, New York, March
25–May 3, 1964, *Jack Tworkov*, #40, p. 16, ill. p. [36];
traveled to: The Washington (D.C.) Gallery of Modern
Art, Washington, D.C., May 8–June 21

National Gallery of Art, Washington, D.C., May 19–
July 21, 1968, *Paintings from the Albright-Knox Art
Gallery*, ill. p. 62

Museo Nacional de Bellas Artes, Buenos Aires, October
23–November 30, 1969, *109 obras de Albright-Knox Art
Gallery*, #48, p. 59, ill.

References

S[idney] T[illim], "In the Galleries/Jack Tworkov," *Arts*,
vol. 35, no. 7, April, 1961, p. 53, ill.

Dore Ashton, "Art/Jack Tworkov," *Arts and Architecture*,
vol. 78, no. 5, May, 1961, p. 5, ill.

Victor Vasarely
Mindanao, 1952–55
Inscribed lower center "Vasarely"

Exhibitions

Galerie Denise René, Paris, November–December 1955,
Vasarely, #44

Palais des Expositions, Charleroi, Belgium, July 5–September 14, 1958, *L'Art du XXIᵉ siècle*, #122

Albright-Knox Art Gallery, Buffalo, December 8, 1958–
January 18, 1959, *Contemporary Art—Acquisitions 1957-
1958*, #40, ill. p. [40]

Galerie Denise René, Paris, November–December, 1959,
Tableaux cinetiques, #4

Victor Vasarely
Bora III, 1964
Inscribed on reverse "Vasarely"

Exhibitions

National Gallery of Art, Washington, D.C., May 19–
July 21, 1968, *Paintings from the Albright-Knox Art
Gallery*

Albright-Knox Art Gallery, Buffalo, June 17–September 1,
1969, *Contemporary Art—Acquisitions 1966-1969*, #29

Museo Nacional de Bellas Artes, Buenos Aires, October
23–November 30, 1969, *109 obras de Albright-Knox Art
Gallery*, #22, p. 78

Albright-Knox Art Gallery, Buffalo, March 4–April 9,
1972, *Movement, Optical Phenomena and Light: Kinetic
and Optic Painting and Sculpture in the Albright-Knox
Art Gallery*

Victor Vasarely
Vega-Nor, 1969
Not inscribed

Exhibition

Albright-Knox Art Gallery, Buffalo, March 4–April 9,
1972, *Movement, Optical Phenomena and Light: Kinetic
and Optic Painting and Sculpture in the Albright-Knox
Art Gallery*

Andy Warhol
100 Cans, 1962
Not inscribed

Exhibitions

Albright-Knox Art Gallery, Buffalo, November 19–December 15, 1963, *Mixed Media and Pop Art*, #72

Milwaukee Art Center, April 9–May 9, 1965, *Pop Art
and the American Tradition*, #67, ill. p. 2

Albright-Knox Art Gallery, Buffalo, September 30–October
30, 1966, *Contemporary Art—Acquisitions 1963-1965*,
#42, ill. p. 37

National Gallery of Art, Washington, D.C., May 19–
July 21, 1968, *Paintings from the Albright-Knox Art
Gallery*, ill. p. 92

The Hayward Gallery, London, July 9–September 3, 1969,
Pop Art, #149

Museo Nacional de Bellas Artes, Buenos Aires, October
23–November 30, 1969, *109 obras de Albright-Knox Art
Gallery*, #91, color ill. p. 102

Albright-Knox Art Gallery, Buffalo, July 25–September 6,
1971, *¿Kid Stuff?*, #46, ill. p. [19]

References

Robert Doty, "Pop Art," *Gallery Notes*, The Buffalo Fine
Arts Academy, vol. XXVII, no. 2, Spring, 1964, pp.
7–8, ill. p. 8

Burton Wasserman, *Modern Painting—The Movements,
The Artists, Their Work*, Davis Publications, Inc.,
Worcester, Mass., 1970, #78, p. 109

Fritz Wotruba
Seated Figure, 1959
Not inscribed

Exhibitions

Fine Arts Associates, New York, March 8–April 2, 1960, *Fritz Wotruba/Sculpture*, #26, ill. p. [14]

Marlborough-Gerson Gallery, New York, March, 1964, *Wotruba*, #22, ill. front cover, p. 17

Albright-Knox Art Gallery, Buffalo, June 17–September 1, 1969, *Contemporary Art—Acquisitions 1966–1969*, #122, ill. p. 64

Albright-Knox Art Gallery, Buffalo, July 21–August 27, 1972, *Continental Painting and Sculpture, 1942–1972, in the Albright-Knox Art Gallery*, checklist, #[126]

References

George Dennison, "Month in Review," *Arts Magazine*, vol. 34, no. 7, April, 1960, p. 50

Werner Hofmann, "Über das Werk/Fritz Wotrubas," *Quadrum*, no. 10, 1961, p. 60, ill. p. 58

Hilton Kramer, "Notes on Wotruba and Spaventa," *Arts Magazine*, vol. 38, no. 7, April, 1964, p. 20, ill. p. 18

"Letters from 31 Artists," *Gallery Notes*, The Buffalo Fine Arts Academy, vol. XXXI, no. 2, and vol. XXXII, no. 2, Spring, 1970, p. 44, ill.

Jack Youngerman
Delfina, 1961
Inscribed on reverse across center "Youngerman/1961/DELFINA"

Exhibitions

Betty Parsons Gallery, New York, November 27–December 16, 1961, *Jack Youngerman*, reproduced on poster

National Gallery of Art, Washington, D.C., May 19–July 21, 1968, *Paintings from the Albright-Knox Art Gallery*, color ill. p. 86

Museo Nacional de Bellas Artes, Buenos Aires, October 23–November 30, 1969, *109 obras de Albright-Knox Art Gallery*, #79, p. 90, ill.

Yvarel (Jean-Pierre Vasarely)
Polychromatic Diffraction
(Diffraction polychrome), 1970
Inscribed lower center "Yvarel 1970." Inscribed on reverse "Yvarel/"Diffraction Polychrome"/BV-VI-R-O/N°1010/Yvarel"

Exhibitions

Salon d'Automne, Paris, September–October, 1970

Albright-Knox Art Gallery, Buffalo, March 4–April 9, 1972, *Movement, Optical Phenomena and Light: Kinetic and Optic Painting and Sculpture in the Albright-Knox Art Gallery*, checklist, #[60]

Complete Catalogue and Index

Paintings and drawings on paper are not included in this catalogue.

ADAMS, Robert | (British, born 1917)
80–81, 125, 127

Tall Spike Form, 1957
Iron and steel,
90½ x 21 x 16 in.
(229.8 x 53.3 x 40.6 cm.)
Gift of Seymour H. Knox
K58:21

Triangulated Column, 1960
Bronzed steel, 91 x 31 x 31 in.
(231.1 x 78.8 x 78.8 cm.)
Gift of Seymour H. Knox
K61:16

Column, 1961
Steel, 86 x 46¾ in. circum.
(218.4 x 118.8 cm.)
Gift of Seymour H. Knox
K64:21

AFRO (Basaldella) | (Italian, born 1912)
193, 216

Concertino, 1948
Oil and watercolor on canvas,
27½ x 35¼ in.
(69.8 x 89.5 cm.)
Room of Contemporary Art
Fund   RCA 49:3

Fear of the Night, 1952
(pp. 216–17, 407)

AGAM, Yaacov | (Israeli, born 1928)
300–302, 305, 334

Loud Tactile Painting, 1962
Wood and metal,
32 x 42½ in.
(81.3 x 108 cm.)
Gift of Seymour H. Knox
K63:11

The Ninth Power, 1970–71
(pp. 334, 336, 407)

Free Standing Painting, 1971
(pp. 334–35, 407)

AIZENBERG, Roberto | (Argentine, born 1928)
200

Painting (Pintura), 1968–69
Oil on masonite,
25⅝ x 25⅝ in.
(65 x 65 cm.)
Gift of Seymour H. Knox
K70:1

ALBERS, Josef | (American, born Germany
1888)
16, 303–4, 312, 352

*Homage to the Square:
Dedicated,* 1955
Oil on masonite, 43 x 43 in.
(109.2 x 109.2 cm.)
Gift of The Seymour H. Knox
Foundation, Inc.   69:4

*Homage to the Square:
Terra Caliente,* 1963
(pp. 310, 312, 407)

ALECHINSKY, Pierre | (Belgian, born 1927)
197, 228

*Greet the North, Greet the
South (Salut le nord, salut
le sud)* 1962
(pp. 228–29, 407)

ALVIANI, Getulio | (Italian, born 1939)
166, 170, 303

*Structure Composed of
Green/Red Square Elements
(La struttura a elementi
quadri, verde/rosso),* 1968
Aluminum and colored paper
on mirrored base,
27 x 49½ x 25 in.
(68.5 x 125.8 x 63.5 cm.)
Gift of Seymour H. Knox
K68:14

ANDRE, Carl | (American, born 1935)
78, 170

Cock, 1963
Wood, 17 x 6 x 2 in.
(43.2 x 15.2 x 5 cm.)
Members' Council Purchase
Fund 72:8

ANUSZKIEWICZ, Richard | (American, born 1930)
304–5, 321

Water from the Rock,
1961–63
Oil on canvas, 56 x 52 in.
(142.2 x 132.1 cm.)
Gift of Seymour H. Knox
K63:16

Iridescence, 1965
(pp. 319, 321, 407)

*Convex, Concave I
Dimensional*, 1967
Lacquered plywood on
mirrored base,
32 x 50 x 50 in. (incl. base)
(81.3 x 127 x 127 cm.)
Gift of Seymour H. Knox
K67:12

APPEL, Karel | (Dutch, born 1921)
157–58, 164, 166, 197,
202, 226

Flight (La Fuite), 1954
(pp. 226–27, 408)

Fire World, 1957
Oil on canvas, 75½ x 95 in.
(191.8 x 241.2 cm.)
Gift of Seymour H. Knox
K57:12

*Personage and Flower
(Personnage et fleur)*, 1967
Painted plywood and
polystyrene,
71 x 67 x 15 in.
(180.3 x 170.2 x 38.1 cm.)
Gift of Seymour H. Knox
K69:28

ARMAN (Fernandez) | (French, born 1929)
271, 273–74

Toccata and Fugue, 1962
Split violins,
65 x 52½ x 5¼ in.
(165.1 x 133 x 13 cm.)
Gift of Seymour H. Knox
K63:5

ARMITAGE, Kenneth | (British, born 1916)
125, 127–28

Family Going for a Walk,
c. 1951
(fifth in an edition of five)
Bronze, 8 x 10⅝ x 5⅝ in.
(20.3 x 27 x 14.3 cm.)
Gift of Seymour H. Knox
K55:2

*Seated Woman with Arms
Extended*, 1953–57
Bronze, 35 x 16 x 36 in.
(88.9 x 40.6 x 91.4 cm.)
Gift of Seymour H. Knox
K59:6

ARNOLD, Anne | (American, born 1925)

Charlie, 1969
Acrylic on canvas over
wooden construction,
50 x 23 x 27 in.
(127 x 58.5 x 68.5 cm.)
Gift of Seymour H. Knox
K70:15

Charlotte, 1971
Acrylic on canvas over
wooden construction,
30 x 44 x 18 in.
(76.2 x 111.8 x 45.8 cm.)
Gift of Seymour H. Knox
K72:6

ARP, Jean | (French, born Germany,
1887–1966) 76, 157, 160–62,
166–68, 172, 273

*Imaginary Animal (Animal
de rêve)*, 1947
Polished bronze and marble
on wood base,
32 x 12½ x 13 in. (incl. base)
(81.3 x 31.8 x 33 cm.)
Gift of Mr. and Mrs. Gordon
Bunshaft RCA64:4.5

Constellation-Punctuation,
1956 (pp. 172–73, 408)

Star (L'Étoile), 1956 (second
in an edition of three;
grande édition)
Polished bronze, 25 x 13 x 4 in.
(incl. base)
(63.5 x 33 x 10.2 cm.)
Charles Clifton Fund   58:3

*Classical Figure (Figure
classique),* 1964
(pp. 171–72, 408)

ARTHUR, Revington   (American, born 1909)

Don Quixote, 1964
Oil on canvas, 72 x 48 in.
(182.9 x 121.9 cm.)
Gift of the Ford Foundation
RCA65:1

ATHERTON, John C.   (American, 1900–1952)

Villa Rotunda, c. 1942
Oil on canvas, 24¼ x 30¼ in.
(61.5 x 76.9 cm.)
Room of Contemporary
Art Fund   RCA43:10

AVEDISIAN, Edward   (American, born 1936)
347–48

West #2, 1962
Oil on canvas, 81¼ x 68 in.
(206.4 x 172.8 cm.)
Gift of S. Paul Boochever
RCA63:10

AVERY, Milton   (American, 1893–1965)

Bucolic Landscape, 1945
Oil on canvas, 32 x 48 in.
(81.3 x 121.9 cm.)
Room of Contemporary
Art Fund   RCA46:2

BACCI, Edmondo   (Italian, born 1913)

*Event #103 (Avvenimento
#103),* c. 1955
Oil on canvas, 47 x 46¾ in.
(119.4 x 118.8 cm.)
Gift of Seymour H. Knox
K56:2

BACON, Francis   (British, born 1909)
123, 128–29, 132, 152

Man with Dog, 1953
(pp. 150, 152, 408)

BAERTLING, Olle   (Swedish, born 1911)
81, 198, 303

Blanar, 1953
Oil on canvas, 36¼ x 23¼ in.
(92 x 59 cm.)
Gift of Seymour H. Knox
K68:12

XIH, 1966
Painted steel, 110 x 43 x 26 in.
(279.4 x 109.2 x 66 cm.)
Gift of Rose Fried Gallery
RCA68:5

BANNARD, Walter Darby   (American, born 1931)
78, 347

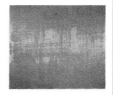

Harbor View #1, 1970
Alkyd resin on canvas,
78 x 93½ in.
(198.1 x 236.8 cm.)
Gift of Seymour H. Knox
K70:16

BASKIN, Leonard   (American, born 1922)

Caprice, 1963
Bronze, 23 x 25½ x 13¾ in.
(58.5 x 64.8 x 35 cm.)
Elisabeth H. Gates Fund
64:10

BAUERMEISTER, Mary   (German, born 1934)
261–63, 284

Four Quarters, 1964–65
(pp. 284–85, 408)

BAUMEISTER, Willi   (German, 1889–1955)
202, 246

Growing, 1952
(pp. 246–47, 408)

BAZIOTES, William | (American, 1912–63)
13–14, 28

White Bird, 1957
(pp. 28, 30, 409)

BECKMANN, Max | (German, 1884–1950)
201, 244

Hotel Lobby, 1950
(pp. 244–45, 409)

BELL, Larry | (American, born 1939)
305

Untitled, 1964
Glass, mirrors, and stainless
steel 63½ x 15¼ x 15¼ in.
(161.3 x 38.8 x 38.8 cm.)
Gift of Seymour H. Knox
K64:31

BENKERT, Ernst G. | (American, born 1928)

Overlap No. 4, 1967
Acrylic on masonite,
24 x 24 in. (61 x 61 cm.)
Gift of Seymour H. Knox
K68:11

BEN-SHMUEL, Ahron | (American, born 1903)

Torso of a Girl, c. 1944
Serpentine, 42 x 9½ x 4½ in.
(106.6 x 24.1 x 11.5 cm.)
Edmund Hayes and
Tracy Funds   45:1

BERKE, Hubert | (German, born 1908)

Malanggan I, 1959
Mixed media,
35½ x 10¾ x 8 in.
(90.2 x 27.3 x 20.3 cm.)
Gift of Seymour H. Knox
K61:20

BERTOIA, Harry | (American, born Italy 1915)
81

Untitled, 1953
Bronzed iron, 33 x 17 x 7 in.
(83.8 x 43.2 x 17.8 cm.)
Gift of Mr. and Mrs. Gordon
Bunshaft   RCA 64:4.3

Untitled Sculptural Screen,
1961
Bronze welded on iron tubes,
81 x 162 x 23 in.
(205.7 x 411.4 x 58.4 cm.)
General Purchase Fund   61:8

BILL, Jacob | (Swiss, born 1942)

Untitled No. 9, 1970
Oil on canvas, 47½ x 47½ in.
(120.6 x 120.6 cm.)
Gift of Seymour H. Knox
K71:19

BILL, Max | (Swiss, born 1908)
77–78, 80–81, 100, 157,
161, 167, 198–99, 236

Construction from a Ring,
1942–63 (pp. 100–101, 410)

*Continuous Surface in Form
of a Column,* 1953–58
Polished brass on stone base,
121 x 4¾ x 4¾ in. (incl.
base) (307.3 x 12 x 12 cm.)
Gift of Seymour H. Knox
K59:7

Field of 32 Parts in 4 Colors,
1965 (pp. 236–37, 410)

*Nine Fields Divided by Means
of Two Colors
(Neun Felder durch
Doppelfarben geteilt),* 1968
Oil on canvas, 47 x 47 in.
(119.4 x 119.4 cm.)
Gift of Seymour H. Knox
K72:3

BIROLLI, Renato | (Italian, born 1906)
193

Rural Scene (Cose rurali), 1954
Oil on canvas, 50¼ x 42 in.
(127.6 x 106.7 cm.)
Gift of Seymour H. Knox
K55:4

BLANCHARD, Carol | (American, born 1919)

Vainglory, undated
Oil on masonite, 20 x 15 in.
(150.8 x 38.1 cm.)
Room of Contemporary
Art Fund   RCA44:22

BLOW, Sandra | (British, born 1925)
132

Painting 1957, 1957
Mixed media on masonite,
59 x 36 in. (149.8 x 91.4 cm.)
Gift of Seymour H. Knox
K58:22

BLUHM, Norman | (American, born 1920)
19–20

Haute Claire, 1962
Oil on canvas, 73 x 122 in.
(185.4 x 309.9 cm.)
Gift of David K. Anderson in
memory of Howard Kellogg, Sr.
RCA64:5

BOGART, Bram | (Dutch, born 1921)

The Fall (La Chute), 1957
Oil on canvas, 44½ x 35½ in.
(113 x 90.2 cm.)
Gift of Seymour H. Knox
K58:23

BOLOTOWSKY, Ilya | (American, born Russia 1907)
351, 386

Scarlet Diamond, 1969
(pp. 386–87, 410)

BONTECOU, Lee | (American, born 1931)
259, 280

Untitled, 1960
(pp. 280–81, 410)

BORDUAS, Paul-Emile | (Canadian, 1905–60)

*Autumn Reception (Réception
automnale)*, 1953
Oil on canvas, 38 x 47 in.
(96.5 x 119.4 cm.)
Gift of The Seymour H. Knox
Foundation, Inc.   71:4.1

BOTO, Martha | (Argentine, born 1925)
157, 166, 170, 305

*Optical Interferences
(Interférences optiques)*, 1965
Wood, aluminum, and
programmed lights,
25½ x 25½ x 14 in.
(64.8 x 64.8 x 35.6 cm.)
Gift of Seymour H. Knox
K67:6

BRIZZI, Ary | (Argentine, born 1930)
200

*Sequences No. 1
(Sequencias No. 1)*, 1969
Acrylic on canvas, 14½ x 59 in.
(36.8 x 149.8 cm.)
Gift of Seymour H. Knox
K70:2

BROOKS, James | (American, born 1906)
18–19, 57, 348

Gant, 1955
Oil on canvas, 53½ x 62½ in.
(135.9 x 158.8 cm.)
Gift of Seymour H. Knox
K57:1

Cooba, 1963
(pp. 55, 57, 410)

BROWN, Jacques | (French, born 1918)

Husserlien, 1959
Oil on tapestry, 50 x 43 in.
(127 x 109.2 cm.)
Gift of Seymour H. Knox
K60:23

BROWN, Joan | (American, born 1938)

*Things Fussing Around the
Moon*, 1959
Oil on canvas, 58½ x 61½ in.
(148.6 x 156.2 cm.)
Gift of Seymour H. Knox
K60:1

BURRI, Alberto | (Italian, born 1915)
195, 259

Composition in White, 1955
Oil on burlap on masonite,
50¾ x 71 in.
(128.9 x 180.3 cm.)
Gift of Seymour H. Knox
K59:20

BURY, Pol | (Belgian, born 1922)
157, 166, 168–69,
300, 324

Nine Balls on Five Planes,
1964 (pp. 324–25, 410)

BUTLER, Reg | (British, born 1913)
79, 125–26, 138, 159

Torso, c. 1950
(pp. 138–39, 411)

Manipulator, 1954
Bronze, 69 x 24 x 17 in. (incl.
base) (175.2 x 61 x 43.2 cm.)
Charles Clifton Fund   60:7

CALCAGNO, Lawrence | (American, born 1916)

Pacific Series, No. IX—Sierra,
1955
Oil on canvas, 45½ x 57½ in.
(115.6 x 146 cm.)
Gift of Seymour H. Knox
K55:5

CALDER, Alexander | (American, born 1898)
160, 273, 299–300, 308

Conger, c. 1950
(pp. 308–9, 411)
The Cone, 1960
(pp. 307–8, 411)

CALLIYANNIS, Manolis | (French, born Greece 1926)

 (bottom left)

*Aeolian Light (Lumière
aeoliene)*, 1957
Oil on canvas, 29 x 40 in.
(73.6 x 101.6 cm.)
Gift of Seymour H. Knox
K58:24

CAMARGO, Sergio de | (Brazilian, born 1930)

Relief No. 278, 1970
Wood relief, painted white,
66½ x 47¼ x 4 in.
(168.9 x 120.6 x 10.2 cm.)
Gift of Seymour H. Knox
K70:18

CARO, Anthony | (British, born 1924)
83–84, 98, 134–35, 166

Georgiana, 1969–70
(pp. 98, 99, 411)

CASCELLA, Andrea | (Italian, born 1920)
162, 166

Capricorno, 1964
Marble, 24 x 27 x 36 in.
(61 x 68.5 x 91.4 cm.)
Charles Clifton Fund   66:3

CASSINARI, Bruno | (Italian, born 1912)
193

The Black Fish, 1951
Oil on canvas, 27¼ x 39 in.
(69.2 x 99 cm.)
Room of Contemporary
Art Fund   RCA52:1

CAVALLON, Georgio | (American, born Italy 1904)

Untitled, 1956
Oil on canvas, 56 x 80 in.
(142.2 x 203.2 cm.)
Gift of Seymour H. Knox
K60:2

CELENTANO, Francis | (American, born 1928)
305

Untitled, 1964
Oil on canvas, 52 x 96 in.
(132 x 243.8 cm.)
Gift of Seymour H. Knox
K65:8

Kinetic Painting III, 1967
Lacquer on masonite,
motorized,
47¼ in. dia. (120 cm.)
Gift of Seymour H. Knox
K68:8

3-61-MT, 1961
Acrylic on masonite,
39¼ x 29¼ in.
(99.7 x 74.3 cm.)
Gift of Seymour H. Knox
K61:10

4-J30-63, 1963
Plexiglass, 64 x 10 x 10 in.
(incl. base)
(162.5 x 25.4 x 25.4 cm.)
Gift of Seymour H. Knox
K63:7

11-67, 1967
(pp. 398–99, 412)

D'ARCANGELO, Allan (American, born 1930)

Landscape, 1968
Acrylic on canvas, 108 x 108 in.
(274.3 x 274.3 cm.)
Gift of Seymour H. Knox
K69:11

DAVIE, Alan (British, born 1920)
128, 130–31, 140

Female, Male (formerly
No. 12), 1955
(pp. 140–41, 412)

Study for "The Key," 1960
Oil on canvas, 48 x 84¾ in.
(121.9 x 215.3 cm.)
Gift of Seymour H. Knox
K66:6

DAVIS, Gene (American, born 1920)

Popsicle, 1968
Acrylic on canvas, 70 x 30 in.
(177.8 x 76.2 cm.)
Gift of Seymour H. Knox
K69:12

DAVIS, Ron (American, born 1937)
401

Plane Sawtooth, 1970
(pp. 400–401, 412)

DEBRÉ, Olivier (French, born 1920)

Gray-Blue-Gray, 1959
Oil on canvas, 39¼ x 39¼ in.
(99.7 x 99.7 cm.)
Gift of The Seymour H. Knox
Foundation, Inc.   71:4.5

DELAHAYE, Jacques (French, born 1928)
160

Wing (L'Aile), 1957
Bronze, 22¼ x 17¼ x 13½ in.
(56.5 x 43.8 x 34.3 cm.)
Gift of Seymour H. Knox
K58:30

DELAUNAY, Sonia (French, born Ukraine 1885)
194, 218, 347

Colored Rhythm, No. 698
(Rythme coloré), 1958
(pp. 218–19, 412)

DENNY, Robyn (British, born 1930)
131

Red Beat 6, 1958
Oil on masonite, 48 x 72 in.
(121.9 x 182.9 cm.)
Gift of Seymour H. Knox
K58:31

DIEBENKORN, Richard (American, born 1922)
20, 68, 351

Woman in a Window, 1957
(pp. 68–69, 413)

DILLER, Burgoyne (American, 1906–65)
78, 351–52, 390

First Theme (Estate
Number 9), 1963–64
(pp. 390 91, 413)

DINE, Jim (American, born 1935)
21, 265–66, 348, 351, 384

Child's Blue Wall, 1962
(pp. 284–85, 413)

DOI, Isamu (American, born Hawaii 1903)

Deep Sleep, 1960
Oil on canvas, 34 x 43 in.
(86.4 x 109.2 cm.)
Gift of The Seymour H. Knox
Foundation, Inc. 71:4.6

DOMOTO, Hisao (Japanese, born 1928)

Painting, 1958
Oil on canvas, 76½ x 83½ in.
(194.3 x 212 cm.)
Gift of Seymour H. Knox
K59:1

*Solution of Continuity
(Solution de continuité),* 1966
Oil and acrylic on canvas,
60 x 60 in. (152.4 x 152.4 cm.)
Gift of Seymour H. Knox
K67:9

DONATI, Enrico A. (American, born Italy 1909)

Habbaku Dancers, 1958
Oil and sand on canvas,
80 x 70 in. (203.2 x 177.8 cm.)
Gift of Seymour H. Knox
K59:8

DORAZIO, Piero (Italian, born 1927)

Stare Mesto I, 1968
Oil on canvas, 79 x 75 in.
(200.6 x 190.5 cm.)
Gift of Seymour H. Knox
K69:21

DOUAIHY, Saliba (American, born Lebanon 1915)

Sea Wind, 1966
Oil on canvas, 52 x 44 in.
(132.1 x 111.8 cm.)
Gift of the artist   RCA67:1

DRUMLEVITCH, Seymour (American, born 1923)

Bronx Bridge, 1949
Oil on canvas, 30 x 40 in.
(76.2 x 101.6 cm.)
Room of Contemporary
Art Fund   RCA50:3

Ardeatine Caves, 1952–53
Oil and lacquer on masonite,
30 x 40 in. (76.2 x 101.6 cm.)
Room of Contemporary
Art Fund   RCA53:2

DRUMMER, John E. (American, born 1934)

Bemo, 1959
Plaster on plywood,
144 x 96 in.
(365.7 x 243.8 cm.)
Gift of Seymour H. Knox
K59:21

DUBUFFET, Jean (French, born 1901)
164–66, 188, 195, 202, 222

*M. Plume, Portrait of Henri .
Michaux,* 1947
(pp. 222–23, 413)

*Path Bordered by Grass
(Chemin bordé d'herbe),* 1956
Collage and oil on canvas,
49 x 45½ in.
(124.5 x 115.5 cm.)
Gift of Seymour H. Knox
K57:2

Borne au logos VII, 1967
(pp. 188, 414)

DUGMORE, Edward (American, born 1915)

Painting 1960-D, 1960
Oil on canvas, 93 x 63 in.
(236.2 x 160 cm.)
Gift of Seymour H. Knox
K60:13

DUNN, Alfred (British, born 1937)
302

Echoes, 1968
Steel, motorized,
42 x 13½ x 16 in.
(106.8 x 33.4 x 40.7 cm.)
Gift of Seymour H. Knox
K69:2

451

ELLIOTT, Philip | (American, born 1903)

Shelocta, Pa., 1943
Oil on canvas, 30¼ x 35½ in.
(76.9 x 90.2 cm.)
Room of Contemporary
Art Fund   RCA43:12

Flame Shaft, 1968
Oil on canvas, 46 x 35 in.
(116.8 x 88.9 cm.)
George Cary Fund   69:1

ERNST, Jimmy | (American, born Germany
1920)

The Chant, 1955
Oil on canvas, 50 x 60 in.
(127 x 152.4 cm.)
Gift of Seymour H. Knox
K55:7

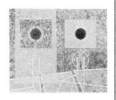

Light (Lumière), 1968
Oil on canvas, 50 x 60 in.
(127 x 152.4 cm.)
Gift of Seymour H. Knox
K69:22

FEININGER, Lyonel | (American, 1871–1956)

Dunes with Ray of Light II,
1944
Oil on canvas, 20 x 35 in.
(50.8 x 88.9 cm.)
Room of Contemporary
Art Fund   RCA44:16

FEITO, Luis | (Spanish, born 1929)

Luminary I, 1959
Oil on canvas, 28¾ x 36¼ in.
(73 x 92.1 cm.)
Gift of The Seymour H. Knox
Foundation, Inc.   71:4.7

FERBER, Herbert | (American, born 1906)
82–83, 112

Green Sculpture II, 1954
(pp. 112–13, 414)

FONTANA, Lucio | (Italian, born Argentina
1899–1968)
165–66, 168, 196, 200, 201,
272

Spatial Concept #2, 1960
Oil on canvas, 20 x 28¾ in.
(50.8 x 73 cm.)
Gift of The Seymour H. Knox
Fondation, Inc.   71:4.8

Natura I, 1961
Bronze, 26 x 31 x 31 in.
(66 x 79 x 79 cm.)
Gift of Seymour H. Knox
K63:27

FRANCIS, Sam | (American, born 1923)
19–20, 66, 194, 343

Blue-Black, 1952
Oil on canvas, 117 x 76¼ in.
(297.2 x 193.7 cm.)
Gift of Seymour H. Knox
K56:3

Untitled, 1956
Oil on canvas, 51 x 38¼ in.
(129.5 x 97.1 cm.)
Gift of David K. Anderson,
in memory of Martha Jackson
RCA70:1

The Whitness of the Whale,
1957–58 (pp. 66–67, 414)

FRANKENTHALER, Helen | (American, born 1928)
19–20, 22–23, 70, 342–45

Round Trip, 1957
(pp. 70–71, 414)

FRASER, Donald Hamilton | (British, born 1929)

*Table and Flowers with
Deck Chairs,* 1958
Oil on canvas, 36 x 48 in.
(91.5 x 121.9 cm.)
Gift of Seymour H. Knox
K58:33

452

FRIEDMAN, Arnold | (American, 1874–1946)

Landscape, c. 1946
Oil on canvas, 20 x 23½ in.
(50.8 x 59.7 cm.)
Gift of Shilling Fund   49:1

FRUHTRUNK, Gunter | (German, born 1923)

*Violet Interferences into Red
(Violette Interferenzen im
Rot)*, 1968
Acrylic on canvas,
64⅝ x 64 in.
(164.1 x 162.5 cm.)
Gift of Seymour H. Knox
K71:2

GABO, Naum | (American, born Russia 1890)
75–77, 80, 82, 161,
166–67, 182, 299

Linear No. 2, Variation,
1962–65 (pp. 182–83, 415)

GARELLI, Franco | (Italian, born 1909)

Figure 2 "Mar," 1958
Bronze, 49 x 21½ x 10 in.
(124.5 x 54.6 x 25.4 cm.)
Gift of Seymour H. Knox
K58:34

GATCH, Lee | (American, 1902–68)

Winter Stone, 1966
Stone and mixed media,
51½ x 36¼ in.
(130.8 x 92.1 cm.)
Charles W. Goodyear Fund
66:5

GEAR, William | (British, born 1915)

Phantom Landscape, 1960
Oil on canvas, 60 x 48 in.
(152.4 x 121.9 cm.)
Gift of Seymour H. Knox
K61:17

GEISSLER, Klaus | (German, born 1933)

Facteur Rhesus, 1963
Mixed media,
50½ x 37 x 23 in.
(128.3 x 94 x 58.4 cm.)
Gift of Seymour H. Knox
K64:17

GERSTNER, Karl | (Swiss, born 1930)
166, 170

Lens Picture No. 15, 1964
Plexiglass lens mounted on
painted Formica,
28½ x 28¼ x 9½ in.
(72.4 x 71.8 x 24.1 cm.),
lens, 16 in. dia. (40.5 cm.)
Gift of Seymour H. Knox
K65:4

GIACOMETTI, Alberto | (Swiss, 1901–66)
82, 127, 157, 160–63, 178

Man Walking, 1960
(pp. 178–79, 415)

GIOIA, Frank di | (American, born 1900)

Night, 1960
Oil on canvas, 39 x 29 in.
(99.1 x 73.7 cm.)
Gift of Mrs. John W. Ames
61:1

GLARNER, Fritz | (Swiss, 1899–1972)
351, 388

Relational Painting #93,
1962 (pp. 388–89, 415)

GOLDBERG, Michael | (American, born 1924)
347

Summer House, 1958
Oil on canvas, 89 x 86 in.
(226 x 218.4 cm.)
Gift of Seymour H. Knox
K58:35

GOODNOUGH, Robert | (American, born 1917)

The Struggle, 1957
Oil on canvas, 44 x 60 in.
(111.8 x 152.4 cm.)
Gift of James I. Merrill
RCA58:2

GORKY, Arshile | (American, born Russia
1904–48)
11–12, 26, 343

The Liver is the Cock's Comb,
1944 (pp. 24, 26, 415)

GOTTLIEB, Adolph | (American, born 1903)
13–15, 38, 342

Frozen Sounds II, 1952
Oil on canvas, 36 x 48 in.
(91.5 x 121.9 cm.)
Gift of Seymour H. Knox
K56:5

Dialogue I, 1960
(pp. 36, 38, 416)

GRIPPE, Peter | (American, born 1912)

Improvisation, 1944
Terra-cotta, 12¾ in.
(32.4 cm.)
Room of Contemporary
Art Fund   RCA44:4

GUERRERO, José | (American, born Spain 1914)

Presence of Black No. 1, 1958
Oil on canvas, 62¼ x 78½ in.
(158.1 x 199.4 cm.)
Gift of Seymour H. Knox
K59:3

GUSTON, Philip | (American, born Canada 1912)
18–19,21, 56

Voyage, 1956
(pp. 54, 56, 417)

Morning, 1959
Oil on canvas, 23⅛ x 28⅞ in.
(58.7 x 73.3 cm.)
Gift of The Seymour H. Knox
Foundation, Inc.   71:4.10

HADZI, Dimitri | (American, born 1921)

Shields IV, 1959–61
Bronze, 8½ x 40 x 30 in.
(incl. base)
(209.6 x 101.6 x 76.2 cm.)
James G. Forsyth Fund
65:18

HAGUE, Raoul | (American, born Turkey 1905)

Mount Marion Walnut,
1952–54
Walnut, 32½ x 36¾ x 26 in.
(incl. base)
(82.6 x 93.3 x 66 cm.)
Gift of Seymour H. Knox
K56:10

HAJDU, Étienne | (Rumanian, born 1907)
157, 160, 166

Livia, 1968
Marble, 20 x 15 x 9 in.
(50.8 x 38.1 x 22.9 cm.)
Gift of Seymour H. Knox
K69:18

HARE, David | (American, born 1917)
80, 92

Sunrise, 1954–55
(pp. 92–93, 417)

Seated Woman, 1958
Bronze, 19¼ x 19 x 16½ in.
(48.9 x 48.2 x 41.9 cm.)
Gift of The Seymour H. Knox
Foundation, Inc.   69:8

HARTIGAN, Grace | (American, born 1922)
20, 62

New England, October, 1957
(pp. 62–63, 417)

HARTUNG, Hans | (French, born Germany 1904)
196, 273–74

Composition, 1951
Oil on canvas, 37¾ x 57 in.
(95.9 x 144.8 cm.)
Gift of Seymour H. Knox
K59:19

T55–28, 1955
Oil on canvas, 19 x 25½ in.
(48.3 x 64.8 cm.)
Gift of The Seymour H. Knox
Foundation, Inc.   71:4.12

HATCHETT, David   (American, born 1948)

Untitled, 1971
Acrylic on canvas, 75 x 85 in.
(190.5 x 215.9 cm.)
Gift of Seymour H. Knox
K71:16

HELD, Al   (American, born 1928)
22–23, 353

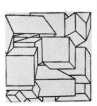

B/WX, 1968
Acrylic on canvas,
114 x 114 in.
(289.5 x 289.5 cm.)
Gift of Seymour H. Knox
K69:7

HEPWORTH, Barbara   (British, born 1903)
125, 162

Curved Form, 1956
Bronze, 35 x 26 x 23½ in.
(88.9 x 66 x 59.7 cm.
Gift of Seymour H. Knox
K58:3

Three Standing Forms, 1964
Slate,
26½ x 24⅞ x 13¹⁵⁄₁₆ in.
(incl. base)
(67.3 x 63.2 x 35.4 cm.)
Gift of Seymour H. Knox
K66:10

HERBIN, Auguste   (French, 1882–1960)
198, 240, 303

Vie No. 1 (Life No. 1), 1950
(pp. 240–41, 418)

HIGGINS, Edward   (American, born 1930)

Untitled, 1959
Welded steel and plaster
on wood base,
42¾ x 26 x 28 in. (incl. base)
(108.5 x 66 x 71.1 cm.)
Gift of Seymour H. Knox
K60:15

HINMAN, Charles   (American, born 1932)

Acropolis, 1965
Acrylic on canvas,
74 x 91 x 7 in.
(188 x 228.5 x 17.8 cm.)
Gift of Seymour H. Knox
K66:1

HITCHENS, Ivon   (British, born 1893)

Tree Landscape, undated
Oil on canvas, 20 x 38¾ in.
(50.8 x 98.5 cm.)
Rome of Contemporary Art
Fund   RCA48:9

HOFLEHNER, Rudolf   (Austrian, born 1916)
82, 162–63

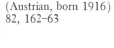

Archon, 1956
Iron, 77 x 35 x 7 in.
(195.6 x 88.9 x 17.8 cm.)
Gift of Mr. and Mrs. Gordon
Bunshaft   61:10

Agon, 1959
Steel, 77½ x 28½ x 18¼ in.
(196.8 x 72.4 x 46.3 cm.)
Gift of Mr. and Mrs. Samuel
M. Kootz   RCA64:2

HOFMANN, Hans   (American, born Germany,
1880–1966)
17–18, 20, 49, 254, 258, 342,
352

Exuberance, 1955
(pp. 48–49, 418)

Summer Night's Dream
(Sommernachtstraum), 1957
(pp. 49–50, 418)

HONEGGER, Gottfried   (Swiss, born 1917)
238

Saugus, 1960
Cardboard collage and encaus-
tic on canvas, 24 x 24 in.
(61 x 61 cm.)
Gift of The Seymour H. Knox
Foundation, Inc.   71:4.13

Permanence, 1961
(pp. 238–39, 418)

Z-611, 1970
Acrylic-tempera on polyester
cast, 70½ x 41 in.
(179 x 104.1 cm.)
Gift of Seymour H. Knox
K70:12

HOSIASSON, Philippe | (French, born Russia 1898)
194

Summer Day 57, 1957
Oil on canvas, 57½ x 45 in.
(146 x 114.3 cm.)
Gift of Seymour H. Knox
K58:5

Composition, 1960
Oil and dry pigment on
canvas, 45½ x 36 in.
(115.6 x 91.4 cm.)
Gift of The Seymour H. Knox
Foundation, Inc.   71:4.14

HOUSE, John Vassar | (American, born 1926)

Game Bird, 1959
Bronze, 16⅜ x 19 x 11 in.
(incl. base)
(41.6 x 48.3 x 27.9 cm.)
Gift of Mr. and Mrs. Manly
Fleischmann, Mrs. Reginald B.
Taylor, Anthony Sisti, and
Charles Cary   60:1

HOYLAND, John | (British, born 1934)
131

No. 42.10.11.61, 1961
Oil on canvas, 68 x 68 in.
(172.7 x 172.7 cm.)
Gift of Seymour H. Knox
K64:34

HULTBERG, John | (American, born 1922)

Italian Journey, 1954
Oil on canvas, 38¼ x 57½ in.
(97.2 x 146 cm.)
Gift of Seymour H. Knox
K55:9

HUNT, Richard | (American, born 1935)

Icarus, 1956
Steel, 78 x 38 x 22½ in.
(198.1 x 96.5 x 57.1 cm.)
Gift of Seymour H. Knox
K59:9

HUXLEY, Paul | (British, born 1938)

Untitled No. 104, 1969
Acrylic on canvas, 88 x 88 in.
(223.5 x 223.5 cm.)
Gift of Seymour H. Knox
K69:31

INDIANA, Robert | (American, born 1928)
261, 263–64, 290, 348, 350–
51, 382

Year of Meteors, 1961
(pp. 382–83, 418)

Star, 1962 (pp. 290–91, 419)

IRWIN, Gwyther | (British, born 1931)

*The Day the Rains Came
Down*, 1959
Paper collage relief on wood,
48 x 33½ in.
(121.9 x 85.1 cm.)
Gift of Seymour H. Knox
K60:22

Bedford Heights, 1964
Collage relief, 38 x 30 in.
(96.5 x 76.2 cm.)
Gift of Seymour H. Knox
K64:29

IRWIN, Robert | (American, born 1928)

Untitled, c. 1962–63
Oil on canvas, 84 x 83 in.
(213.3 x 210.8 cm.)
Gift of Seymour H. Knox
K64:27

JACOBSEN, Robert | (Danish, born 1912)
83, 157, 161–62, 273

Taha, 1961
Iron and steel,
23½ x 14 x 8½ in.
(59.7 x 35.6 x 21.6 cm.)
Gift of The Seymour H. Knox
Foundation, Inc.   K62:8

JARVAISE, James | (American, born 1925)

*Hudson River School
Series #30*, 1957
Oil on masonite, 48 x 66 in.
(121.9 x 167.6 cm.)
Gift of Seymour H. Knox
K60:4

JENKINS, Paul | (American, born 1923)
19–20

The Archer, 1955
Oil on canvas, 51¼ x 37⅞ in.
(130.2 x 81 cm.)
Gift of Seymour H. Knox
K55:10

JENSEN, Alfred | (American, born Guatemala
1903)
352

The Great Mystery II, 1960
Oil on canvas, 50 x 42 in.
(127 x 106.7 cm.)
Gift of Seymour H. Knox
K61:2

JOHNS, Jasper | (American, born 1930)
20–21, 255–56, 266, 270, 305,
348–49, 364

Numbers in Color, 1959
(pp. 364–65, 419)

JONES, Howard | (American, born 1922)
305

Bronze Star, 1967
Spun bronze with programmed
lights, 36 x 36 x 3 in.
(91.5 x 91.5 x 7.5 cm.)
Gift of Seymour H. Knox
K68:3

JORN, Asger | (Danish, born 1914)
164, 197, 230

Untitled, 1961
(pp. 230–32, 419)

JUDD, Donald | (American, born 1928)
78, 259, 262, 296

Untitled, 1969
(pp. 296–97, 419)

KANTOR, Morris | (American, born Russia 1896)

Blue on Blue and Beyond,
1966
Oil on canvas, 44 x 53 in.
(111.8 x 134.6 cm.)
Gift of the American Academy
of Arts and Letters   72:6

KARAHALIOS, Constantin | (Greek, born 1923)

Saint Pierre of Rome, 1963
Mixed media,
63¾ x 38⁵⁄₁₆ in.
(161.9 x 97.2 cm.)
Gift of The Seymour H. Knox
Foundation, Inc.   71:4.15

KAUFFMAN, Craig | (American, born 1932)

Untitled, 1966
Vacuum-molded plexiglass,
77 x 38½ x 4¼ in.
(195.6 x 97.8 x 10.8 cm.)
Gift of Seymour H. Knox
K67:8

KAWABATA, Minoru | (Japanese, born 1911)

Green Curve, 1967
Acrylic on canvas.
65¼ x 84 in.
(165.7 x 213.3 cm.)
Gift of Seymour H. Knox
K68:6

KELLY, Ellsworth | (American, born 1923)
22, 256, 263, 352, 371

New York, N.Y., 1957
(pp. 371–72, 419)

Blue, Yellow and Red, 1968
(pp. 371, 373, 420)

KEMENY, Zoltan | (Swiss, born Rumania, 1907–65)
83, 160, 164

Color-Sadness (Couleur-douleur), 1960
Brass, 35⅝ x 35⅝ x 7½ in.
(90.5 x 90.5 x 19 cm.)
Gift of Seymour H. Knox
K61:14

KEPES, Gyorgy | (American, born Hungary 1906)

Patina, 1959
Oil on canvas, 60 x 60 in.
(152.4 x 152.4 cm.)
Gift of Seymour H. Knox
K60:5

KIENBUSCH, William | (American, born 1914)

Fallen Pine, Camp Island, 1955
Oil on canvas, 26¾ x 40½ in.
(67.9 x 102.9 cm.)
Gift of The Seymour H. Knox Foundation, Inc.   K59:22

KIESLER, Frederick | (American, born Austria, 1896–1965)

Birth of a Lake, undated
Bronze, partly painted, two sections:
upper portion, 28 x 5 x 7 in.
(71.1 x 15.2 x 17.8 cm.);
lower portion, 82 x 32 x 27 in.
(incl. base)
(208.3 x 81.3 x 68.6 cm.)
Anonymous gift   RCA66:8

KINLEY, Peter | (British, born 1926)

Sleeping Figure, 1958
Oil on canvas, 30 x 40 in.
(76.2 x 101.6 cm.)
Gift of Seymour H. Knox
K58:36

KIPP, Lyman | (American, born 1929)
81, 110

Directional I, 1962
Bronze, 44 x 33 x 26 in.
(111.8 x 83.8 x 66 cm.)
Gift of Seymour H. Knox
K62:14

Flat Rate II, 1969
(pp. 110–11, 420)

KITAJ, Ronald B. | (American, born 1932)
132–33, 149, 351

Walter Lippmann, 1966
(pp. 147, 149, 420)

KLEIN, Yves | (French, 1928–62)
165–66, 168, 200, 270–74, 303–4

Lecteur I.K.B. 1960 (No. 1), 1960 (pp. 293, 295, 420)
Lecteur I.K.B. 1960 (No. 2), 1960 (pp. 293, 295, 420)
Lecteur I.K.P. 1960, 1960 (pp. 293, 295, 420)

KLINE, Franz | (American, 1910–62)
18, 46, 129, 196, 257, 346–47

New York, N.Y., 1953
(pp. 46–47, 420)

Requiem, 1958
(pp. 46, 48, 421)

KNATHS, Karl | (American, 1891–1971)

Number Zero—Adam, 1948
Oil on canvas, 40 x 50 in.
(101.6 x 127 cm.)
Room of Contemporary Art
Fund   RCA51:4

KOHN, Gabriel | (American, born 1910)

Pitcairn, 1958
Wood, 22⅝ x 49½ x 24½ in.
(57.5 x 125.8 x 62.2 cm.)
Gift of Seymour H. Knox
K59:12

KOONING, Willem de | (American, born The Netherlands 1904)
17–21, 32, 257, 342, 346–47, 350

Gotham News, c. 1955
(pp. 32–33, 421)

KRAMER, Harry (German, born 1925)
302

Cylinder with Three Paws
(Cylindre à trois pattes), 1964
Wire, wood, and metal,
motorized,
28¾ x 32 x 19¼ in.
(73 x 81.3 x 48.9 cm.)
Gift of Seymour H. Knox
K65:9

KRUSHENICK, Nicholas (American, born 1929)
352–53, 396

Lotus Europa, 1969
(pp. 396–97, 422)

KUWAYAMA, Tadaaki (Japanese, born 1932)

Untitled, 1961
Water soluble paint on rice
paper on canvas,
96 x 72½ in.
(243.8 x 184.1 cm.)
Gift of Seymour H. Knox
K62:8

LAMIS, Leroy (American, born 1925)
305–6

Construction #31—II, 1965
Plexiglass,
12½ x 12¼ x 12½ in.
(31.8 x 31.1 x 31.8 cm.)
Gift of Seymour H. Knox
K65:10

LANYON, Peter (British, 1918–64)
132

Lulworth, 1956
Oil on canvas, 72 x 47 in.
(182.9 x 119.4 cm.)
Gift of Seymour H. Knox
K58:6

Sky, 1956
Oil on masonite, 40 x 36 in.
(101.6 x 91.4 cm.)
Gift of The Seymour H. Knox
Foundation, Inc.   71:4.16

LASSAW, Ibram (American, born Egypt 1913)
83

Theme and Variations #1,
1957
Bronze and copper,
47¼ x 25½ x 13½ in.
(120 x 64.8 x 34.3 cm.)
Gift of Seymour H. Knox
K57:14

Cytherea, 1961
Copper sheet with phosphor-
bronze, silicon-bronze, brass,
and nickel-silver,
84 x 57 x 42 in.
(213 x 144.8 x 106.7 cm.)
Gift of the artist and
Seymour H. Knox   K64:20

LATASTER, Gerard (Dutch, born 1920)
197

Icarus, 1957
Oil on canvas, 29½ x 39 in.
(74.9 x 99.1 cm.)
Gift of Seymour H. Knox
K58:37

Departing from Red, 1961
Oil on canvas, 51½ x 47½ in.
(130.8 x 120.7 cm.)
Gift of Seymour H. Knox
K62:19

LEAVITT, Phillip (American, born 1898)

Red Window, 1960
Oil on masonite, 24 x 18 in.
(61 x 45.7 cm.)
Gift of Alexander D. Read
RCA61:1

LE CLAIR, Charles (American, born 1914)

The Collector, 1944
Oil on canvas, 30 x 25 in.
(76.2 x 63.5 cm.)
Anonymous gift   44:3

LEE, Doris Emerick | (American, born 1905)

Country Wedding, 1942
Oil on canvas, 30 x 44½ in.
(76.2 x 113 cm.)
Room of Contemporary Art
Fund RCA43:7

Summer, 1958
Gouache on board, 23 x 26 in.
(58.4 x 66 cm.)
Gift of Seymour H. Knox
K58:38

LÉGER, Fernand | (French, 1881–1955)
166, 180, 202, 349

The Walking Flower (La Fleur qui marche), 1951
(pp. 180–81, 422)

LE PARC, Julio | (French, born Argentina 1928)
77, 157, 169, 199, 301, 303,
305, 328

*Unstable-continual Light
(Instabile-continuel lumière)*,
c. 1962
Metal, wire, and wood,
31½ x 31½ in. (80 x 80 cm.)
Gift of Seymour H. Knox
K63:18

*14 Series, No. 2 (Série 14
No. 2)*, 1970
(pp. 326, 328, 422)

LESLIE, Alfred | (American, born 1928)
347

Soldier's Medal, 1959
Oil on canvas, 92 x 119 in.
(233.6 x 302.2 cm.)
Gift of Seymour H. Knox
K60:6

Hialeah, 1961
Oil on canvas, 95⅞ x 66 in.
(243.5 x 167.6 cm.)
Gift of The Seymour H. Knox
Foundation, Inc. K61:14

LEVI, Josef | (American, born 1938)
304

Simurgh, 1965
Acrylic, perforated metal, and
fluorescent light,
45 x 57 x 6½ in.
(114.3 x 144.8 x 16.5 cm.)
Gift of Seymour H. Knox
K66:3

LEWY, Kurt | (Belgian, born Germany,
1898–1963)

#169, 1959
Oil on canvas, 36 x 28½ in.
(91.5 x 72.4 cm.)
Gift of Mrs. Lilli Lewy and
Miss Doris Meltzer RCA68:3

LEYDEN, Ernst van | (American, born The
Netherlands 1892)

Sensations, 1961
Cloth and paper collage on
canvas, 51 x 38¼ in.
(129.5 x 97.1 cm.)
Gift of Mr. and Mrs. Gordon
Bunshaft K64:4.2

LIBERMAN, Alexander | (American, born Russia 1912)
81, 102

Iota III, 1961
Oil on canvas, 80 x 45 in.
(203 x 114.3 cm.)
Gift of Seymour H. Knox
K62:3

Bond, 1969 (pp. 102–3, 422)

LICHTENSTEIN, Roy | (American, born 1923)
21, 202, 265, 268–70, 348–50,
378

Head—Red and Yellow, 1962
(pp. 378–79, 422)

LIPCHITZ, Jacques | (French, born Lithuania 1891)
76, 157, 161–62, 174

Sacrifice, 1948
(pp. 174–75, 422)

LIPTON, Seymour | (American, born 1903)
82, 108

Sea King, 1955
(pp. 108–9, 423)

LOEWENSBERG, Verena | (Swiss, born 1912)

Untitled No. 1, 1969–70
Oil on canvas, 40 x 40 in.
(101.6 x 101.6 cm.)
Gift of Seymour H. Knox
K71:20

LOUIS, Morris | (American, 1912–62)
22–23, 342–46, 356

Alpha, 1960
(pp. 356–57, 423)

LUKIN, Sven | (American, born Latvia 1934)

Egypt, 1965
Acrylic on canvas over wood
construction, 94 x 65 x 24 in.
(238.1 x 165 x 61 cm.)
Gift of Seymour H. Knox
K66:5

LYE, Len | (American, born New Zealand
1901)
301

Grass, 1965
Stainless steel and wood,
motorized and programmed,
36 x 35⅜ x 8½ in.
(incl. base)
(91.5 x 90 x 21.5 cm.)
Gift of Howard Wise Gallery
RCA65:2

MacBRYDE, Robert | (English, born 1913)

Still Life, 1948
Oil on canvas, 28 x 36 in.
(71.1 x 91.5 cm.)
Room of Contemporary Art
Fund   RCA48:8

MacENTYRE, Eduardo A. | (Argentine, born 1929)
200

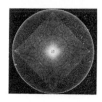

*Generative Painting (Pintura
generativa)*, 1969
Acrylic on canvas,
39½ x 39½ in.
(100 x 100 cm.)
Gift of Seymour H. Knox
K70:3

McEWEN, Jean | (Canadian, born 1923)

Painting, undated
Oil on canvas, 30 x 30 in.
(76 x 76 cm.)
Gift of Women's Committee
of the Montreal Museum of
Fine Arts   RCA63:7

MacIVER, Loren | (American, born 1909)

Night Shadows, 1961
Oil on canvas, 48 x 55 in.
(121.9 x 139.7 cm.)
George Cary Fund   61:7

MACK, Heinz | (German, born 1931)
168–69, 200–201, 305

White Light Dynamo, 1964
Wood and glass, motorized,
59¼ x 59¼ x 12 in.
(150.5 x 150.5 x 30.5 cm.)
Gift of Seymour H. Knox
K65:5

Simona, 1965
Lenses and plexiglass,
100⅜ x 13 x 22 in.
(incl. base)
(255.6 x 33 x 55.9 cm.)
Gift of Seymour H. Knox
K66:12

Zig-Zag, 1965
Plexiglass and aluminum on
mirror base, 85 x 11½ x 3 in.
(216.6 x 29.2 x 7.6 cm.);
base, 1½ x 13 x 28 in.
(3.8 x 33 x 71.1 cm.)
Gift of Seymour H. Knox
K66:13

Monument of Mirrors, 1966
Plexiglass and mirrors,
70¼ x 10½ x 29 in.
(incl. base)
(178.5 x 27 x 74 cm.)
Gift of Seymour H. Knox
K66:14

MAGARINOS, Victor | (Argentine, born 1924)

Painting (Pintura), 1965
Oil on canvas, 75 x 92 in.
(190 x 234.6 cm.)
Gift of The Seymour H. Knox
Foundation, Inc.   70:6

MALICH, Karel | (Czech, born 1924)
81–82

Black and White, 1964–65
Painted wood and aluminum,
86 x 12¾ x 13¼ in.
(218.6 x 32.5 x 34 cm.)
Gift of Seymour H. Knox
K68:2

MALLARY, Robert | (American, born 1917)
259–60

Apothecary, 1960
Polyester, paper, and crushed
stone on plywood,
74 x 49¾ x 3½ in.
(188 x 126.4 x 9 cm.)
Gift of Seymour H. Knox
K63:23

MANNUCCI, Edgardo | (Italian, born 1904)

Idea No. 16, 1958, 1958
Bronze, 57½ x 33½ x 22 in.
(146 x 85 x 56 cm.)
Gift of Seymour H. Knox
K59:14

MANZÙ, Giacomo | (Italian, born 1908)
(pp. 186–87)

Standing Cardinal, 1957
(pp. 186–87, 423)

MARCA-RELLI, Conrad | (American, born 1913)
60, 348

Beach Stand, 1949
Oil on canvas, 25½ x 32 in.
(64.8 x 81.3 cm.)
Gift of Mr. and Mrs. Gordon
Bunshaft   RCA64:4.4

Odalisque, 1957
(pp. 58, 60 ,424)

MARCKS, Gerhard | (German, born 1889)

Freya, 1949
Bronze, 62 x 20 x 15 in.
(157.5 x 50.9 x 38.1 cm.)
Gift of Elisabeth H. Gates
61:4

MARGO, Boris | (American, born Russia 1898)

From Elements of Evening,
1957
Oil on canvas, 47½ x 32 in.
(120.6 x 81.3 cm.)
Gift of Seymour H. Knox
K58:8

MARINI, Marino | (Italian, born 1901)
161–63, 191

Acrobats and Horse, 1951
Gouache and ink on canvas,
38¼ x 28⅛ in.
(97.2 x 71.4 cm.)
Gift of Seymour H. Knox
K54:2

Dancer, 1952
(pp. 191–92, 424)

MARISOL (Escobar) | (American, born France 1930)
264–65, 294, 348

The Generals, 1961–62
(pp. 292, 294, 424)

Baby Girl, 1963
Wood and mixed media,
74 x 35 x 47 in.
(188 x 88.9 x 119.4 cm.)
Gift of Seymour H. Knox
K64:8

462

MASSEY, Jack | (American, born 1925)

Piazza, 1960
Gouache and plastic on
canvas, 68½ x 78⅞ in.
(174 x 200 cm.)
Gift of The Seymour H. Knox
Foundation, Inc.   71:4.19

MASSON, André | (French, born 1896)
12, 79, 202

In the Forest, 1944
Tempera, oil, and sand on
canvas, 25 x 15 in.
(63.5 x 38.1 cm.)
Room of Contemporary Art
Fund   RCA44:17

MATHIEU, Georges | (French, born 1921)
196, 213–74

*For the Definitive Alienation
of Logos (Pour une alienation
definitive du logos)*, 1955
Oil on canvas, 38 x 77 in.
(96.5 x 195.5 cm.)
Gift of Mr. and Mrs. Arthur
A. Goldberg   71:7

First Avenue, 1957
Oil on canvas, 60 x 60 in.
(152.5 x 152.5 cm.)
Gift of Seymour H. Knox
K58:9

MATTA (Echaurren) | (Chilean, born 1912)
202, 212

*Poly-joueurs des cartes
(Card Players)*, c. 1957
(pp. 212–13, 424)

MEADOWS, Bernard | (British, born 1915)
125, 127

Startled Bird, 1955
(second in an edition of six)
Bronze, 24 x 17 x 11 in.
(61 x 43.2 x 28 cm.)
Gift of Seymour H. Knox
K58:39

MILKOWSKI, Antoni | (American, born 1935)
80, 96

Diamond–#I of III, 1967
(pp. 96–97, 425)

MILLONZI, Victor | (American, born 1915)
305

Standing Blue, 1966
Neon and stainless steel,
programmed,
66½ x 12½ x 11½ in.
(168.9 x 31.8 x 29.8 cm.)
Anonymous gift   RCA68:1

MIRKO (Basaldella) | (Italian, 1910–69)

Chimera, undated
Bronze, 36½ x 28 x 11 in.
(92.7 x 71.1 x 27.9 cm.)
Gift of Mr. and Mrs. Gordon
Bunshaft, in memory of
Mr. and Mrs. David Bunshaft
58:4

MIRÓ, Joan | (Spanish, born 1893)
11, 12, 79, 82, 160, 206, 273,

*Woman and Bird in the Night
(Femme et oiseau dans la
nuit)*, 1945 (pp. 206–7, 425)

MITCHELL, Joan | (American, born 1926)
19–20, 72, 347–48

*George Went Swimming at
Barnes Hole, but It Got Too
Cold*, 1957 (pp. 72–73, 425)

Blue Territory, 1972
(pp. 72, 74, 425)

MONCLOA, Benjamin | (Peruvian, born 1927)

Caucus Room, 1965
Acrylic on canvas, 55 x 59 in.
(139.7 x 149.8 cm.)
Gift of Seymour H. Knox
K66:8

OKADA, Kenzo | (American, born Japan 1902)
348

Dynasty, 1956
Oil on canvas, 80 x 60 in.
(203 x 152.4 cm.)
Gift of Seymour H. Knox
K57:7

White and Gold, 1961
(pp. 59, 61, 428)

O'KEEFFE, Georgia | (American, born 1887)

Green Patio Door, 1955, 1955
(pp. 404–5, 428)

OKIMOTO, Jerry Tsukio | (American, born 1924)

Study #3, 1957
Oil on canvas, 52 x 60 in.
(132.1 x 152.4 cm.)
Gift of Seymour H. Knox
K58:14

Mobile Painting #17, 1963
Acrylic on canvas,
21½ x 40 in.
(54.6 x 101.6 cm.)
Gift of Seymour H. Knox
K63:20

OLDENBURG, Claes | (American, born Sweden 1929)
21, 265–67, 270, 282, 348

Glace en dégustation
(Ice Cream Being Tasted),
1964
Painted plaster, porcelain, and
metal spoon, 3½ x 9½ x 6 in.
(8.9 x 24.1 x 15.2 cm.)
Gift of Seymour H. Knox
K66:9

Soft Manhattan #1
(Postal Zones), 1966
(pp. 282–83, 429)

OLITSKI, Jules | (American, born Russia 1922)
22–23, 342, 345–47, 350, 374

Second Tremor, 1969
(pp. 374–75, 429)

ORTMAN, George | (American, born 1926)
352

Aton, 1964
Oil on canvas, mounted on
masonite, 84 x 96 in.
(213.3 x 243.9 cm.)
Gift of Seymour H. Knox
K64:28

OUBORG, Piet | (Dutch, born 1893)

Bright and Black Shining,
1952
Oil on canvas, 22½ x 36 in.
(57.1 x 91.5 cm.)
Room of Contemporary Art
Fund   RCA53:3

PAOLOZZI, Eduardo | (British, born 1924)
80, 131, 142

Japanese War God, 1958
(pp. 142–43, 429)

PARKER, Raymond | (American, born 1922)
21–22, 348

Untitled, 1959
Oil on canvas, 68½ x 69 in.
(174 x 175.2 cm.)
Gift of Seymour H. Knox
K60:9

PASMORE, Victor | (British, born 1908)
131

Abstract in Red, No. 3, 1960
Oil on plywood, 60 x 60 in.
(152.4 x 152.4 cm.)
Gift of Seymour H. Knox
K60:21

PAVIA, Philip | (American, born 1912)

Yankee Clipper, 1965
Marble, 50 x 32 x 29 in.
(127 x 81.3 x 73.5 cm.);
pedestal, 27 x 32 in. diam.
(68.6 x 81.3 cm.)
George Cary Fund   67:3

PEARSON, Henry

(American, born 1914)
303–4

Relax, Relax, 1964
Oil on canvas, 40 x 28 in.
(101.5 x 71 cm.)
Gift of Seymour H. Knox
K65:6.2

Gandabrod Ball II, 1965
Oil on papier-mâché,
12 in. dia. (30.5 cm.)
Gift of Seymour H. Knox
K65:11

PEDERSEN, Carl-Henning

(Danish, born 1913)
197–98, 234

Flying Bird, 1951
(pp. 234–35, 429)

PENALBA, Alicia

(French, born Argentina 1918)
157, 160, 164

Chrysalis (Chrysalide), 1961
Bronze, 17½ x 32 x 19 in.
(44.5 x 81.3 x 48.3 cm.)
Charles Clifton Fund   65:20

PEPPER, Beverly

(American, born 1924)
82, 104

Zig-Zag. 1967
(pp. 104–5, 429)

PEVSNER, Antoine

(French, born Russia,
1884–1962)
75, 77–78, 80, 157, 161,
166–67, 184

*Construction in the Egg
(Construction dans l'oeuf),*
1948 (pp. 184–85, 430)

PHILLIPS, Helen

(American, born 1913)

*Abstract Form (Forme
abstraite),* 1967
Alabaster, 32 x 8 x 8½ in.
(81.3 x 20.3 x 21.6 cm.)
Gift of Seymour H. Knox
K67:10

PHILLIPS, Peter

(British, born 1939)
132

War/Game, 1961
Oil and wood, 85½ x 61⅝ in.
(217.1 x 156.5 cm.)
Gift of Seymour H. Knox
K64:33

PICASSO, Pablo

(French, born Spain 1881)
12, 14, 75–77, 79–80, 82, 126,
157, 161 62, 176, 193, 202–3,
248–49, 351

*Female Bather Playing
(Baigneuse jouant),* 1958
(pp. 176–77, 430)

The Artist and His Model,
1964 (pp. 248–49, 430)

PIENE, Otto

(German, born 1928)
168, 200, 242

Any Fire Flower, 1964
(pp. 242–43, 430)

PISTOLETTO, Michelangelo

(Italian, born 1933)
275, 286

Sacra Conversazione, 1963
(pp. 286–87, 430)

Philodendron, 1965
Painted tissue paper on
stainless steel, 47 x 47 in.
(119.4 x 119.4 cm.)
Gift of The Seymour H. Knox
Foundation, Inc.   471:4.22

POLESELLO, Rogelio

(Argentine, born 1939)
330

Painting (Pintura), 1969
(p. 330, 431)

POLIAKOFF, Serge

(French, born Russia,
1906–69)
77, 252

Composition, 1953
(pp. 252–53, 431)

POLLOCK, Jackson (American, 1912–56)
13, 16–17, 19–21, 27, 129, 130, 197, 257, 343

Convergence, 1952
(pp. 25, 27, 431)

POMODORO, Arnaldo (Italian, born 1926)
163, 166

The Cube, 1962
(edition of two)
Polished bronze,
45 x 45 x 26 in.
(114.3 x 114.3 x 66 cm.)
Gift of Elisabeth H. Gates
65:23

POONS, Larry (American, born Japan 1937)
22, 303, 313, 347, 350

Orange Crush, 1963
(pp. 311, 313, 431)

POUSETTE-DART, Richard (American, born 1916)
14–15, 64

In the Forest, 1957
(pp. 64–65, 432)

PRENTICE, David (British, born 1936)

Passer-Welsh Green, 1964
Oil and aluminum on masonite,
52½ x 48 x 3⅛ in.
(133.4 x 121.9 x 8 cm.)
Gift of Seymour H. Knox
K64:32

RATTNER, Abraham (American, born 1895)

Bird Bath, 1944
Oil on canvas, 25½ x 21¼ in.
(64.8 x 54 cm.)
Room of Contemporary Art
Fund   RCA46:3

RAUSCHENBERG, Robert (American, born 1925)
20–21, 254–55, 265, 268,
270–71, 348–51, 361

Painting with Red Letter S,
1957 (pp. 361–62, 432)

Ace, 1962
(pp. 361, 363, 432)

REINHARDT, Ad (American, 1913–67)
15–16, 42, 78, 305

No. 15, 1952, 1952
(pp. 42–43, 432)

REZVANI, Serge (French, born Iran 1928)

Composition, 1959
Oil on canvas, 28¾ x 21¼ in.
(73 x 54 cm.)
Gift of Seymour H. Knox
K59:27

RICHTER, Vjenceslav (Yugoslavian, born 1917)
169, 305

Rasver 1, 1968
Aluminum, 70 x 18¼ x 20 in.
(177.8 x 46.5 x 50.9 cm.)
Gift of Seymour H. Knox
K69:6

RICKEY, George (American, born 1907)
337–38

Peristyle: Five Lines, 1963–64
(pp. 337–39, 433)

RILEY, Bridget (British, born 1931)
133–34, 144, 304

Drift No. 2, 1966
(pp. 144–45, 433)

RIOPELLE, Jean-Paul (Canadian, born 1923)
196–97, 224

Composition in White, 1955
Oil on canvas, 37⅞ x 51 in.
(96.2 x 129.5 cm.)
Gift of The Seymour H. Knox
Foundation, Inc.   71:4.24

Preo, 1964 (pp. 224–25, 433)

RIVERS, Larry (American, born 1923)
20, 271, 349, 402

The Final Veteran, 1960
(pp. 402–3, 433)

ROBIROSA, Josefina | (Argentine, born 1932)

Strangers II (Forasteros II),
1969
Oil on canvas, 59 x 59 in.
(149.9 x 149.9 cm.)
Gift of Seymour H. Knox
K70:6

ROESCH, Kurt | (American, born Germany
1905)

Imagined Music, 1957
Oil on canvas, 40 x 55 in,
(101.6 x 139.7 cm.)
Gift of Seymour H. Knox
K58:15

RONALD, William | (Canadian, born 1926)

Arrival #4, 1960
Oil on canvas, 50 x 50 in.
(127 x 127 cm.)
Gift of Seymour H. Knox
K60:18

ROSATI, James | (American, born 1912)
82, 106

Big. Red. 1970–71
(pp. 106–7, 433)

ROSENQUIST, James | (American, born 1933)
269–70, 348, 350–51, 380

Nomad, 1963
(pp. 380–81, 433)

ROSENTHAL, Bernard | (American, born 1914)
81

Sun Ikon, 1959
Brass, 39 x 48 in.
(99 x 121.9 cm.)
Gift of Seymour H. Knox
K60:10

Jericho II, 1963
Bronze and brass,
79 x 29 x 30 in.
(200.6 x 73.7 x 76.2 cm.)
Charles Clifton Fund   64:3

ROTH, Frank | (American, born 1936)

Agincourt, 1958
Oil on canvas, 72 x 66 in.
(182.9 x 167.6 cm.)
Gift of Seymour H. Knox
K58:43

ROTHKO, Mark | (American, 1903–70)
13–15, 17, 22, 44, 129, 303,
342

Orange and Yellow, 1956
(pp. 44–45, 434)

RUSSO, Alexander | (American, born 1922)

Winter Plant, 1957
Oil on canvas, 82¼ x 49¾ in.
(209.1 x 126.5 cm.)
Gift of Seymour H. Knox
K57:8

SAMARAS, Lucas | (Greek, born 1936)
261–62, 322, 305–6

Mirrored Room (formerly
Room No. 2), 1966
(pp. 322–23, 434)

Transformation: Boxes,
1966–67
12 boxes, painted cardboard,
4 to 7 in. h. (10.2 to 17.8 cm.)
Gift of Seymour H. Knox
K69:4

SANDER, Ludwig | (American, born 1906)
352, 392

Composition—Blue, 1960
Oil and crayon on canvas,
20¼ x 24⅛ in.
(51.4 x 61.3 cm.)
Gift of The Seymour H. Knox
Foundation, Inc.   71:4.26

Untitled, 1963
(pp. 392 93, 434)

SANTOMASO, Giuseppe | (Italian, born 1907)
193

Castilian Earth I, 1959
Oil on canvas, 51 x 63 in.
(129.5 x 160 cm.)
Gift of Seymour H. Knox
K62:4

SATO, Tadashi | (American, born 1923)

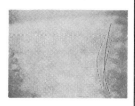

*Composition #10—Three
Lines*, 1957
Oil on canvas, 37 x 51 in.
(94 x 129.5 cm.)
Gift of Seymour H. Knox
K58:17

SAURA, Antonio | (Spanish, born 1930)

Portrait 64 (Retrato 64), 1959
Oil on canvas, 23¾ x 28½ in.
(60.3 x 72.4 cm.)
Gift of Mr. and Mrs. Magee
Wyckoff   RCA68:2

SCARPITTA, Salvatore | (Italian, born America 1919)

Directory, 1960
Painted fabric over metal,
75 x 60 in. (190.5 x 152.4 cm.)
Gift of Seymour H. Knox
K60:12

SCHANKER, Louis | (American, born 1903)

Number 9, 1951
Oil on canvas, 42½ x 44 in.
(108 x 111.8 cm.)
Room of Contemporary Art
Fund   RCA52:9

SCHMIDT, Julius | (American, born 1923)

Untitled, 1966
Bronze,
31½ x 18¾ x 17⅛ in.
(80 x 47.5 x 43.5 cm.)
Gift of Seymour H. Knox
K67:2

SCHNEIDER, Gerard | (French, born Switzerland
1896)
196

Painting 61-C, 1957
Oil on canvas, 45 x 57½ in.
(114.3 x 146 cm.)
Gift of Seymour H. Knox
K58:18

SCHÖFFER, Nicolas | (French, born Hungary 1912)
78, 157, 166, 168–69, 340

Spatiodynamique 22, 1954
(pp. 340–41, 434)

SCHUMACHER, Emil | (German, born 1912)
259

Iwan, 1960
Oil on canvas, 67 x 51 in.
(170.2 x 129.5 cm.)
Gift of Mr. and Mrs. Arthur
A. Goldberg   71:8

SCHWABACHER, Ethel | (American, born 1903)

Morning, 1957
Oil on canvas, 65 x 78 in.
(165.1 x 198.1 cm.)
Gift of Seymour H. Knox
K59:17

SCHWITTERS, Kurt | (German, 1887–1948)
201–2, 208, 260

Difficult, 1942–43
(pp. 208–9, 434)

SCOTT, William | (British, born Scotland 1913)
128–30

Blue Painting, 1960
(pp. 146, 148, 435)

Nile Valley: Morning, 1962
Oil on canvas, 63 x 68 in.
(160 x 172.8 cm.)
Gift of Mrs. Martha Jackson
RCA67:4

SEDGLEY, Peter | (British, born 1930)
303, 305

Polarity, 1966
Acrylic on canvas, 72 x 72 in.
(182.9 x 182.9 cm.)
Gift of Seymour H. Knox
K68:5

SEGAL, George | (American, born 1924)
265–66, 288

Cinema, 1963
(pp. 288–89, 435)

SELIGMANN, Kurt | (American, born Switzerland,
1900–1962)

*Souvenir of America
(Souvenir d'Amérique)*, 1943
Oil on masonite, 23 x 32 in.
(58.4 x 81.3 cm.)
Room of Contemporary Art
Fund   RCA43:11

SEPESHY, Zoltan | (American, born Hungary
1898)

Saturday Afternoon, 1942
Tempera on gesso panel,
25¼ x 33¼ in.
(64.1 x 84.5 cm.)
Room of Contemporary Art
Fund   RCA43:8

SERPAN, Iaroslav | (French, born Czechoslovakia
1922)

Cricket (Tsepheej), 1957
Oil on canvas, 36¼ x 66 in.
(92.5 x 167.6 cm.)
Gift of Seymour H. Knox
K57:11

SHAHN, Ben | (American, 1898–1969)

Spring, 1947
Tempera on masonite,
17 x 30 in. (43.2 x 76.2 cm.)
Room of Contemporary Art
Fund   RCA48:2

SHAPIRO, Seymour | (American, born 1927)

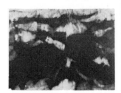

Phantasmagoria, 1961
Oil on board, 71¼ x 95½ in.
(181 x 242.5 cm.)
Gift of Seymour H. Knox
K62:2

SHAW, Kendall | (American, born 1924)

Southampton, 1968
Acrylic on canvas (six panels),
96 x 168 in.
(243.8 x 426.7 cm.)
Gift of Seymour H. Knox
K70:14

SHEA, Dorothy | (American, 1924–63)

Bridge Series: Structure #32,
1962
Oil on canvas, 94 x 102½ in.
(238.1 x 259.7 cm.)
Gift of Mrs. William Berger
RCA66:2

SHIVITZ, Barbara | (American, born 1936)

9/15/59, 1959
Oil on masonite, 48 x 48 in.
(121.9 x 121.9 cm.)
Gift of L. M. Angeleski
RCA60:2

SHOW-YU, Lin | (British, born Formosa 1933)

Painting Relief, 1962
Aluminum and oil on canvas,
50 x 40 in. (127 x 101.5 cm.)
Gift of Seymour H. Knox
K63:13

SIGNORI, Sergio | (Italian, born 1906)
166

Venus, 1957
Marble, 31½ x 10 x 5 in. (incl.
base) (80 x 25.4 x 12.7 cm.)
Gift of Seymour H. Knox
K61:25

SIRONI, Mario | (Italian, 1891–1961)

Composition, 1951
Oil on canvas, 27½ x 35½ in.
(69.8 x 89.2 cm.)
Room of Contemporary Art
Fund   RCA52:3

SMITH, David | (American, 1905–65)
77, 79, 82–84, 88–89, 258

Tank Totem IV, 1953
(pp. 88–90, 435)

Cubi XVI, 1963
(pp. 88–89, 91, 436)

SMITH, Hassel | (American, born 1915)

Number 4, 1960, 1960
Oil on canvas, 69½ x 68 in.
(176.5 x 172.7 cm.)
Gift of Seymour H. Knox
K60:19

SMITH, Tony | (American, born 1912)
80–81, 94

Cigarette, 1961–68
(pp. 94–95, 436)

SOBRINO, Francisco | (French, born Spain 1932)
157, 166, 169, 200, 301, 305–6

*Permutational Structure
(Structure permutationnelle),*
1963–66 (first in an edition
of three)
Plexiglass,
43¼ x 11¾ x 11½ in.
(109.8 x 30.5 x 29.2 cm.)
Gift of Seymour H. Knox
K69:1

SOFFER, Sasson | (American, born Iraq 1925)

Along II, 1960
Encaustic on masonite,
48 x 96 in.
(121.9 x 243.8 cm.)
Gift of Seymour H. Knox
K61:6

The Tides, 1962–63
Encaustic on canvas,
108 x 180 in.
(274.2 x 457.2 cm.)
Gift of Seymour H. Knox
K63:4

SOMAINI, Francesco | (Italian, born 1926)
160

Vertical, 1959
Bronze, 43 x 28 x 19 in.
(incl. base)
(109.2 x 71.1 x 48.2 cm.)
Gift of Seymour H. Knox
K66:11

SOTO, Jesús Raphael | (Venezuelan, born 1923)
77, 168, 300, 304, 331

*Wood—Iron Rods (Bois–tiges
de fer),* 1964 (pp. 331, 436)

SOULAGES, Pierre | (French, born 1919)
160, 196, 220

3 April 1954, 1954
Oil on canvas, 76¾ x 51¼ in.
(194.9 x 130.2 cm.)
Gift of Mr. and Mrs. Samuel
M. Kootz   RCA58:3

4 July 1956, 1956
(pp. 220–21, 436)

STAËL, Nicholas de | (French, 1914–55)
194, 196, 214, 348

Landscape in Vaucluse No. 2,
1953 (pp. 214–15, 436)

STAMOS, Theodoros | (American, born 1922)
13–14, 31, 348

Levant for E.W.R., 1958
(pp. 29, 31, 436)

STANCZAK, Julian | (American, born Poland 1928)
304

Unrest, 1963
Polymer and tempera on
canvas, 45 x 55½ in.
(114.3 x 141.1 cm.)
Gift of Seymour H. Knox
K64:37

STANKIEWICZ, Richard | (American, born 1922)
21, 83, 257–58, 271, 273, 278

Our Lady of All Protections,
1958 (pp. 278–79, 437)

STELLA, Frank | (American, born 1936)
78, 255, 303, 342, 345–47,
350, 366–67

Jill, 1959 (pp. 366, 368, 437)

Fez, 1964 (pp. 366, 369, 437)

Lac Laronge III, 1969
(pp. 366–67, 370, 437)

STERNE, Hedda | (American, born Rumania
1916)

Alaska I, 1958
Oil on canvas, 70¾ x 110¼ in.
(179.7 x 279.4 cm.)
Gift of Seymour H. Knox
K58:44

STILL, Clyfford | (American, born 1904)
14–17, 22, 40, 352

1945–K, 1945
Oil on canvas, 50 x 31 in.
(127 x 78.8 cm.)
Gift of the artist   64:5.3

July 1945-R, 1945
Oil on canvas, 69 x 32 in.
(175.3 x 81.3 cm.)
Gift of the artist   64:5.4

September 1946, 1946
Oil on canvas, 60 x 27½ in.
(152.4 x 69.8 cm.)
Gift of the artist   64:5.5

1946-L, 1946
Oil on canvas, 71 x 46 in.
(180.3 x 116.8 cm.)
Gift of the artist   64:5.6

1946-N 1946
Oil on canvas, 71 x 45 in.
(180.3 x 114.3 cm.)
Gift of the artist   64:5.7

January 1947, 1947
Oil on canvas, 62 x 45 in.
(157.5 x 114.3 cm.)
Gift of the artist   64:5.8

1947-8-A, 1947
Oil on canvas, 45 x 40 in.
(114.3 x 101.6 cm.)
Gift of the artist   64:5.9

1947-G, 1947
Oil on canvas, 62½ x 59 in.
(158.1 x 149.8 cm.)
Gift of the artist   64:5.10

1947-8-W No. 2, 1947
Oil on canvas, 108½ x 88 in.
(275.5 x 223.8 cm.)
Gift of the artist   64:5.11

January 1948, 1948
Oil on canvas, 79 x 60 in.
(200.6 x 152.4 cm.)
Gift of the artist   64:5.13

July 1948, 1948
Oil on canvas, 58½ x 49 in.
(148 x 124.5 cm.)
Gift of the artist   64:5.12

1948-B, 1948
Oil on canvas, 77½ x 69½ in.
(196.8 x 176.5 cm.)
Gift of the artist   64:5.14

1948-E, 1948
Oil on canvas, 82 x 69 in.
(208.5 x 175.2 cm.)
Gift of the artist   64:5.15

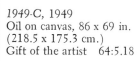

1948-M, 1948
Oil on canvas, 58 x 55 in.
(147.3 x 139.7 cm.)
Gift of the artist   64:5.16

1949, 1949
Oil on canvas, 47½ x 38½ in.
(120 x 97.8 cm.)
Gift of the artist   64:5.17

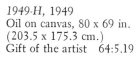

1949-C, 1949
Oil on canvas, 86 x 69 in.
(218.5 x 175.3 cm.)
Gift of the artist   64:5.18

1949-H, 1949
Oil on canvas, 80 x 69 in.
(203.5 x 175.3 cm.)
Gift of the artist   64:5.19

1949-M, 1949
Oil on canvas, 93 x 69½ in.
(236.5 x 176.5 cm.)
Gift of the artist   64:5.20

January 1950-D, 1950
Oil on canvas, 94 x 69 in.
(239 x 175.3 cm.)
Gift of the artist   64:5.24

October 1950, 1950
Oil on canvas, 80 x 68½ in.
(203.5 x 174 cm.)
Gift of the artist   64:5.21

November 1950, 1950
Oil on canvas, 80 x 68 in.
(203.5 x 172.8 cm.)
Gift of the artist   64:5.22

November 1950 No. 2, 1950
Oil on canvas, 92½ x 79½ in.
(235.2 x 202.6 cm.)
Gift of the artist   64:5.23

1951-E, 1951
Oil on canvas, 117 x 143 in.
(297.3 x 363.5 cm.)
Gift of the artist   64:5.25

1951-L No. 2, 1951
Oil on canvas, 114 x 96 in.
(289.8 x 244.1 cm.)
Gift of the artist   64:5.26

November 1953, 1953
Oil on canvas, 114 x 81½ in.
(289.8 x 206.7 cm.)
Gift of the artist   64:5.29

1954, 1954
Oil on canvas, 113½ x 156 in.
(288.8 x 296.5 cm.)
Gift of Seymour H. Knox
K57:10

November 1954, 1954
Oil on canvas, 114 x 95 in.
(289.8 x 241.5 cm.)
Gift of the artist   64:5.27

September 1955, 1955
Oil on canvas, 114 x 95 in.
(289.8 x 241.5 cm.)
Gift of the artist   64:5.28

1957-D No. 1, 1957
Oil on canvas, 113 x 159 in.
(288.2 x 403.8 cm.)
Gift of Seymour H. Knox
K59:26

April 1962, 1962
(pp. 40–41, 437)

1963-A, 1963
Oil on canvas, 114 x 75½ in.
(289.7 x 191.8 cm.)
Gift of the artist   64:5.31

STRUYCKEN, Peter   (Dutch, born 1939)

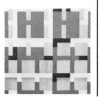

Structure XI-6F, 1967
Lacquer on plexiglass,
39½ x 39½ in.
(100.3 x 100.3 cm.)
Gift of Seymour H. Knox
K68:7

STUART, Ian (Irish, born 1926)

H, 1962
Wood, glass, and mixed media,
25½ x 19⅜ x 3¼ in.
(64.8 x 49.5 x 8.2 cm.)
Gift of Seymour H. Knox
K64:18

Pastoral, 1962
Iron and wood on slate base,
43 x 22 x 10½ in.
(109.2 x 55.9 x 26.7 cm.)
Gift of Seymour H. Knox
K64:19

STUEMPFIG, Walter (American, 1914–70)

Trajan and the Children,
c. 1944
Oil on canvas, 30 x 39 in.
(76.2 x 99.1 cm.)
Room of Contemporary Art
Fund   RCA44:19

SUGAÏ, Kumi (French, born Japan 1919)

Untitled, 1954
Oil on canvas, 23 x 19¼ in.
(58.5 x 48.9 cm.)
Gift of Mr. and Mrs. Gordon
Bunshaft   RCA64:4.6

Aooni, 1960
Oil on canvas, 77 x 51 in.
(195.5 x 129.5 cm.)
Gift of Keith Wellin   71:9

Calm Before the Storm, 1961
Oil on canvas, 63½ x 45 in.
(161.3 x 114.3 cm.)
Gift of Seymour H. Knox
K61:19

SUTHERLAND, Graham (British, born 1903)
123, 130, 153

Thorn Trees, 1945
(pp. 151, 153, 437)

TADASKY (Kuwayama) (Japanese, born 1935
303, 305, 329

Untitled B 133, 1964
(pp. 327, 329, 438)

#E-111, 1969
Acrylic on canvas, 60 x 60 in.
(152.4 x 152.4 cm.)
Gift of Seymour H. Knox
K69:24

TALMAN, Paul (Swiss, born 1932)
301–2

K-121, Black/White, 1965
Plexiglass, 47 x 47 x 1¾ in.
(119.4 x 119.4 x 4.5 cm.)
Gift of Seymour H. Knox
K67:1

TAM, Reuben (American, born 1916)

Edge of Place, 1948
Oil on canvas, 19¼ x 44 in.
(52 x 111.8 cm.)
Room of Contemporary Art
Fund   RCA50:2

TAMAYO, Rufino (Mexican, born 1899)

Fruit Vendors, 1952
Oil on canvas, 59½ x 79 in.
(151.1 x 200.6 cm.)
Gift of Seymour H. Knox
K54:3

TANGUY, Yves (American, born France,
1900–1955)
202, 210

Indefinite Divisibility
(Divisibilité indéfinie), 1942
(pp. 210–11, 438)

TÀPIES (Puig), Antonio | (Spanish, born 1923)
160, 195, 259

Constructions of Shah Abbas,
1950
Oil on canvas, 34¼ x 43 in.
(87.6 x 109.2 cm.)
Room of Contemporary Art
Fund   RCA52:4

Painting, 1956
Oil on canvas, 44 x 57 in.
(111.8 x 144.8 cm.)
Gift of Seymour H. Knox
K57:9

Relief over Black Space, 1958
Oil on canvas, 77 x 51 in.
(195.6 x 129.5 cm.)
Gift of Mr. and Mrs. Gordon
Bunshaft   63:11

TARTY, Vicente | (Spanish, born 1923)

Tropical Moonlight, 1952
Oil on canvas, 27½ x 22 in.
(69.8 x 55.9 cm.)
Gift of Mr. and Mrs. T.
Edward Hanley   RCA53:1.1

THARRATS, Joan-Josep | (Spanish, born 1918)

Zurbale, 1962
Oil on canvas, 32¾ x 39¼ in.
(83.2 x 99.7 cm.)
Gift of Andres J. Escoruela
RCA66:1

THIEBAUD, Wayne | (American, born 1920)
351

Yo-Yos, 1963
Oil on canvas, 24 x 24 in.
(61 x 61 cm.)
Gift of Seymour H. Knox
K63:24

THORNTON, Leslie | (British, born 1925)

Large Seated Figure with Chair
(Version II), 1960
Welded bronze,
46½ x 24 x 29 in.
(118.1 x 61 x 73.7 cm.)
Gift of Seymour H. Knox
K60:17

TIBBLE, Geoffrey | (British, born 1909)
124

Hairdressing, No. 3, 1948
Oil on canvas, 54 x 42 in.
(137.2 x 106.7 cm.)
Room of Contemporary Art
Fund   RCA48:5

TINGUELY, Jean | (Swiss, born 1925)
157, 162, 166, 168–69, 255,
257, 265, 271–73, 300, 332

Peut-être No. 11 (Maybe
No. 11), c. 1959
Metal relief, motorized,
28 x 28¾ in. (71.1 x 73 cm.)
Gift of Philip Johnson
RCA62:1

Cocktail au cheval (Cocktail
on Horseback), 1966
(pp. 332–33, 439)

TOBEY, Mark | (American, born 1890)
342–43, 354

Red Man—White Man—
Black Man, 1945
(pp. 354–55, 439)

Coming and Going, 1970
(pp. 354–55, 439)

TOMASELLO, Luis | (Argentine, born 1915)
200, 306

Chromoplastic Atmosphere
No. 106 (Atmosphère
chromoplastique no. 106),
1963
Painted wood-cubes on canvas,
40 x 39¼ x 2½ in.
(101.5 x 99.7 x 6.4 cm.)
Gift of Seymour H. Knox
K64:22

TOMLIN, Bradley Walker　(American, 1899–1953)
18–19, 34

No. 12—1952, 1952
(pp. 34–35, 439)

TOYOFUKU, Tomonori　(Japanese, born 1925)

Sui (4 Elements) 1, 1964
Wood on metal base,
83 x 16½ x 8½ in.
(210.8 x 41.9 x 20.3 cm.)
Gift of Seymour H. Knox
K65:1

TRÖKES, Heinz　(German, born 1913)

Between Clouds and Crystals,
1951
Oil on canvas, 24¼ x 29½ in.
(61.6 x 74.9 cm.)
Room of Contemporary Art
Fund　RCA52:5

TSAI　(American, born China 1928)
302

Harmonic Sculpture #11,
1968
Stainless steel, motorized, and
stroboscope, 42 in., 17 in. dia.
(106.7, 43.3 cm. dia.)
Gift of Seymour H. Knox
K68:13

TUNNARD, John　(British, born 1900)

Flower for 1945, 1945
Tempera on masonite,
28¾ x 24½ in.
(73 x 62.2 cm.)
Room of Contemporary Art
Fund　RCA48:3

TURNBULL, William　(British, born Scotland 1922)
131

Abstract #25, 1958
Oil on canvas, 78 x 58 in.
(198.1 x 147.3 cm.)
Gift of The Seymour H. Knox
Foundation, Inc.　61:13

Cortez, 1960
Bronze, 57 x 24 x 15 in.
(incl. rosewood base)
(144.8 x 61 x 38.1 cm.)
Gift of Seymour H. Knox
K61:23

TWORKOV, Jack　(American, born Poland 1900)
18–19, 52, 348

East Barrier, 1960
(pp. 52–53, 440)

UBAC, Raoul　(Belgian, born 1910)
157, 160, 194

Still Life, 1951
Oil on canvas, 28¾ x 39¼ in.
(73 x 100.3 cm.)
Room of Contemporary Art
Fund　RCA52:6

Fields (Champs), 1964
Slate, 39 x 25½ x 2¾ in.
(99.1 x 64.8 x 7 cm.)
Charles Clifton Fund　66:2

UECKER, Gunther　(German, born 1930)
168, 200, 305

Overgrowth, 1962
Nails on canvas over wood,
43½ x 43½ x 4 in.
(110.5 x 110.5 x 10.2 cm.)
Gift of Seymour H. Knox
K64:30

UHLMANN, Hans　(German, born 1900)
81, 166

Growth, 1952
Bronze, 68 x 43½ x 22½ in.
(172.7 x 110.5 x 57.1 cm.)
Gift of Seymour H. Knox
K59:18

URBAN, Albert　(American, born Germany,
1909–59)

Painting 1959, 1959
Oil on canvas, 68 x 70 in.
(172.7 x 177.8 cm.)
Gift of Seymour H. Knox
K60:14

VASARELY, Victor
(French, born Hungary 1908)
78, 198–99, 300–301, 303–5,
314

Mindanao, 1952–55
(pp. 314–15, 440)

Bora III, 1964
(pp. 314, 316, 440)

Vega-Nor, 1969
(pp. 314, 317, 440)

VASS, Gene
(American, born 1922)

Two Persons (Deux Personages), 1957
Oil on canvas, 60 x 51 in.
(152.5 x 129.5 cm.)
Gift of Seymour H. Knox
K58:20

Eleventh Street, 1960
Oil on canvas, 72 x 87 in.
(182.9 x 220.9 cm.)
Gift of Seymour H. Knox
K60:20

VAUGHAN, Keith
(British, born 1912)
124

Bathers by a Gray Sea, 1947
Oil on canvas, 25 x 30 in.
(63.5 x 76.2 cm.)
Room of Contemporary Art
Fund   RCA48:4

VIANI, Alberto
(Italian, born 1906)
166

Chimera, 1962
Bronze, 83½ x 39¾ x 48¾ in.
(212 x 101 x 123.8 cm.)
Gift of Seymour H. Knox
K67:3

VIDAL, Miguel Angel
(Argentine, born 1928)
200, 304

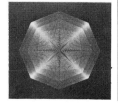

Focus of Light (Focos de luz),
1969
Acrylic on canvas,
51¼ x 51¼ in.
(130.2 x 130.2 cm.)
Gift of Seymour H. Knox
K70:7

VISSERT'T HOOFT, Martha
(American, born 1906)

Fall of Related Objects
(Tribute to Charles Forte),
1948
Oil on canvas, 18 x 14¼ in.
(45.8 x 36.2 cm.)
Gift of A. Conger Goodyear
Trust   70:2.4

WAKITA, Aijiro
(Japanese, born 1942)

Untitled, 1967,
Lead wire over plaster, in two
parts, 16 in. dia. (40.6 cm.)
and 6½ in. dia. (9.1 cm.)
Gift of Seymour H. Knox
K67:11

WARHOL, Andy
(American, born 1930)
21, 265, 267–68, 270, 274,
348–50, 376

100 Cans. 1962
(pp. 376–77, 440)

WEBER, Idelle
(American, born 1932)

Reflection, 1962
Acrylic on canvas, 79 x 71 in.
(203.2 x 180.3 cm.)
Gift of Seymour H. Knox
K63:2

WEISS, Harvey
(American, born 1922)

Departure from Venice, 1961
Bronze, 28¾ x 24 x 12 in.
(incl. base)
(73.2 x 61 x 30.5 cm.)
Gift of the Ford Foundation
RCA64:3

WESLEY, John
(American, born 1928)

*George Washington and
Three Indians*, 1963
Oil on canvas, 72 x 72 in.
(182.9 x 182.9 cm.)
Gift of Seymour H. Knox
K64:4

WESSELMANN, Tom | (American, born 1931)
270, 348, 350

Still Life #20, 1962
Mixed media, 48 x 48 x 5½ in.
(121.9 x 121.9 x 14 cm.)
Gift of Seymour H. Knox
K62:16

WILLENBECHER, John | (American, born 1936)
263

Change Game, 1964
Wood and plastic,
28⅝ x 20 x 3¼ in.
(72.5 x 50.8 x 8.3 cm.)
Gift of Seymour H. Knox
K64:14

WINES, James | (American, born 1932)
83, 260

Metro, 1962
Iron and cement,
28 x 27 x 13 in. (incl. base)
(71.1 x 68.5 x 33 cm.)
Charles Clifton Fund   65:10

WINTER, Fritz | (German, born 1905)
194

Composition in Red and Blue,
1953
Oil on burlap, 45¼ x 57½ in.
(114.9 x 146 cm.)
Gift of Seymour H. Knox
K54:4

Within Space, 1954
Oil on paper on canvas,
29½ x 39½ in.
(74.9 x 100.3 cm.)
Gift of Mr. and Mrs. Gordon
Bunshaft   RCA64:4.1

WOTRUBA, Fritz | (Austrian, born 1907)
161, 163, 189

Seated Figure, 1959
(pp. 189–90, 441)

WRAY, Richard | (American, born 1933)

Eva Plus Five, 1962
Mixed media on canvas
(two panels), 114 x 138 in.
(289.5 x 350.5 cm.)
Gift of the Ford Foundation
RCA63:6

YOUNG, Peter | (American, born 1940)

Number 22-1968, 1968
Acrylic on canvas, 108 x 96 in.
(276.2 x 245.8 cm.)
Members' Council Purchase
Fund   P71:17

YOUNGERMAN, Jack | (American, born 1926)
352, 394

Delfina, 1961
(pp. 394–95, 441)

Roundabout, 1970
Acrylic on canvas, 96 in. dia.
(244.5 cm.)
Gift of Seymour H. Knox
K71:17

YVARAL (Jean-Pierre
Vasarely) | (French, born 1934)
199, 301, 303–4, 320

Acceleration #15, Series B,
1962
Vinyl cords and painted wood,
24¼ x 23½ x 3¼ in.
(61.5 x 59.7 x 8.2 cm.)
Gift of Seymour H. Knox
K63:19

Polychromatic Diffraction
(*Diffraction polychrome*), 1970
(pp. 318, 320, 441)

ZERBE, Karl | (American, born Germany
1903)

Gloucester Alley, 1943
Encaustic on presswood,
28½ x 36 in.
(72.4 x 91.5 cm.)
Room of Contemporary Art
Fund   RCA44:6

479